LYLE PRICE GUIDE
TO
DOULTON

MICK YEWMAN

LYLE PRICE GUIDE
TO
DOULTON

While every care has been taken in the compiling of information contained in this volume, the publishers cannot accept any liability for loss, financial or otherwise, incurred by reliance placed on the information herein.

All prices quoted in this book are based on forty years of experienced dealing backed by accurate and up-to-date reports obtained from a variety of auctions in various countries during the twelve months prior to publication and are converted to dollars at the rate of exchange prevalent at the time of sale.

Mick Yewman is rightfully acclaimed as the international expert on Doulton for his knowledge of the subject is unsurpassed. He was born in Essex in 1926 and started collecting Doulton as a boy but by 1947 he was seriously engaged in building up a comprehensive collection.
His early career included war time service in the Royal Navy; some time as an amateur boxer and as a car dealer until 1967 when he opened his Abridge Auction Rooms. This auction house has made the little Essex village a Mecca for all serious Doulton collectors because it is one of the leading specialist Doulton salerooms in the world. Dealers and collectors from all parts of the globe flock to the Abridge auctions which turn over more than 5,000 lots of Doulton each year.

A CIP catalogue record for this book is available from the British Library.

ISBN 0-86248-117-1

Copyright © Lyle Publications MCMXC
Glenmayne, Galashiels, Scotland TD1 3NR

Printed and bound in Great Britain by
Butler & Tanner Ltd, Frome and London

CONTENTS

The History of Doulton 7
Advertising Wares 33
Animal Figures 39
Art Pottery 47
    Chang 50
    Chinese Jade 52
    Faience 52
    Flambe 56
    Holbein Ware 60
    Impasto 60
    Morrisian Ware 60
    Sets 61
    Sung 62
    Titanian 64
Character Jugs 65
Figures 101
Kingsware 289
Loving Cups & Jugs 301
Miscellaneous Ware 311
    Ash Bowls 311
    Ash Trays 311

Bookends 312
Busts 312
Dickens Tinies 313
Musical Jugs 314
Napkin Rings 314
Sugar Bowls 314
Table Lighters 315
Teapots 316
Tobacco Jars 317
Toothpick Holders 317
Wall Vases 317
Wall Masks 318
Panels 319
Series Ware 329
Stoneware 341
Toby Jugs 417
    Doultonville Tobies 419
    Small Seated Tobies 422
Artists & Assistants 423
Marks 430
Index 433

The publishers wish to express their sincere thanks to the following for their involvement and assistance in the production of this volume:

Text by LIZ TAYLOR & MICK YEWMAN
Edited by TONY CURTIS
CHARLES BORTHWICK
ANNETTE CURTIS
EELIN McIVOR
NICKY FAIRBURN
LESLEY MARTIN
TRACEY BLACK
LOUISE SCOTT-JONES
FRANK BURRELL
JONN DUNLOP
DONNA BONAR
JAMES BROWN
EILEEN BURRELL

ACKNOWLEDGEMENTS

ABRIDGE AUCTION ROOMS, Market Place, Abridge, Essex
DORIS AMES
BILL & LILY BRETT
BERYL BURGESS (Toby Jug Museum, St Ives, Cornwall)
CHRISTIE'S 85 Old Brompton Road, London
DAVID COPE, Stand Even, Kidsgrove, Stoke-on-Trent
FRED DEARDEN
GILLIAN DENMARK
LEAH & GERALD FITERSTEIN
HENRY GIBBONS
DOROTHY GREEN
P. HATFIELD (Lambeth Archives Dept.)
PETER JACKMAN
PHILLIPS, Blenstock House, New Bond Street, London
TOM POWER
SOTHEBY'S, Booth Mansion, Watergate Street, Chester
PHILIP SPRINGTHORPE (Photographer)
LOUIS TAYLORS, Hanley, Stoke-on-Trent
KEN WHITBREAD (Photographer)
FLORENCE MARY YEWMAN

The author and publishers would like to express special thanks to all of the auction houses and specialist dealers and collectors who have given so generously of their time and expertise and in particular they would like to mention the help given by ROYAL DOULTON in assisting in the compilation of this book.

THE HISTORY OF DOULTON

"**B**etter to bear with singularity than crush individuality" said Henry Doulton when critics complained about the variable output of his pottery studio.

He knew that the artists and potters who worked for him were producing treasures for ordinary people at reasonable prices and also for future generations of collectors. Even though some of the hundreds of thousands of designs and individual items that were produced under the Doulton name were calculated to appeal to the bizarre and overdecorated taste of the High Victorians, there were many others of such high quality and originality that they have never lost their artistic quality and appeal.

A study of the trade catalogues of the Doulton Company gives a staggering glimpse into the enormous range of their products and the free scope which both John and Henry Doulton gave to the people who worked for them.

There never was a style 'trademark' in Doulton, each potter and artist was free to interpret influences and fashions in their own way and the result was an upsurge of creative talent which has never been equalled by any commercial enterprise in Britain.

In its Lambeth factory the company provided an opportunity for artistic creation and self expression to an army of men and women who otherwise would have lived and died in obscurity without exercising their enormous talents. Men like George Tinworth, an illiterate who became an R.A., or Frank Butler who was deaf and dumb and

whose expertise at creating beautiful pieces of pottery enthralled visitors to the Doulton works, owed everything to the liberal minded attitudes of John and particularly Henry Doulton.

The Studio also provided an outlet for the talents of artistic women and paved the way for more employment equality between the sexes. The names of Hannah and Florence Barlow, Louisa Davis and the two Elizas, Simmance and Sayers would never be remembered today if it had not been for the fact that they were allowed and encouraged to work at Lambeth.

It is to the credit of Henry Doulton in particular that this creativity burst into life for he was the archetypal Victorian business man, forward thinking, energetic and entrepreneurial who took over a well established business and turned it into a world famous name.

He was not however a woolly minded do-gooder for his company first of all had to turn out a profit but still he was prepared, for the sake of an ideal, to sponsor and finance a pottery studio side by side with the money making commercial factory. In the 1860's the Lambeth Studio made a loss for several years until the public began to appreciate the quality and enormous originality of the work that was being produced there.

The Doulton story began with Henry's father John, a native of Fulham who was reputed to be the best thrower of pint pots in London. He worked as an apprentice with John Dwight, called 'the father of English

7

Terracotta panel above the entrance to Doulton House, modelled by George Tinworth, showing Sir Henry Doulton in the artists' studios.

The entrance to Doulton House on the corner of Lambeth High Street and Black Prince Road (formerly Broad St.) which housed the offices, artists' studios and showrooms.

Saltglazed stoneware jug depicting Lord Nelson by Doulton & Watts, Lambeth, circa 1830.   *$450 £280*

costs and the clean air legislation. In its 19th century heyday however it made a fine sight on the south bank of the Thames because the original works were rebuilt as an Italianate Palace, modelled on the Palazzo Vecchia of Florence on the advice of Henry Doulton's friend, John Ruskin of "The Stones of Venice" fame. The 233 foot high factory chimney was disguised as a campanile.

While John Doulton and his original partners were running the business they concentrated on making earthenware beer bottles, chimney pots, ridge tiles and garden vases. Now and again however they would produce a good selling pot 'figure'; for example the model of George IV's unfortunate Queen Caroline which they made in 1820 and also figures of contemporary heroes including Nelson and even of enemies like Napoleon, which were very much in demand with the poorer class of customers at the time.

In 1832 while the country was afire with enthusiasm for the Reform Bill which extended the male franchise, Doulton and Watts, like several other companies, brought out what are known as Reform flasks. They were really stone glazed bottles for gin but the upper half was modelled on the figure of a popular politician of the time. Because they were designed for such a utilitarian purpose few of those flasks still exist but the few that do are highly prized — and priced — by collectors.

By the time Watts left the firm and it became Doulton and Company, Henry, John's second son had joined his father in spite of his parents' wish that he become a Baptist preacher. The lure of pottery making was too much for Henry. His father proudly exhibited outside the door of their works a vast pottery urn which was Henry's handiwork. It was reputed to be the largest stoneware vessel in the world and could hold 300 gallons. However, it also seems likely that the lure of business made preaching pale into insignificance for the energetic Henry who turned out to be a prime example of Victorian enterprise and ingenuity.

pottery', who was carrying on the ancient tradition of saltglaze pottery making in Fulham. In 1815 young John, who had saved the considerable sum of £100, went into partnership in a pottery with a widow called Jones and a journeyman called Watts. They were established at Vauxhall, opposite the gate of the famous Vauxhall Pleasure Gardens, once the haunt of the fashionable beaux and belles of 18th century London.

The widow disappeared from the scene fairly quickly but Watts and Doulton continued in business. It is said that in the beginning their pottery sign board had "Watts and Doulton" on one side and "Doulton and Watts" on the other but after a short time they called themselves only Doulton and Watts until 1853 when Mr Watts retired.

By this time the firm had moved to Lambeth High Street, to a property with a large garden which was to become the nucleus of the famous Lambeth Pottery Works. It was to stay there until 1956 when it closed down because of rising transport

No idea was too novel for him to give it serious consideration. Edwin Chadwick, the pioneer of improved sanitation, was a friend of Henry's and persuaded him that a better sewage and water supply system was the only way of freeing Britain's crowded cities of the scourge of cholera that stalked them every summer. Chadwick's theories originally must have seemed the theorising of a crank for at the beginning of the 19th century even doctors believed that the cholera infection was spread through the air – they never guessed it was water borne. Henry Doulton however listened to Chadwick and was one of the first to start making earthenware sewage and water pipes. Many of the drainpipes and conduits made during Henry Doulton's lifetime are still in use beneath city streets today.

He designed a self-adjusting joint for water pipes and before long was extending the firm's product lines into baths, lavatories, washbasins and other sanitary fitments to cope with the new 'bathroom' craze which was to sweep the country. This branch of the business was to culminate in a magnificent order for fitting out the bathrooms of the Savoy Hotel in London with 237 specially designed baths.

At the height of their production the Doulton Works were turning out one fifth of the sewer pipes made in Britain at a rate of ten miles a week and exporting them all over the world.

Ever inventive, Henry took a chemistry course and also designed air tight jars for keeping food and a screw top bottle. He recognised the enormous potential of the new industries and inventions that were to transform Victorian Britain into the modern age and devised chemical resistant earthenware for use in telephone and electrical systems.

It was Henry's idea to install steam power in the factory to drive the potters' wheels and by doing so he put his firm in the forefront of the pottery industry because it was a good ten years before any competitor followed his example.

The development of the company into art pottery would not have been possible without the sound financial base provided by the industrial and sanitary side. By the 1860's however John and Henry Doulton were presiding over a company of enormous capacity and world fame. At the time when their finances were beginning to be established on a very stable basis, Henry was prepared to take a chance and found a Pottery Studio in the corner of his works.

The Prince of Wales with Henry Doulton, 1885.

In doing so he was responding to a prevalent theory among the intelligentsia that art and industry should be able to co-exist. That theory was continued and fostered by the Doulton Company right till the end of the First World War and to a lesser extent after as well but by the 1930's the new generation of studio potters were rejecting the Victorian ideas of a creative collaboration between art and industry.

Henry Doulton was first approached by John Sparkes, head of the newly formed Lambeth School of Art, in the late 1850's with the proposition that some of the students should be allowed to try their hand at potting. At first the idea met with little response from John Doulton but his son was to return to it later and set aside a corner of the factory for a few Lambeth School of Art students. It is noticeable that many of them were people who would have worked at lowly or manual trades without this opportunity. Tinworth, a universally acknowledged artistic genius, was a wheelwright before Sparkes took him up and he and the famous Barlows were among the first intake to the Lambeth Studio.

Henry Doulton was ahead of his time too in his ability as a publicist for he was quick to realise the value of the exhibitions which were organised all over the world in the 19th century and, having an acute sense of what was going to be important, he never missed an opportunity to display his firm's goods. This was the medium that presented the work of his studio potters to the world.

Henry had joined his father's firm in 1835 and when the Great Exhibition was unveiled in Hyde Park in 1852, Doulton and Company exhibited but the pieces on show were all industrial items except for a figure of Old Father Time and some terracotta garden vases.

By 1862 however the Lambeth Studio had been established in a small way and in the London Exhibition of that year Doulton's exhibited their first piece of art pottery – a reproduction of a 16th century Rhenish salt cellar.

In the Paris Exhibition of 1867 however the work of George Tinworth was on the Doulton stand and it created a sensation which was followed at the London International Exhibition of 1871 where the robust and virile work of Hannah and Arthur Barlow was first displayed. Queen Victoria was so impressed by the Doulton ware in the exhibition that she ordered some to be sent to Buckingham Palace.

The Doulton name had now begun to have another meaning than just pipes and conduits. At the Vienna Exhibition of 1873 a distinctive cobalt blue glaze which the company was using was given the official name of 'Doulton blue' and in the Philadelphia Centennial Exhibition of 1876,

which perhaps marked the zenith of the Lambeth Pottery, they won five first class awards. There was such a great interest in the pieces from the American public that a cult for Doulton began which continues to this day. American collectors are among the most enthusiastic and knowledgeable in the world. Their original enthusiasm was only intensified by the Chicago International Exhibition of 1893 where the firm showed 1,500 items from its Lambeth and its recently acquired Burslem factory.

Some of the items displayed over the years were of such magnificence that they stopped the public in its tracks. For example for the Glasgow Exhibition of 1888 Doulton's made an Indian pavilion of glazed and enamelled terracotta with stained glass windows which had also been manufactured by the company. The firm's success at international exhibitions continued into the 20th century for at the Brussels Exhibition of 1958 they were the winners of the only Gold Medal awarded to a British pottery manufacturer.

They expanded rapidly throughout the 19th century and in 1877 Henry Doulton bought an earthenware factory called Pinder Bourne and Company in Burslem, Staffordshire. In spite of antagonism and opposition from rival potteries there who regarded him as a southern incomer and upstart, he set about energising the new acquisition with his own brand of magic and in 1882 the name was changed to Doulton and Company, Burslem. His firm now had major factories in London and in Staffordshire where they were able to draw on the long established potting skills of the local population. It was in Burslem that Doulton's began to manufacture bone china in 1885 when a new wing was built onto the factory for that purpose. As in Lambeth, a Studio for creative artists and potters was established and the variety of their output was truly dazzling.

Sir Henry Doulton died in 1897, loaded with honours and success. He was given the Albert Medal by the Royal Society of Arts in 1885 and in 1887 he was knighted by

Queen Victoria, the first potter ever to be awarded the honour of a knighthood.

Part of his achievement was the creation of an artistic environment that encouraged individual creation. It must have been exhilarating to be on the staff of the Studios belonging to Doulton because their artists were given a free hand, there was no official guidelines about what sort of thing they should be turning out, no production line theories of any kind.

This manner of handling artists produced results. Not only did they create exactly the sort of thing that the mass of the public wanted to buy but they also produced in enormous volume. Hannah Barlow, at her peak, made 30 different original pieces every week and hundreds of thousands of other individual pieces were turned out by the rest of the Doulton artists. They signed their work with their initials or monograms and took a personal pride in their creations, a pride that was fostered and encouraged by their employer.

When the staff of the Lambeth Studio expanded from a handful of people to 200 by 1880 and later doubled by the end of the century, the firm enjoyed a world dominance in decorative pottery. Both factories were constantly trying to devise new ways of firing and producing exotic glazes or experimenting with new colours. C. J. Noke who joined Doulton from the Worcester Pottery in 1889 and later became the Artistic Director of Burslem, concentrated on producing a range of experimental transmutation glazed wares as good as those made by Sevres, Copenhagen or Dresden. He devised the Titanian glaze which gave a Copenhagen style look to pottery. Noke also experimented in recreating some of the Oriental techniques of the past and his work resulted in the famous Flambé, Sung, Chinese jade and Chang pottery. In the 1890's he also guided the firm into one of its most successful lines, the production of figure models. The first of these, a range of Shakespearian characters, were shown at the Chicago Exhibition in 1893.

Bone china vase featuring Pan playing his pipes, in Sung glazes by Charles Noke, 7in. high, circa 1925. $1,000 £650

Bone china tobacco jar with elephant finial on cover, Sung glazes, 6in. high, circa 1936. $520 £325

Sung glaze bone china tiger, 9in. long, circa 1925. $560 £350

Bowl with prunus flowers and Sung glazes, bone china, 9¾in. diam., circa 1920. $600 £375

Eliza Simmance, 1873-1928.

death knell and though it produced the well designed range of blue plaques for the LCC which mark houses in London where famous people lived, and the Festival of Britain brought a surge of short lived energy, the Studio finally closed in 1956. That closure marked a 90 year long association between art and industry in Lambeth. Burslem however continued and carried on the success story.

Another interesting aspect of the Doulton story is the fact that while they had a famous name for producing decorative pottery they were also turning out a huge variety of other products. Not only did they continue to make sanitary and industrial goods, but they had a huge output of garden ornaments, especially in the 19th century when the age of the public park began. They made drinking fountains, garden seats, urns, edgings, pots and sundials for every sort of garden from that of a stately home to the suburban villa. After the First World War the spacious age of gardening declined but the Doulton artists then turned their

As the Lambeth Studio was getting into full swing Henry Doulton converted a group of workers' houses into individual studios where his protégès were encouraged to work without managerial interference and this policy proved to be a hothouse for talent. Creativity was allowed its head and pieces were produced with leaves or lace pressed into the glaze as the artists' fancies took them. The potters also devised new techniques like *pâte sur pâte*, as used by Florence Barlow and Eliza Simmance, and their work reflects the styles and fashions of the day. Doulton designs over the years show the influence of Japanese and Primitive art as well as the rising Art Nouveau which they were among the first to popularise, producing a range of distinctive items for Liberty's.

The First World War brought a running down to the Lambeth Studio but it survived on a reduced scale under J. H. Nott, producing some notable items including a range of Persian inspired designs. The Second World War however marked its

Linnie Watt, 1875-1890.

Doultons' premises, formerly Stiff & Sons, on the corner of Broad St. (now Black Prince Road) and the Albert Embankment, circa 1909.

attention to creating decorative things for the smaller garden including garden gnomes but some of the imaginative artefacts installed in urban housing estates of the 1920's and '30's were produced for them by academic sculptors like Gilbert Bayes.

The firm also specialised in architectural work and was particularly well known for decorative tiles which were used both to beautify the interiors and exteriors of buildings. The famous Oyster Bar in Edinburgh's Café Royal is a lovely example of Doulton tile work and many hospital wards, especially children's wards, throughout the country were decorated with tile pictures. Those that survive today are highly prized.

The great upsurge in building in the latter half of the 19th century gave the company an enormous boost and they found that terracotta was an invaluable building and decorative material. Designs made in terracotta could be easily mass reproduced and it was also longer lasting and less liable to atmospheric pollution damage than stone.

Examples of terracotta work by Doulton's can still be seen on London's Savoy Hotel and Royal Court Theatre.

Doulton's also made a huge range of advertising wares and collectors now look out for things like model feet they produced for Dr Scholl's; for ceramic pump handles; ashtrays and stoneware whisky bottles. For many years these were a profitable sideline of a multifacetted business which today continues its diversification with ceramics for the aerospace and textile industries.

Today Doulton and Co. is part of the Pearson Group and is still the largest producer of ceramic products in the U.K. with interests in glass, industrial and sanitary wares, engineering and building materials as well as producing the world famous Royal Doulton decorative pieces and tableware at Burslem. The artists in the Doulton factory continue the long artistic tradition laid down by their distinguished predecessors. They are still carrying on Henry Doulton's dream-making collectors' pieces for future generations.

15

ADVERTISING WARES

Before the advent of plastics, ceramics were used on an enormous scale for the production of advertising items.

Doultons were involved with the beer and spirit trade from the beginning of the 19th century and they produced all manner of promotional items for these industries ranging from public house tiled or terracotta frontages and ceramic beer pump handles to ashtrays and spittoons for public bars.

Some of the other advertising artefacts produced by the company included perfume bottles moulded like figures and plaques painted with portraits of Queen Victoria advertising soap or toothpaste.

One of the more unusual advertising commissions came Doulton's way in the 1950's when they were asked to make a Toby jug depicting the American industrialist Clifford Cornell, head of the Cleveland Flux Company of Ohio. He was a great fan of Winston Churchill and commissioned Doulton to make a Toby jug of him imitating the one they had recently produced of Churchill. Another oddity was a moulded

William Grant character jug, specially commissioned by William Grant & Sons Ltd, limited edition of 500, 1986. $640 £400

white china foot which was made to advertise Dr Scholl's Zino pads.

The collecting of Doulton ceramic advertising ware is a growing field and items are eagerly sought out by enthusiasts.

The International Collection, a set of four character liqueur flasks made for Pick-Kwik Wines & Spirits, complete with stand.   *$295 £185*

ANIMAL FIGURES

Before 1912 only a few animal figures were produced by the Doulton potteries but among them were the highly successful Flambe Ware figures.

However by the time of World War One, Charles J. Noke launched a new line, very realistic figures of animals and birds which proved to be highly popular with the buying public.

In the beginning they were used to decorate ashtrays, bookends and other household objects but later they began to be produced as freestanding figures in their own right. Great care was taken to model and paint them as close to reality as possible.

In 1936 limited numbers of earthenware figures of goats, calves and deer were made by artist Raoh Schorr but one of the first series which were produced in large numbers for an eager public was the Championship Dog range, which was launched in 1939. At least 41 models were made and many of them are still in production.

The Chatcull Range of animal figures was started in 1940 with figures modelled by artist Joe Ledger who named the series after his home, Chatcull Hall. Most of these are now out of production.

In 1973 yet another artist, Robert Jefferson started animal figure modelling and his Jefferson range of limited editions still continues today.

ART POTTERY

The most astonishing aspect of Doulton Art Pottery is its range and the variety of styles and techniques introduced by the company.

These were developed in the Lambeth Studios established by Henry Doulton from 1867 onwards. The Studio was financed by the far more prosaic side of the business, sanitary and chemical ceramics.

Henry Doulton provided creative artists with the opportunity of expressing themselves in pottery and it is to his credit that he allowed their talents and eccentricities full flowering. There was never

Play Goers, by George Tinworth, salt glazed stoneware, 5in. high, circa 1884.
$1,920 £1,200

any attempt to impose a 'house style' on them.

"The personal is the true vivifying element in art," he said.

The first big name in Art Pottery was that of George Tinworth who began making little models of mice and children, mainly for his own amusement. Many of those were never exhibited.

He was followed by over 400 enthusiastic artists who worked at Lambeth over the years. They not only experimented with the sort of sculptures that could be produced in pottery but also in the intricacy of decorative painting and devised a great range of glazing and firing techniques.

One of the innovators in this respect was William Rix among whose discoveries was a way of reproducing the marbling effect found in 18th century 'agate' wares. Charles J. Noke at Burslem was to carry on the Rix tradition, producing the famous Flambe and Chang glazes among others.

CARRARA WARE . . .

. . . got its name because it looks like Italian Carrara marble and is a dense off-white stoneware with a slightly transparent crystalline matt glaze which is occasionally crackled. The effect was achieved by using more Cornish china clay than usual in the mixture. It was mainly produced between 1887 and 1903 but some examples were still being made in the 1920's when it had a short lived revival.

CHANG WARE . . .

. . . was named after a Chinese master potter of the Sung Dynasty and it was an effort by Doulton to produce glazes which old Chinese potters had also tried to create. The first Chang pottery appeared in 1925 and was characterised by thick textured layers of flowing glaze in lustrous colours which gave a lava like appearance. It was used on vases, some of them festooned with dragons or lizards.

Carrara Ware vase decorated with a scene of children playing, by Ada Dennis, Josephine Durtnall, Mary Denley and Katherine Smallfield, 9¼in. high, circa 1890. $880 £550

THE HISTORY OF DOULTON

CHINESE JADE . . .

. . . In 1920, after years of experimentation, Charles J. Noke achieved his ambition of reproducing jade in ceramic. His simulated jade was used to make libation cups, figures and bowls and examples of it are now very rare because only a limited number of pieces were successfully made.

CROWN LAMBETH . . .

. . . is a fine earthenware remarkable for the richness and transparency of the decorations. It was decorated by hand painting on biscuit ware and after glazing, was re-fired and re-painted several times. Crown Lambeth was first shown in the Chicago Exhibition of 1893 and was much admired but production ceased after 1903 because heavy kiln losses meant the line was a loss maker.

Dragon vase in Chang glazes, earthenware, 7½in. high, circa 1920. $4,480 £2,800

Royles Patent Toilet Aquarius, earthenware, height with jug inside bowl 12in., circa 1891.

CRYSTALLINE WARE . . .

. . . the surface of the glaze sparkled because zinc oxide was mixed in the glaze compound and it was kept in a high kiln temperature for long periods. It was invented by Cuthbert Bailey who left Doulton's in 1907 but examples of crystalline ware were produced till 1914 when production ceased because of the expense caused by the high number of failures in firing.

CYPRUS WARE . . .

. . . In 1878 Cyprus was annexed to Britain by the Treaty of Berlin and Doulton's celebrated the occasion by introducing Cyprus Ware. It is recognisable by the lotus and hatched designs, based on ancient vases excavated on the island of Cyprus about the time of the Annexation. Not a great number of pieces were made and the name is mainly found on Lambeth Faience vases and bowls produced during 1879.

FLAMBE . . .

. . . the name describes the streaky, flame like effect of the deep blood red glaze which was produced by mixing copper oxide and other minerals and allowing certain amounts of oxygen to be admitted to the kiln during firing. The technique was first discovered by Bernard Moore, a chemist and innovator who worked in conjunction with Doulton at the turn of the century. After two years' experimentation the first examples of Flambe were shown at the St Louis Exhibition of 1904 and it had a huge appeal. Although it is expensive to make, Flambe is still being produced.

IMPASTO . . .

. . . the unusual effect of Impasto is achieved by fusing two harmonious pigments and firing with very little gloss. Colour was applied to raw clay and potters used a small amount of relief to add to reality. Impasto colours were browns, yellows, greens and blues and its production in the last quarter of the 19th century coincided with one of the most artistic periods of the Lambeth Pottery. The first piece was brought out of the kiln during a visit from Princess Alexandra in February 1879 and it continued in production until 1914, though the numbers produced dwindled after 1906.

Bone china Penguin with flambe glazes, 9in. high, circa 1930.   *$270 £170*

Impasto Ware vase by K. Rodgers, 10in. high, circa 1885.   *$400 £250*

MARQUETERIE WARE . . .

. . . this is the rarest of the Lambeth wares. Invented in 1886, it was patented in 1887 under the joint names of Doulton and Rix, and was a simulation of the different coloured wood inlays made by cabinetmakers. This was achieved in pottery by cutting thin slices of coloured clay in various patterns. Marqueterie Ware was produced in large quantities until 1906 when it ceased because of heavy production costs.

Luscian Ware bone china vase with blue bells painted by Louis Bilton, 5½in. high, circa 1895. $320 £200

MORRISIAN WARE . . .

. . . derives its name from the decorations of Morris dancers with which it was decorated. It was made between 1901 and 1924 at Lambeth and some items were designed by A. Pierce. Other items, not marked as Morrisian but with the same sort of decoration, were painted with figures of golfers in 17th century costume.

PERSIAN WARE . . .

. . . was based on Eastern designs with blue, green and orange colouring. Persian ware was produced between 1884 and 1912 and was influenced by the work of William de Morgan. It was used in tiles and panels for wall decoration as well as in pottery. The painting on a white slip coating was done before the glazing and firing.

Bone china teapot with raised paste gilding and exotic birds painted by J. Birbeck, 5½in. high, circa 1910. $400 £250

SUNG . . .

. . . is remarkable for the mottled and veined effect of the glaze produced by high temperatures during firing. The first examples of Sung were exhibited at the British Industry Fair at the Crystal Palace in 1920 and they were of animal and figure models. One of the best known is the elephant and the lustrous green Buddha. Each piece was signed by Charles J. Noke who developed the glaze.

Bone china Buddha decorated with Sung and lustre glazes, 4in. high, circa 1920. $1,200 £750

TITANIAN WARE . . .

. . . the name derives from titanium oxide which gives this ware its characteristic smoky blue colour. It was developed by Charles J. Noke during the early years of World War One and was often decorated with transfer printings of birds of paradise or, during the 1920's when the Tutankhamen fever was at its height, with Egyptian designs. Artists involved were Allen, Raby, Tittensor and Henri.

VELLUMA WARE . . .

. . . was only produced between 1911 and 1914 and as a consequence is extremely rare. The offwhite glaze has a parchment like texture, hence the name. The earthenware shapes were brought from Burslem and painted at Lambeth with transfers from etchings by A. E. Pearce and W. Rowe. The designs are usually landscapes or figure subjects.

Bone china vase with Japanese lady by H. Tittensor, under Titanium glazes, 14½in. high, circa 1919. $2,000 £1,250

CHARACTER JUGS

The first Royal Doulton Character Jug, titled 'John Barleycorn Old Lad' was produced in the early 1930's from a design and model by Charles Noke. As the popularity of the jugs grew, many new characters were introduced including 'Sairey Gamp', 'Parson Brown', 'Dick Turpin' and 'Old Charley'. Some of these jugs are still in production today but many of the earlier designs were discontinued in the sixties.

One of the first to be withdrawn was the Churchill character jug made during the Battle of Britain and designed as a Loving Cup by C. J. Noke. It is cream coloured with two black handles and bears the inscription 'Winston Churchill Prime Minister of Britain 1940'. It was withdrawn after only eighteen months however because, it is said, Churchill himself was not pleased with the likeness. Because so few were produced this jug is an extremely rare and desirable item, coveted by collectors throughout the world, and a fair estimate of its price at auction today is five thousand pounds.

Churchill character jug designed by Charles Noke, introduced 1940, D6170 bearing the inscription 'Winston Spencer Churchill Prime Minister of Britain 1940', 'this loving cup was made during the "Battle of Britain" as a tribute to a great leader'.

Old King Cole musical jug with yellow crown, D6014, issued 1939. $2,400 £1,500

The two faces of Mephistopheles D5757 designed by H. Fenton, issued 1937-1948.
$1,440 £900

Another notable jug is the 'Drake' designed by Mr H. Fenton and introduced in 1940. In the first version the rim is the character's hair but in later versions the rim is his hat. The earlier jug, known as 'The Hatless Drake', bears the inscription 'Drake He Was A Devon Man' and production was limited. Today the hatless version can sell for around £1,700 but the hatted version is less sought after and sells for only about £60.

H. Fenton was also the designer of the red haired, brown haired and white haired clowns. The first two were introduced in 1937 and withdrawn in 1942. Today in auction they can sell for around £1,250. The white haired version, which was introduced in 1951 and withdrawn in 1955, sells for between £550 and £650. In the 1950's however it sold for under £5.

Other favourite jugs are the Cockney costermonger and his wife ''Arry and 'Arriet', introduced in the mid 1940's and withdrawn by 1960. The ''Arry' is usually predominantly brown in colour but if there are buttons on his hat and collar he is known as a 'Brown Pearly Boy'; a version with a blue collar and white buttons is the 'Blue Pearly Boy'. The latter is the most rare and sells for around £2,250.

''Arriet' too is predominantly brown with a green hat and handle, but if she has a blue collar and a maroon hat she is 'Blue Pearly Girl', which is extremely rare and can command a price of between £3,000 and £4,500.

Small details such as the colours of buttons, triangles or hair can represent the difference between hundreds and thousands of pounds for an item. Each jug bears the Doulton backstamp and is numbered according to the firm's numbering system which greatly assists collectors.

TOBY JUGS

The name 'Toby' has long associations with conviviality and it was used by Shakespeare in his Toby Belch and by Laurence Sterne in his character Uncle Toby in 'Tristram Shandy'. Today it has come to signify a jug made like a seated male figure in a tricorn hat with a pipe or a mug of beer on his knee. This is particularly due to the creations of Doulton who took up and developed the long history of the Toby jug and made it beloved by a vast collecting public.

From 1815 when John Doulton first set up his business, the firm made Toby jugs but the earliest examples were only brown salt glazed as they had been for centuries. In 1925 however coloured Toby jugs were added to the range by Harry Simeon and their potential was immediately recognised by Charles J. Noke who made their colours even more vivid and developed them into one of the company's best selling lines.

One of the distinguishing marks of the Toby jug is that one corner of his tricorn hat is always used as a pourer for the beverage he carries.

Charlie Chaplin toby jug, 11in. high, issued 1918. $6,400 £4,000

FIGURES

The first highly skilled figure maker who worked for Doulton was George Tinworth, the Lambeth sculptor, but his figure output was small.

However in 1889 Charles J. Noke left the Royal Worcester Company where he was already showing his prodigious talent as a sculptor and went to work for Doulton's at Burslem. The son of an antique dealer who appreciated the fine vases and figures made by Derby, Bow, Chelsea, Meissen and Sevres, he was fired with the ambition of recreating the once greatly admired Staffordshire figure making industry. For the Chicago Exhibition of 1893 he made several figures including 'Jack Point' and 'Lady Jester'.

During the next five years more figures followed including Noke's 'Pierrot'; 'Geisha' and the double figures 'Oh Law!' and 'Double Jester'. The latter figure today sells for £1,700 because it was only produced in small numbers.

These figures, though finely modelled, were of dull colours and did not sell well so Noke's figure making was suspended until

Contentment designed by Leslie Harradine.

around 1912 when he re-introduced a figure range which was released to the public in 1913 after Queen Mary, on a visit to Burslem, exclaimed "What a Darling!" at the sight of a figure called 'Bedtime' modelled by Charles Vyse.

'Bedtime' was re-christened 'Darling' and proved to be one of the most popular Doulton figures ever produced. It is still in production.

The colours of the new figures were bolder and a group of very talented sculptors worked on them. One of the most notable was Harry Tittensor, (1914-21), a local art master, His 'Europa and The Bull' today sells for £1,200 and his 'Princess Badoura' for a remarkable £6,500.

The work of Leslie Harradine, who began his career at the Lambeth Studio before emigrating to Canada but returned to work at Burslem after World War One, was filled with vitality. His 'Contentment' and 'The Goose Girl' showed his ability to capture movement and he also had a great talent for picking subjects which caught the public fancy. His 'Old Balloon Seller' is still in production today and is one of the most popular Doulton figures ever.

The quality of the range which now

Darling designed by Charles Vyse.

Old Balloon Seller designed by Leslie Harradine.

studying the anatomy of animals and people, as well as ensuring that all costume details are absolutely correct. Her 'Matador and The Bull' is a good example of this and today the figure sells for £2,000 to collectors. Her group, produced in an edition of 12, entitled 'The Marriage of Art and Industry', (today's price £2,500), showing a man and a woman, the tree of knowledge and doves of peace, was centrepiece for the Doulton stand at the Brussels Exhibition of 1958. It helped them win the only Grand Prix awarded to a pottery firm at the exhibition.

Even figures which are still in production can command large prices among collectors. An example is St George by W. K. Harper. This is the third version of St George produced by Doulton and was introduced in 1978. Its price at auction is £3,000.

numbers over 2,000 is superb. Limited editions of figures and wall masks were produced by Richard Garbe, an R.A. and Professor of Sculpture at the Royal College of Art who modelled for Doulton's between 1934 and 1939. His 'West Wind', which today fetches a price of £1,900, was produced in an edition of only 25 and originally sold for just over £8. Most of his wall masks, made of special porcelain with an ivory glaze, were in editions of 100.

Figure making still continues at Burslem with more than 200 still in production. The star of our times is Margaret (Peggy) Davies who was born and brought up in the pottery district of Burselm and, after studying at Burslem College of Art, began work as an assistant to Clarice Cliff. Her association with Doulton began in 1939 and she has worked for them ever since, producing a vast range of figures ranging from her Kate Greenaway children to period characters from English history and a modelled head of Queen Elizabeth II.

Her work is notable for meticulous research which can be clearly seen in the 'Indian Brave' (today's price £2,000). She takes great care in researching her subject,

St George designed by W. K. Harper.

KINGSWARE

In 1899 a new method of stoneware production was introduced at Burslem which involved applying colour slips of subdued greens, yellows and reddish browns to the interior of plaster moulds in which a

A pair of Kingsware beakers decorated with landscape scenes, 4in. high. $52 £35

design was impressed. When another brown slip was poured in the colours fused to give a deep and soft effect to the embossed design.

Kingsware was mostly used for the production of pottery flasks to hold whisky and they were produced in enormous quantities, usually in editions of 1,000, for firms like John Dewar and Sons of Perth; Bullock Lade; Greenlees and Watson and the Hudson's Bay Company.

The glaze was most commonly a dark treacle brown but more unusual was a paler yellow called the 'Kingsware yellow glaze'.

The flasks were embossed with designs emphasising the pleasures of drinking and figures like Falstaff and the Sporting Squire were especially popular. These were often modelled by Arthur Bailey who worked between 1912 and 1932.

Some of the flasks had silver fittings and they are more likely to have survived than the everyday specimens.

Sir Francis Drake jug, designed by Noke & Fenton, issued in 1933 in a limited edition of 500, together with the original invoice for the Drake jug, dated May 14th 1932 for £1. 5 shillings.

LIMITED EDITION LOVING CUPS AND JUGS

O ne of Charles J. Noke's greatest talents was giving the public what it wanted and in 1930 he hit upon the idea of producing a range of limited editions of loving cups and jugs, ornately embossed and decorated to a certain theme.

They were modelled on the slip cast relief jugs which had been made in Staffordshire during Victorian times but were much more intricate and colourful.

The first one produced was 'The Master of Foxhounds Presentation Jug'. It was modelled in low relief with rich glowing colours painted by William Grace and it set the style of the lip and handle of the jug or cup continuing the theme.

The following year 'The Regency Coach Jug' appeared and it was followed by a new one each year including the 'Dickens Dream Jug'; 'The Shakespeare Jug' and 'Robin Hood and His Merry Men'. The maximum number in each edition was 1,000 and each jug or cup bore a certificate of authenticity.

Some were produced to coincide with significant dates like the one made in 1932 for George Washington's birth bicentenary which was designed for the American market. In 1953 a loving cup was issued for the coronation of Queen Elizabeth II by Cecil Noke and in 1977 another edition of only 250 was produced by Richard Johnson for her Silver Jubilee.

SERIES WARE

" A dorn yet serve some useful purpose" was the reasoning behind the very successful introduction of Series Ware which was the brain child of Charles J. Noke who joined Doulton's in 1889.

He realised that standard pottery shapes could be decorated with popular images and sold as 'novelty art wares' to the general public who were not able to afford the more expensive creations of individual artists.

Designs, many of them by Noke himself, were transfer printed onto plates, jugs,

George Washington Bicentenary Jug, designed by C. J. Noke & H. Fenton, 10¾in. high, issued 1932 in a limited edition of 1000, colour variation on handle.

$7200 £4500

Moorish Gateway, a Series Ware rack plate, designed by H. Allen, introduced 1926, withdrawn 1945, D4601, 9½in. diam. $27 £18

bowls, mugs and tea sets. Refined earthenware or bone china was used and the transfer prints were handcoloured which gave the technique the name of 'print and tint'.

The first series issued was the 'Isthmian Games' in 1889 and it was followed by a new theme almost every year till World War Two. They include Olde Worlde England, characters from legend, song or story, motoring scenes, characters from Dickens and hunting scenes. Collectors could buy everything from tooth brush holders to dinner plates with their favourite theme and the craze for collecting them continues today.

In the 1970's Doulton's revived Series Ware when they issued sets of plates for special events and anniversaries called "Collectors' International".

STONEWARE

The production of saltglazed stoneware had been carried on at Lambeth for centuries when John Doulton first went into the pottery business there in 1815.

At first his firm continued the prevalent output of cheap mass produced items like bottles, jugs and barrels and it was not until John's son Henry joined the business that more complex modelling and detail began to be introduced.

It was Henry who diversified into architectural stoneware and who started to turn his Lambeth Pottery into a centre for the production of decorative stoneware.

In 1866 he took into the company a group of students from the Lambeth School of Art and in the Paris Exhibition of 1867 their work was highly acclaimed.

The people who produced decorative stoneware at this time included the three famous Barlows, Frank Butler, George Tinworth and many others including women like Eliza Simmance. At first designs were fairly simple and incised but this led on to 'pâté sur pâté' work which involved building up a raised outline by delicate brushwork and to far more sophisticated designs of incised and carved stylised foliage which were a precursor of the Art Nouveau styles.

Stoneware manufacture ceased entirely at Lambeth in 1956 and had only been on a limited scale there since 1914 but today there is a great resurgence of interest in it among collectors.

ARTHUR BARLOW (1871-78) . . .

. . . died sadly young while his talent was in its full flowering. He was one of the first students to be accepted from the Lambeth School of Art by Henry Doulton in his Lambeth Pottery Works. Arthur Barlow's work is distinctive because of its subtle colours and his flowing use of the foliate scroll.

FLORENCE BARLOW (1873-1909) . . .

. . . was the third member of the Barlow family to work for Henry Doulton. After 1877 she made an arrangement with her more famous sister Hannah that she would only paint birds and leave the animals to Hannah. Florence was a skilled exponent of the 'pâté sur pâté' technique but throughout her career her style stayed relatively unchanged.

Florence E. Barlow, 1873-1909.

HANNAH BARLOW (1871-1913) . . .

. . . was the most famous Doulton artist who maintained an incredible level of output and variety throughout her career. Like her brother and her sister Florence she was a student at Lambeth School of Art, and when she made history by being the first female artist to be employed by Henry Doulton, she paved the way for hundreds of women who came after her. Some of her best pieces were paintings of animals for which she had a strong affection and she maintained a small private zoo at her home. Her best period was between the 1870's and the late 1880's. It is interesting to note that Hannah actually lost the use of her right hand early in her career and retrained herself to use her left.

Hannah B. Barlow, 1871-1913.

FRANK BUTLER (1872-1911) . . .

. . . became one of the best known personalities of the art world during the last quarter of the 19th century when the press discovered that he was a deaf mute who could create things of fascination and beauty from clay. He was one of the early stoneware designers working at Lambeth and often went to exhibitions where he worked in front of the public on the company's stand. His greatest talent was for folding soft clay into myriad shapes and the Indian Pavilion used as a centrepiece for Doulton's exhibit in the Glasgow Exhibition was his work. His peak was between 1872 and 1890 but when the Art Nouveau fashion developed he adopted it with enthusiasm, adapting his designs to the new styles.

LESLIE HARRADINE (1902-1915) . . .

. . . was a gifted artist with a great flair for capturing movement, who modelled at Lambeth from 1902 until 1915 when he emigrated to Canada. He returned to Britain after serving in World War One and for the rest of his life freelanced for Doulton's at Burslem producing some of their most notable figures including the Old Balloon Seller and the Beggar's Opera series. He is best known for his series of Dickens' characters, produced at a rate of about two a month for almost 40 years, and for his set of spirit flasks modelled on 20th century politicians in the same way as the Reform Flasks of 1832 were modelled on the politicians of that time.

EDITH LUPTON (1876-?) . . .

. . . her early work was incised stylised foliage but, after 1880, she turned to 'pâté sur pâté' and pierced vases. Her death is recorded in 1896 but it is not known exactly when she stopped working for Doulton though she is thought to have still been producing work in 1892.

MARK MARSHALL (1879-1912) . . .

. . . a gifted stoneware modeller who produced imaginative dragons, lizards and grotesque creatures, some of them moulded and some in limited editions. He was much influenced by the Art Nouveau movement and translated its ideas into pottery.

ELIZA SIMMANCE (1873-1928) . . .

. . . first assisted on the production of Barlow vases and silicon pieces but after 1900 her work became much more free and all her pieces thereafter were signed. Her output was enormous and her most characteristic work shows finely incised 'pâté sur pâté' decorations of flowers and blossoms.

GEORGE TINWORTH (1866-1913) . . .

. . . was the illiterate son of a Walworth wheelwright who became an artistic genius with a world famous reputation. He studied sculpture at Lambeth School of Art and was one of the first students to work for Henry Doulton who quickly recognised his talents. He produced many terracotta panels with religious themes as well as humorous figures of people and animals and incised and painted vases and jugs.

BIBELOTS . . .

. . . were small trifles which could be given as presents. They range from ring trays and inkwells to match strikers and bookends. They were produced in very large numbers and, though many of them were the work of major artists, they are nearly always unsigned.

COMMEMORATIVE WARE . . .

. . . large numbers of these were produced to mark historical events like centenaries and military actions during the 19th and early 20th centuries. Many of the designs were by John Broad and most had applied, moulded decorations.

DOULTON AND SLATER'S WARE

. . . is also known as 'Chine' and is easily recognised because it was decorated by lace pressed into the stoneware body while still soft. It was then glazed, decorated and gilded with applied motifs. The technique was the invention of John Slater who was Art Director at Burslem between 1887 and 1914.

MINIATURES . . .

. . . were very popular during the last quarter of the 19th century because they made amusing gifts. They were scaled down glazed stoneware copies of popular lines of vases and jugs and great care was taken to ensure the proportions were true. Many of the miniatures were decorated by major artists.

NATURAL FOLIAGE WARE . . .

. . . was produced by pressing real leaves into soft clay and the impressions were joined by twigs which were incised before the vase was glazed. This Ware was produced between 1886 and 1936.

SILICON WARE . . .

. . . is a hard, smooth, high fired stoneware with a thin glaze. It was produced in the greatest quantities between 1880 and 1912 and decorated by some of the most famous Doulton artists. Carved, pierced, gilt or lustre painted Silicon Ware can be found in considerable quantities and the predominant colours are light blue and white on buff or brown bodies.

Stoneware jug commemorating the Golden Jubilee of Queen Victoria, 9in. high, circa 1897. $176 £110

SIMULATED WARE . . .

. . . is a type of ware in which silicon bodies have been painted to look like some other material. For example there are pottery cricket balls or cast iron weights as well as jugs that look as if they were made of copper with painted on joints and rivets and a lustre glaze. They were even given a coating of simulated verdigris. Very popular when they first appeared, were leatherwork jugs with black silicon bodies that had a dark textured surface stitched with imitation waxed threads. This range was produced from 1887, when the simulated copper first appeared, until around 1910.

SPORTING SUBJECTS . . .

. . . comprise a series of stoneware mugs and jugs decorated with relief figures of famous sportsmen. They were introduced in 1880 and the figures were the work of John Broad. One of the best examples is his W. G. Grace jug showing the famous cricketer in eight different poses.

ADVERTISING WARES

Stoneware matchstriker and holder made for Worthingtons, 4in. high, circa 1900.
$72 £45

Match-holder and striker advertising 'Sir Edward Lee's Old Scotch Whisky', with the slogan 'As supplied to the House of Commons'.
$64 £40

Small character jug liqueur flask made for W. Walklate Ltd. depicting 'Rip Van Winkle', 4in. high.
$61 £38

Cream jug made for the Savoy Hotel, London, 3¾in. high, circa 1930, c.m.l. & c.
$16 £10

Scotsman and Irishman whisky flasks in a wooden tantalus designed for Asprey & Co. of New Bond St., London.
$5600 £3500

A pin tray with a map of New Zealand, circa 1928.
$38 £24

Doulton whisky jug made for Charles Wilkinson & Co., featuring Burns Cottage, Ayr.
$96 £60

Pick-Kwik character jug inscribed 'Pick-Kwik, Derby, Sells Jim Beam Whiskey', circa 1984.
$67 £42

A whisky bottle made for Bell's Old Scotch Whisky, 7¾in. high, circa 1950.
$24 £15

33

Small character jug liqueur
flask made for W. Walklate Ltd.
depicting 'Falstaff', 4in. high.
$61 £38

Doulton Lambeth Improved
Foot Warmer. $32 £20

Doulton Lambeth stoneware
match-holder and striker for
John Dewar & Sons.
$64 £40

Display sign of a Beefeater for
Illustrated London News, 8in.
high. $1376 £850

A Doulton Lambeth stoneware
sanitary fountain. $48 £30

Display sign for 'Army Club
Cigarettes' depicting the bust of
a soldier. $128 £80

A small 'Auld Lang Syne'
whisky flagon depicting an Inn
scene, 4in. high. $56 £35

Pick-Kwik character jug, 4in.
high, made in a limited edition
of 2000, circa 1982. $67 £42

Charrington Toby jug inscribed
'Toby Ale', 9¹/₄in. high.
$180 £120

A Royal Doulton advertising model of a bulldog, 14.7cm. high, c.m.l. & c., Rd. no. 645658. **$960 £600**

A Doulton Lambeth stoneware ashtray match holder, 'Queen Anne's Mansion'. **$48 £30**

Small character jug liqueur flask for W. Walklate Ltd. depicting 'Poacher', 4in. high. **$61 £38**

A Royal Doulton figural bottle for Sandiman's Port, 10¼in. high, circa 1920-1956, c.m.l. & c. **$72 £45**

A Royal Doulton advertising jug, William Grant, Specially Commissioned for Wm. Grant & Sons Ltd., limited edition of 500, 1986. **$640 £400**

Whisky flask in the form of a crow made for National Distillers of Kentucky, circa 1954. **$240 £150**

Royal Doulton Dewar's whisky moonflask, printed design no. 181, circa 1919, 8in. high. **$400 £250**

'The McCallum', a large Kingsware character jug made for D. & J. McCallum Whisky Distillers, circa 1930. **$2320 £1450**

Early 20th century 'Big Ben Scotch Whisky' jug. **$144 £90**

A miniature stoneware bottle
vase for Jas. Shoolbred & Co.,
circa 1902, 2¹/₂in. high.
$48 £30

A stoneware match striker made
for Bass, 'Bottled Bass', 3¹/₂in.
high, circa 1919, c.m.l. & c.
$70 £44

A replica decanter made for
Fortnum & Mason, as held in
their crypt dated 1700 A.D., 7 in.
high, c.m.l. & c. $61 £38

An earthenware presentation
beaker, 'Victoria R.I. Diamond
Jubilee', made for Lewis &
Hyland, Ashford, circa 1897.
$72 £45

Pip, Squeak and Wilfred, an
ashtray made for The Daily
Mirror, Fetter Lane, London,
4in. high, circa 1930.
$432 £270

A tea caddy made for 'Twinings
of the Strand', June 1953, 7in.
high. $104 £65

An ashtray made for
Chessington and Paignton Zoo
& Circus, circa 1950, c.m.l. & c.
$16 £10

A stoneware barge made for
Downey, 4 Pratt St., Lambeth,
circa 1890. $112 £70

An ashtray made for Craven 'A'
cigarettes, circa 1930.
$45 £28

A paperweight made for Veale
Chifferiel & Co., silicon ware,
circa 1890, 2³/₄in. high.
$112 £70

A small cream jug made for The
Waldorf Hotel, 2¹/₂in. high,
circa 1920. $16 £10

A pin tray made for the Sneyd
Collieries & Brickworks Co.
Ltd., Staffordshire, circa 1930,
c.m.l. & c. $38 £24

'Cawdor Castle', a Series Ware
dish made for R.G. Giles, Pool,
nr. Leeds, circa 1928.
$45 £28

The Major bust ashtray made
for Army Club Cigarettes,
5¹/₂in. high, circa 1920.
$88 £55

A Doulton & Co. Ltd. stoneware
brush pot, circa 1902, 3¹/₄in.
high, c.m.l. & c. $19 £12

A pin tray made for Hughes,
North St., Belfast, 'God Bless
The Cat', c.m.l. & c.
$96 £60

Counter display sign for
Grossmith's perfume, 'Tsang
Ihang' the perfume of Tibet,
circa 1923. $720 £450

A Doulton stoneware ashtray for
pipes, circa 1900, DLE.
$45 £28

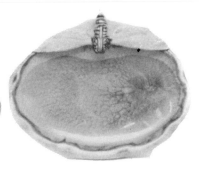

An ashtray for Doulton & Co. Ltd., Sanitary Dept. Showroom, Lambeth, circa 1930, c.m.l. & c. $35 £22

A Royal Doulton stoneware match striker advertising Dewar's Whisky, 2½in. high, c.m.l. & c. $48 £30

A stoneware soap dish made for Wright's Coal Tar Soap, circa 1960. $70 £44

Royal Doulton wireless loudspeaker made for Artandia Ltd. in the form of a feathered cockatoo perched on a rock, 15½in. high. $240 £150

A Doulton stoneware inkwell 'For Office Use Only', circa 1902. c.m.l. & c. $61 £38

A water jug made for William Younger & Co., circa 1920. $56 £35

'Glen Garry Old Highland Whisky' jug with blue lettering, 7½in. high. $96 £60

A stoneware jug made for Style & Winch Ltd., 4¼in. high, circa 1910. $70 £44

Royal Doulton 'Ginger Wine' barrel made for Rawlings, complete with tap, 10in. high. $192 £120

ANIMAL FIGURES

Character Dog, head turned, HN2508, 2½in. high, withdrawn 1985. $48 £30

English Setter, HN1050, 3¾in.high, c.m., withdrawn 1985. $56 £35

Irish Setter, HN1055, 5¼in. high, withdrawn 1985. $64 £40

Persian Cat, HN999, 5in. high, c.m.l. & c., withdrawn 1985. $61 £38

Cocker Spaniel & Pheasant, HN1138, 5¼in. high, withdrawn 1985. $104 £65

Cocker Spaniel, HN1036, 5in. high, c.m., withdrawn 1985. $67 £42

Character Dog, standing, HN2509, 2¹/₂in. high, withdrawn 1985. $56 £35

Character Kitten, cleaning paw, HN2583, 2in. high, c.m., withdrawn 1985. $45 £28

French Poodle, HN2631, 5¹/₂in. high, c.m.l. & c., withdrawn 1985. $61 £38

Cairn, sitting, K11, 2¹/₄in. high, c.m., withdrawn 1985. $64 £40

Scottish Terrier, begging, K10, 3¹/₂in. high, withdrawn 1985. $64 £40

Collie, HN1059, 3¹/₂in. high, c.m.l. & c., withdrawn 1985. $64 £40

Cocker Spaniel, K9, 2½in. high, c.m.l. & c., withdrawn 1985. $64 £40

Character Kitten, HN2584, 1¾in. high, c.m., withdrawn 1985. $45 £28

Three Terrier Puppies, in a basket, HN2588, 2¾in.
high, c.m.l. & c., withdrawn 1985. $45 £28

Scottish Terrier, sitting, K18, 2¼in. high, c.m.,
withdrawn 1985. $64 £40

Character Dog, bone in mouth, HN1159, 3¾in.
high, withdrawn 1985. $61 £38

A Royal Doulton figure of a bulldog draped in the
Union Jack, 7in. high, printed marks. $1040 £650

Character Dog, with plate, HN1158, 3in. high, withdrawn 1985.   **$64 £40**

Character Dog, with brown ball, HN1103, 2¹/₂in. high, withdrawn 1985.   **$51 £32**

Welsh Corgi, HN2559, 3¹/₂in, c.m., withdrawn 1985.   **$61 £38**

Siamese Cat, standing, HN2660, 5¹/₄in. high, c.m., withdrawn 1985.   **$45 £28**

Bulldog, white, small, HN1074, 3¹/₄in. high, withdrawn 1985.   **$77 £48**

River Hog, HN2663, 3¹/₂in. high, c.m.l. & c., withdrawn 1985.   **$176 £110**

ANIMAL FIGURES

Puppy in a basket, HN2585, 2in. high, withdrawn 1985. $48 £30

Cocker Spaniels, asleep, HN2590, 1³/₄in. high, c.m.l. & c., withdrawn 1985. $48 £30

Labrador, HN2667, 5in. high, c.m., withdrawn 1985. $61 £38

Fox Terrier, small, HN1014, withdrawn 1985. $61 £38

Rough Haired Terrier, HN1014, 4in. high, c.m., withdrawn 1985. $61 £38

Cocker Spaniel, HN1020, 5¹/₄in. high, c.m., withdrawn 1985. $61 £38

Royal Doulton 'Fox in Red Frock Coat', HN100, 16cm. high, c.m.l. & c.   **$336 £210**

Dachshund, HN1128, 3³/₄in. high, c.m., withdrawn 1985.   **$61 £38**

The Gude Grey Mare, HN2519, 7³/₄in. high, withdrawn 1985.   **$352 £220**

Boxer, HN2643, 6¹/₂in. high, withdrawn 1985.   **$64 £40**

Dalmation, HN1113, 5¹/₄in. high, withdrawn 1985.   **$70 £44**

A Royal Doulton model, 'Kingfisher', 10.5cm. high, c.m.l. & c.   **$88 £55**

ANIMAL FIGURES

A Royal Doulton Cairn begging, HN2589, 4in. high, withdrawn 1985. $64 £40

English Setter and Pheasant, HN2529, 8½in. high, c.m.l. & c., withdrawn 1985. $288 £180

Cocker Spaniel, in a basket, HN2586, 2¾in. high, c.m.l. & c., withdrawn 1985. $56 £35

Siamese Cat, sitting, HN2655, 5¼in. high, withdrawn 1985. $45 £28

English Setter, HN1049, 7¾in. x 12¼in., c.m., withdrawn 1985. $88 £55

Collie, medium, HN1058, 5¼in. high, withdrawn 1985. $72 £45

Pride of the Shires, HN2528, 9in. high, withdrawn 1985. $256 £160

A Royal Doulton character kitten, curled asleep, HN2581, withdrawn 1985, 1¹/₂in. high. $45 £28

Huntsman Fox, HN6448, 4¹/₂in. high, c.m.l. & c., withdrawn 1985. $61 £38

Bulldog, with the Union Jack draped over his back, c.m.l. & c. Large $416 £260; Small $384 £240; Min. $416 £260

Royal Doulton model of a rhinoceros, by Leslie Harradine, 6¹/₄in. high. $896 £560

Tiger on Rock, a Royal Doulton Prestige figure, HN2639, 11¹/₂ x 14in., c.m.l. & c. $880 £550

ART POTTERY

Doulton crackleglaze plate with shaped edge. $35 £22

Doulton crackleglaze Deadwood teapot. $77 £48

Doulton Burslem Royles Patent self pouring teapot, circa 1900. $144 £90

A Doulton Lambeth coffee pot painted with a purple iris, circa 1879. $352 £220

Doulton Art Pottery jardiniere with a blue ground and applied flowers, 8³/₄in. high. $144 £90

An oviform pate-sur-pate vase decorated with birds by Florence Barlow, 15in. high. $560 £350

Doulton jug of tapered cylindrical form decorated with a bird on a branch, by Florence Barlow, circa 1890. $320 £200

A Royal Doulton blue and white oval plaque, printed with a mother and child picking flowers, 14in. wide. $400 £250

A Doulton Burslem baluster vase painted with an Edwardian lady, by H.G. Theaker, 10¹/₄in. high. $528 £330

A Royal Doulton Art Pottery vase decorated with stylised flowers, 8in. high, circa 1910. $96 £60

A pair of Doulton Lambeth stoneware vases by Florence E. Barlow, circa 1906. $480 £300

Royal Doulton Art Pottery vase, 9in. high, circa 1910, $160 £100

Doulton Lambeth Carrara Ware vase with flared neck by Josephine Durtnall, 16in. high. $720 £450

Royal Doulton bowl, Japanese Fan, designed by H. Tittensor, introduced 1921, withdrawn 1938. $480 £300

Royal Doulton vase painted by Ethel Beard, 13in. high. $192 £120

One of a pair of Royal Doulton baluster shaped vases, by Francis C. Pope, 8³/₄in. high. $224 £140

Pair of Royal Doulton cylindrical vases painted by L. Johnson, 30cm. high. $832 £520

Doulton Lambeth ewer by Hannah Barlow, decorated with a pate-sur-pate frieze of dogs, 11in, high. $480 £300

Royal Doulton pottery
jardiniere, cobalt blue glazed,
9in. diam. $136 £85

A Doulton Lambeth Silicon
Ware oviform vase, by Edith D.
Lupton and Ada Dennis,
20.5cm. high, dated 1885.
$352 £220

A Royal Doulton earthenware
globular vase, 21.8cm. high,
c.m.l. & c. $120 £75

Doulton Lambeth vase by
Florence Barlow, decorated in
pate-sur-pate with an owl,
12½in. high. $464 £290

Pair of Doulton saltglazed
stoneware baluster vases, circa
1906/7, 12½in. high.
$480 £300

A Doulton Crown Lambeth two-
handled vase and cover
decorated with panels of wild
flowers by Emma Harrison,
circa 1889. $480 £300

A large Doulton Burslem vase
and cover, painted by G. White,
signed, circa 1910, 20¾in. high.
$1360 £850

A Royal Doulton jug decorated
with a maiden wearing a flowing
dress, 10½in. high. $240 £150

A fine hand painted vase with
bird and flower decoration,
11in. high. $640 £400

CHANG

A Chang bowl by Noke and Nixon, 8in. diam.　$960 £600

A Royal Doulton Chang vase by Nixon and Noke, 9¼in. high, circa 1925.　$1920 £1200

Royal Doulton Chang bowl by Nixon and Noke, circa 1930.　$1600 £1000

Royal Doulton Chang vase by Noke and Moore, 7½in. high, circa 1935.　$880 £550

A Chang vase by Noke and Nixon, 10in. high.　$4400 £2750

A Chang vase by Noke and Nixon, 10in. high.　$2000 £1250

Royal Doulton Chang vase by Noke and Nixon, 8¾in. high.　$1600 £1000

A Chang vase by Noke and Nixon, 7in. high.　$1280 £800

Royal Doulton Chang vase by Nixon and Noke, 5¾in. high, circa 1920.　$800 £500

CHANG

A Chang bowl by Noke and
Nixon, 5in. high. $1360 £850

A Chang vase by Noke and
Nixon, 5in. high. $1280 £800

A Chang bowl by Noke and
Nixon, 8in, diam. $1840 £1150

A Chang vase by Noke and
Nixon, 10in. high. $1920 £1200

A Chang vase by Noke and
Nixon, 8in. high. $1400 £900

The Chang Potter lamp base by
Noke and Nixon, 10¹/₂in. high.
$4480 £2800

Royal Doulton Chang vase by
Noke and Nixon, 10¹/₄in. high.
$1360 £850

Royal Doulton Chang vase by
C.J. Noke and Harry Nixon,
7¹/₂in. high, circa 1930.
$1920 £1200

A Chang vase by Noke and
Nixon, 5in. high. $960 £600

CHANG

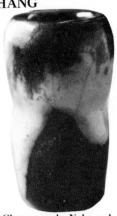

A Chang vase by Noke and Nixon, 8in. high. $1520 £950

A Royal Doulton 'Chang' jar and cover, by Harry Nixon, 8in. high. $1120 £700

A Chang vase by Noke and Nixon, 9in. high. $1600 £1000

CHINESE JADE

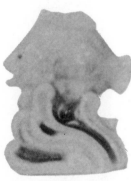

A Chinese jade model of a fish in white and green by Noke, $3^{1}/_{4}$in. high. $1080 £675

Royal Doulton Chinese jade two-handled bowl in white and green, $3^{1}/_{2}$in. high. $512 £320

'Leaping Salmon', a large Chinese jade figure, signed Noke and Nixon, $11^{1}/_{2}$in. high, circa 1930. $1760 £1100

FAIENCE

Royal Doulton faience vase by John H. McLennan, decorated with panels representing Earth and Water, $13^{1}/_{2}$in. high. $368 £230

A pair of Doulton Lambeth faience oil lamp bases decorated by Esther Lewis, $10^{1}/_{4}$in. high. $720 £450

A Doulton Lambeth faience vase painted with stylised flowers, by Emily Gillman, $9^{1}/_{4}$in. high. $176 £110

FAIENCE

A Doulton Lambeth faience
wall plaque decorated with
fruit and foliage, 13¾in. diam.
$192 £120

Doulton Lambeth faience vase
decorated with daffodils and
narcissi, 10½in. high.
$176 £110

Doulton Lambeth faience vase
with the artist's monogram for
Mary Butterton, circa 1880.
$288 £180

Doulton Lambeth faience vase
by Mary Capes, decorated with
flowers, circa 1878. $224 £140

A Doulton Lambeth faience
coffee service painted with
azaleas, dahlias and dog roses,
circa 1879. $352 £220

One of a pair of Doulton faience
vases decorated by Katherine
Smallfield, 12½in. high.
$576 £360

A large Doulton Lambeth
faience plaque by Florence E.
Lewis, 15½in. diam., circa 1880.
$288 £180

Pair of Doulton Lambeth faience
vases decorated with sprays of
leaves and flowers by Mary M.
Arding, 14¾in. high, circa 1880.
$512 £320

Doulton faience moonflask
decorated with leaves and wild
flowers, 14¼in. high.
$608 £380

FAIENCE

A Doulton Lambeth stoneware vase, signed initials of Florence E. Barlow, impressed date for 1880, 10in. high.　$264 £165

A Doulton Lambeth faience wall plaque, painted by L. Watt, 51cm. diam.　$400 £250

A faience vase decorated with leaves and flowers, by Josephine A. Durtnall, 5in. high, circa 1876.　$104 £65

A Doulton Lambeth vase by Kate Rogers, decorated with wild flowers, 8in. high.　$240 £150

A pair of Doulton faience vases by Fanny Stable, decorated with dragons amongst clouds, 11½in. high, circa 1879.　$720 £450

A faience vase decorated with panels of flowers, by Alberta L. Green, 9¼in. high, circa 1882.　$208 £130

A Doulton Lambeth faience moonflask, decorated by H. Barlow.　$608 £380

Doulton Lambeth faience two-handled vase decorated with a band of wild flowers by Margaret M. Challis, 7½in. high, circa 1880.　$176 £110

Doulton Lambeth faience wall plaque, 'Old Cottage, Bromley, Kent', by Esther Lewis, 14¾in. diam., circa 1882.　$336 £210

FAIENCE

A faience vase decorated with entwined leaves and fruit, 8$\frac{1}{2}$in. high, circa 1877. $160 £100

A faience teapot decorated with flowers, by Gertrude Smith, 6in. high, circa 1889. $160 £100

A faience vase decorated with flowers and birds, by Josephine A. Durtnall, 10$\frac{1}{2}$in. high, circa 1887. $224 £140

Royal Doulton faience vase and cover, by Ada Dennis, Esther Lewis and Mary Denley, 24in. high, circa 1885. $5600 £3500

A Doulton Lambeth faience tile panel, 61.5 x 20.6cm., printed c.m. on reverse of each. $432 £270

Doulton Lambeth faience water jug decorated with flowers, 7$\frac{1}{2}$in. high. $93 £58

A large Doulton faience moon-fask decorated with flowers and fruit, 14$\frac{1}{4}$in. high. $608 £380

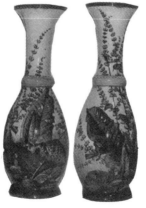

Pair of Doulton Lambeth faience vases decorated with sprays of leaves, by Mary M. Arding, 14$\frac{1}{4}$in. high, circa 1880. $512 £320

Doulton Lambeth faience wall plaque by Helen A. Arding, circa 1880. $224 £140

FLAMBE

A Doulton Lambeth flambe ashtray with elephant heads on the corners, by Moore, 3¹/₂in. wide.
$176 £110

A Royal Doulton flambe figure of a crab, 4¹/₂in. wide.
$400 £250

The Dragon, a Royal Doulton flambe figure, 2085, introduced 1973, 7¹/₂in. high.   Rec. Retail Price

Royal Doulton flambe jardiniere decorated with a desert scene. $448 £280

Royal Doulton flambe model of a collie dog, 7³/₄in. high, circa 1926. $480 £300

A Royal Doulton flambe figure modelled as a seated Buddha, 6³/₄in. high, possible by C.J. Noke.
$928 £580

Rhinoceros, a Royal Doulton flambe figure, 615, introduced 1973, 9¹/₂in. long.   Rec. Retail Price

Royal Doulton flambe model of a terrier, 5¹/₄in. high, circa 1930. $272 £170

FLAMBE

Pig Dish, 2¹/₂in. high x 4¹/₂in. long, silver mounted, circa 1927. $480 £300

Tiger, snarling, HN225, 2¹/₂in. high x 9in. long, circa 1930. $400 £250

Guinea Fowl, Model 69, 3in. high. $192 £120

Pomegranate, 2³/₄in. high. $240 £150

Monkeys, embracing, Model 486, 5¹/₂in. high.
                    $224 £140

Fox, sitting, head up, Model 102, 9½in. high, designed by Noke, introduced 1962, withdrawn 1965. $275 £170

'The Cat' sitting, a Royal Doulton flambe model 2259, 11¹/₂in. high.   Rec. Retail Price

A Royal Doulton flambe model of a pair of penguins, 15cm. high, c.m.l. & c. $128 £80

FLAMBE

Mallard, Model 654, 4in. high, designed by Noke, introduced 1920, withdrawn 1961. $312 £195

Fox, slinking, full length, Model 29, 2½in. high x 12in. long. $192 £120

Leaping Salmon, Model 666, 12in. high, designed by Noke, introduced 1940, withdrawn 1950. $480 £300

Elephant, a Royal Doulton flambe model 489A, 5½in. high.   Rec. Retail Price

Monkey, dunce's cap, HN972, 5½in. high. $480 £300

Penguin, double, Model 103, HN133, 6in. high, circa 1929. $192 £120

Pigeons, two fantail, Model 46, 3¾in. high. $320 £200

A Royal Doulton flambe model of a bulldog, 14.2cm. high, c.m.l. & c., impressed date 10.26, no. 135. $1600 £1000

FLAMBE

Tiger, Model 1809, 5¹/₂in. long.   Rec. Retail Price

Two foxes, curled asleep, Model 15, 4in. long.
$192 £120

Royal Doulton flambe Buddha, signed Noke, 8in.
high. $640 £400

Fish, group of, Model 682, 6¹/₂in. high, circa 1921.
$432 £270

Dobermann Pinscher, a Royal Doulton
figure, HN2645, 6in. high, withdrawn 1985, c.m.
$64 £40

Mouse, on cube, Model 1164, HN255, 2¹/₂in. high,
circa 1908. $320 £200

A Royal Doulton flambe model of an elephant,
16.8cm. high, c.m.l. & c., signed Noke. $288 £180

Elephant, trunk down, 12in. high, circa 1930.
$880 £550

ART POTTERY

HOLBEIN WARE

A Royal Doulton Holbein Ware plaque, by Walter Nunn, 11.4 x 18.3cm. image area, c.m.l. & c.
$640 £400

A Holbein Ware vase with silver rim, 9in. high.
$320 £200

A large Royal Doulton Burslem Holbein Ware jardiniere decorated with four cavaliers playing cards, 13¼in. high, signed W. Nunn.
$720 £450

IMPASTO

A Doulton Lambeth Impasto jardiniere decorated with wild flowers by Rosa Keen, 10½in. high.
$288 £180

A Doulton Lambeth Impasto vase decorated with chrysanthemums, by Rosa Keen, 11in. high.
$264 £165

A Doulton Lambeth Impasto wall plaque decorated with chrysanthemums, by Frances Linnell, 14½in. diam., circa 1882.
$184 £115

MORRISIAN WARE

Doulton Burslem Morrisian Ware teapot with a frieze of girls dancing, 8in. high.
$160 £100

Doulton Burslem Morrisian Ware tobacco jar and cover decorated with a band of dancing girls, 5½in. high.
$144 £90

A Doulton Burslem Morrisian Ware teapot decorated with a band of dancing maidens, 7¾in. high, circa 1899
$160 £100

SETS

A Royal Doulton 'Tango' pattern porcelain part coffee set, coffee pot, 20.75cm. high, c.m.l. & c., impressed dates 1.1.35 and 2.1.35. $356 £220

A Doulton Burslem porcelain fruit set, by Walter Slater, each piece painted in natural colours with dandelion buds and clocks, flowers and leaves, b.r.m. & c., England Rd. no. 72067. $640 £400

A Royal Doulton 'Aubrey' shape toilet set comprising a large bowl, jug, chamber pot, soap dish and toothbrush holder, decorated with Art Nouveau floral motifs in sepia, rust, blue and yellow colours. $480 £300

SUNG

Royal Doulton Sung model of a rabbit, 4in. long, circa 1928.
$480 £300

Royal Doulton Sung vase decorated with a leopard in a mountainous landscape, 6³/₄in. high.
$200 £125

Royal Doulton Sung bowl decorated with stylised flowers, 9in. diam., circa 1920. $480 £300

Royal Doulton Sung vase by Noke, decorated with a peacock painted by A. Eaton, 10¹/₂in. high. $480 £300

A large Royal Doulton Sung vase by Arthur Eaton, decorated with dragons amongst clouds, 13in. high, circa 1930.
$1280 £800

Royal Doulton Sung vase decorated by A. Eaton, 14¹/₂in. high.
$1088 £680

Royal Doulton Sung vase by Charles Noke and Fred Moore, 10¹/₄in. high, circa 1930.
$416 £260

A Royal Doulton Sung vase and cover, circa 1926, 13in. high.
$528 £330

A Royal Doulton Sung vase by Noke, 6³/₄in. high, circa 1928.
$640 £400

SUNG

Royal Doulton Sung vase
painted with fish swimming
among weeds, 6¼in. high, circa
1930. $240 £150

A Royal Doulton Sung ashtray
by Charles Noke and Fred
Moore, 3¾in. square.
                    $200 £125

A Royal Doulton Sung vase by
Charles Noke and Fred Moore,
7in. high, circa 1930.
                    $240 £150

A tall Royal Doulton Sung vase
by Charles Noke and F. Allen,
11½in. high, circa 1930.
                    $512 £320

Royal Doulton Sung vase signed
by A. Eaton, 5¾in. high.
                    $1152 £720

Royal Doulton Sung vase decorated with a peacock by Arthur
Eaton, 8½in. high, circa 1925.
                    $880 £550

Royal Doulton Sung vase by
Noke, decorated with flying
birds, 8¾in. high. $800 £500

Royal Doulton Sung bowl decorated with a band of geometric
ornament, 8in. diam., circa
1925. $400 £250

Royal Doulton Sung tobacco jar
and cover of hexagonal form,
6¼in. high, circa 1930.
                    $400 £250

TITANIAN WARE

A Royal Doulton Titanian Ware teapot, 6¹/₂in. high, circa 1920. $80 £50

A Royal Doulton Titanian Ware vase by F. Henri, decorated with a cat seated beneath a crescent moon. $432 £270

Royal Doulton Titanian Ware sugar bowl and cover, 4¹/₄in. high, circa 1922. $80 £50

Royal Doulton Titanian figure, 'The Smiling Buddha', by Noke, issued in 1921, withdrawn 1938. $960 £600

A pair of Royal Doulton Cecil Aldin Titanian glazed Series ware vases, 15.5cm. high, D4525. $560 £350

Royal Doulton Titanian figure of 'Blighty', 11¹/₂in. high, circa 1919. $640 £400

Royal Doulton Titanian vaes by Harry Allen decorated with a long eared owl, 13in. high. $560 £350

A Royal Doulton Titanian bowl decorated with a dragon, 14¹/₂in. diam. $160 £100

A Royal Doulton Titanian Ware teapot, 6¹/₂in. high, circa 1922. $45 £28

ANNE BOLEYN D6644
Designer: D. Tootle
Size: Large
Issued: 1975-
Rec. Retail Price

ANNE BOLEYN D6650
Designer: D. Tootle
Size: Small
Issued: 1980-
Rec. Retail Price

ANNE BOLEYN D6651
Designer: D. Tootle
Size: Mini
Issued: 1980-
Rec. Retail Price

ANNE OF CLEVES D6650
Designer: M. Abberley
Size: Small
Issued: 1987
Rec. Retail Price

ANNE OF CLEVES D6651
Designer: M Abberley
Size: Mini
Issued: 1987
Rec. Retail Price

ANNE OF CLEVES D6653
Designer: M. Abberley
Size: Large
Issued: 1980
Price: $160 £100 (Ears Up)

ANNE OF CLEVES D6653
Designer: M. Abberley
Size: Large
Issued: 1980-
Rec. Retail Price

ANNIE OAKLEY D6732
Designer: S. Taylor
Size: Medium
Issued: 1985-1988
Price: $40 £25

ANTIQUE DEALER
(Kevin Francis) D6809
Limited edition of 5000
Designer: G. Blower
Size: Large
Issued: 1988
Price: $104 £65

ANTONY AND CLEOPATRA
D6728 Limited edition of 9500
Designer: M. Abberley
Size: Large
Issued: 1985-
Price: $90 £55

APOTHECARY D6567
Designer: M. Henk
Size: Large
Issued: 1963-1983
Price: $77 £48

APOTHECARY D6574
Designer: M. Henk
Size: Small
Issued: 1963-1983
Price: $50 £32

ANNE OF CLEVES D6653

ANNIE OAKLEY D6732

ANTIQUE DEALER D6809

APOTHECARY D6581
Designer: M. Henk
Size: Mini
Issued: 1963-1983
Price: $45 £28

ARAMIS D6441
Designer: M. Henk
Size: Large
Issued: 1956-
Rec. Retail Price

ARAMIS D6454
Designer: M. Henk
Size: Small
Issued: 1956-
Rec. Retail Price

ARAMIS D6508
Designer: M. Henk
Size: Mini
Issued: 1960-
Rec. Retail Price

ARAMIS D6828
(Peter Jones) New colourway
Limited edition of 1000
Designer: M. Henk
Size: Large
Issued: 1988
Price: $80 £50

'ARD OF EARING D6588

'ARD OF EARING D6588
Designer: D. Biggs
Size: Large
Issued: 1964-1967
Price: $720 £450

'ARD OF EARING D6591
Designer: D. Biggs
Size: Small
Issued: 1964-1967
Price: $560 £350

'ARD OF EARING D6594
Designer: D. Biggs
Size: Mini
Issued: 1964-1967
Price: $720 £450

'ARRIET D6208
Designer: H. Fenton
Size: Large
Issued: 1947-1960
Price: $160 £100

'ARRIET D6236
Designer: H. Fenton
Size: Small
Issued: 1947-1960
Price: $72 £45

'ARRIET D6250
Designer: H. Fenton
Size: Mini
Issued: 1947-1960
Price: $64 £40

'ARRIET D6256
Designer: H. Fenton
Size: Tiny
Issued: 1947-1960
Price: $120 £75

'ARRY D6207
Designer: H. Fenton
Size: Large
Issued: 1947-1960
Price: $160 £100

ATHOS D6827

'ARRIET D6208

'ARRY D6235
Designer: H. Fenton
Size: Small
Issued: 1947-1960
Price: $72 £45

'ARRY D6249
Designer: H. Fenton
Size: Mini
Issued: 1947-1960
Price: $64 £40

'ARRY D6255
Designer: H. Fenton
Size: Tiny
Issued: 1947-1960
Price: $128 £80

ATHOS D6439
Designer: M. Henk
Size: Large
Issued: 1956-
Rec. Retail Price

ATHOS D6452
Designer: M. Henk
Size: Small
Issued: 1956-
Rec. Retail Price

ATHOS D6509
Designer: M. Henk
Size: Mini
Issued: 1960-
Rec. Retail Price

ATHOS D6827
(Peter Jones) New colourway
Limited edition of 1000
Designer: M. Henk
Size: Large
Issued: 1988
Price: $80 £50

AUCTIONEER (Kevin Francis)
D6838 Limited edition of 5000
Designer: G. Blower
Size: Large
Issued: 1988
Price: $104 £65

AULD MAC D5823
Designer: H. Fenton
Size: Large
Issued: 1937-1985
Price: $64 £40

AULD MAC D5824
Designer: H. Fenton
Size: Small
Issued: 1937-1985
Price: $40 £25

AULD MAC D6253
Designer: H. Fenton
Size: Mini
Issued: 1937-1985
Price: $29 £18

AULD MAC D6257
Designer: H. Fenton
Size: Tiny
Issued: 1946-1960
Price: $144 £90

BACCHUS D6499
Designer: M. Henk
Size: Large
Issued: 1959-
Rec. Retail Price

ANTONY AND CLEOPATRA   D6728

ARAMIS D6828   **APOTHECARY D6567**

AUCTIONEER   D6838   **AULD MAC D6253**

BACCHUS D6505
Designer: M. Henk
Size: Small
Issued: 1959-
Rec. Retail Price

BACCHUS D6521
Designer: M. Henk
Size: Mini
Issued: 1960-
Rec. Retail Price

BEEFEATER D6206
Designer: H. Fenton
Size: Large
Issued: 1947-
Rec. Retail Price

BEEFEATER D6233
Designer: H. Fenton
Size: Small
Issued: 1947-
Rec. Retail Price

BEEFEATER D6251
Designer: H. Fenton
Size: Mini
Issued: 1947-
Rec. Retail Price

BEEFEATER (GR on handle) D6206
Designer: H. Fenton
Size: Large
Issued: 1947-1953
Price: $96 £60

BEEFEATER (GR on yellow handle) D 6206
Designer: H. Fenton
Size: Large
Issued: 1947-1953
Price: $880 £550

BEEFEATER (GR on yellow handle) D 6206
Designer: H. Fenton
Size: Small
Issued: 1947-1953
Price: $720 £450

BEEFEATER (GR on handle) D6233
Designer: H. Fenton
Size: Small
Issued: 1947-1953
Price: $64 £40

BEEFEATER (GR on handle) D6251
Designer: H. Fenton
Size: Mini
Issued: 1947-1953
Price: $64 £40

BEEFEATER D6806 (Collectors' Club)
Designer: R. Tabbenor
Size: Tiny
Issued: 1988
Rec. Retail Price

BENJAMIN FRANKLIN D6695
Designer: E. Griffiths
Size: Small
Issued: 1982-1988
Price: $40 £25

BEEFEATER   D6206

BENJAMIN FRANKLIN D6695

BUZ FUZ D5838

BLACKSMITH D6571
Designer: D. Biggs
Size: Large
Issued: 1963-1983
Price: $77 £48

BLACKSMITH D6578
Designer: D. Biggs
Size: Small
Issued: 1963-1983
Price: $52 £32

BLACKSMITH D6585
Designer: D. Biggs
Size: Mini
Issued: 1963-1983
Price: $48 £30

BONNIE PRINCE CHARLIE D6858
Designer: W.K. Harper
Size: Large
Issued: 1990
Rec. Retail Price

BOOTMAKER D6572
Designer: D. Biggs
Size: Large
Issued: 1963-1983
Price: $77 £48

BOOTMAKER D6579
Designer: D. Biggs
Size: Small
Issued: 1963-1983
Price: $52 £32

BOOTMAKER D6586
Designer: D. Biggs
Size: Mini
Issued: 1963-1983
Price: $48 £30

BUFFALO BILL D6735
Designer: S. Taylor
Size: Medium
Issued: 1985-1988
Price: $40 £25

BUSKER D6775
Designer: S. Taylor
Size: Large
Issued: 1988
Rec. Retail Price

BUZ FUZ D5838
Designer: L. Harradine &
          H. Fenton
Size: Intermediate
Issued: 1938-1948
Price: $136 £85

BUZ FUZ D5838
Designer: L. Harradine &
          H. Fenton
Size: Small
Issued: 1948-1960
Price: $80 £50

CAPTAIN AHAB D6500
Designer: G. Sharpe
Size: Large
Issued: 1959-1985
Price: $64 £40

BUSKER D6775

BOOTMAKER D6572

BLACKSMITH D6571

BACCHUS D6499

BUFFALO BILL D6735

CAPTAIN AHAB D6500

CAPTAIN AHAB D6506
Designer: G. Sharpe
Size: Small
Issued: 1959-1985
Price: $48 £30

CAPTAIN AHAB D6522
Designer: G. Sharpe
Size: Mini
Issued: 1960-1985
Price: $40 £25

CAP'N CUTTLE D5842
Designer: L. Harradine
Size: Intermediate
Issued: 1938-1945
Price: $120 £75

CAP'N CUTTLE D5842
Designer: L. Harradine
Size: Small
Issued: 1948-1960
Price: $80 £50

CAPTAIN HENRY MORGAN D6467
Designer: G. Sharpe
Size: Large
Issued: 1958-1982
Price: $80 £50

CAPTAIN HENRY MORGAN D6469
Designer: G. Sharpe
Size: Small
Issued: 1958-1982
Price: $56 £35

CAPTAIN HENRY MORGAN D6510
Designer: G. Sharpe
Size: Mini
Issued: 1960-1982
Price: $40 £25

CAPTAIN HOOK D6597
Designer: M. Henk & D. Biggs
Size: Large
Issued: 1965-1971
Price: $416 £260

CAPTAIN HOOK D6601
Designer: M. Henk & D. Biggs
Size: Small
Issued: 1965-1971
Price: $384 £240

CAPTAIN HOOK D6605
Designer: M. Henk & D. Biggs
Size: Mini
Issued: 1965-1971
Price: $368 £230

CARDINAL D5614
Designer: C. Noke
Size: Large
Issued: 1936-1960
Price: $90 £70

CARDINAL D6033
Designer: C. Noke
Size: Small
Issued: 1939-1960
Price: $57 £42

CARDINAL D6129

CAVALIER D6114

CAPTAIN HOOK D6597

CARDINAL D6129
Designer: C. Noke
Size: Mini
Issued: 1940-1960
Price: $48 £30

CARDINAL D6258
Designer: C. Noke
Size: Tiny
Issued: 1947-1960
Price: $128 £80

CATHERINE HOWARD D6645
Designer: P. Gee
Size: Large
Issued: 1978-1989
Price: $48 £30

CATHERINE HOWARD D6692
Designer: P. Gee
Size: Small
Issued: 1984-1989
Price: $29 £18

CATHERINE HOWARD D6693
Designer: P. Gee
Size: Mini
Issued: 1984-1989
Price: $16 £10

CATHERINE OF ARAGON D6643
Designer: A. Maslankowski
Size: Large
Issued: 1975-1989
Price: $48 £30

CATHERINE OF ARAGON D6657
Designer: A. Maslankowski
Size: Small
Issued: 1981-1989
Price: $29 £18

CATHERINE OF ARAGON D6658
Designer: A. Maslankowski
Size: Mini
Issued: 1981-1989
Price: $20 £12

CATHERINE PARR D6664
Designer: M. Abberley
Size: Large
Issued: 1981-1989
Price: $48 £30

CATHERINE PARR D6752
Designer: M. Abberley
Size: Mini
Issued: 1987-1989
Price: $20 £12

CATHERINE PARR D6751
Designer: M. Abberley
Size: Small
Issued: 1987-1989
Price: $29 £18

CAVALIER D6114
Designer: H. Fenton
Size: Large
Issued: 1940-1960
Price: $96 £60

CATHERINE OF ARAGON D6643

CATHERINE PARR D6664

Mini D6693

CATHERINE HOWARD D6645

Small D6692

CAPTAIN HENRY MORGAN D6467

CAP'N CUTTLE D5842

CAVALIER D6173
Designer: H. Fenton
Size: Small
Issued: 1941-1960
Price: $56 £35

CAVALIER D6114
Designer: H. Fenton
Size: Large (with goatee
        beard)
Issued: 1940-1942
Price: $1920 £1200

CHELSEA PENSIONER D6817
Designer: S. Taylor
Size: Large
Issued: 1989
Rec. Retail Price

CHIEF SITTING BULL AND GEORGE ARMSTRONG CUSTER D6712
Limited edition of 9500
Designer: M. Abberley
Size: Large
Issued: 1984-
Price: $120 £75

CHURCHILL (Natural) D6170
Two handled Loving Cup, very rare
Designer: C. Noke
Size: Large
Issued: 1940-1941
Price: $26400 £16500

CHURCHILL (White) D6170
Two handled Loving Cup, rare
Designer: C. Noke
Size: Large
Issued: 1940-1941
Price: $8000 £5000

CHURCHILL D6849 (Lawleys)
Designer: S. Taylor
Size: Small
Issued: 1989
Price: $80 £50

CITY GENT D6815
Designer: S. Taylor
Size: Large
Issued: 1988
Rec. Retail Price

CLARK GABLE D6709
Designer: S. Taylor
Size: Large
Issued: 1984-
Price: $3520 £2200

CLOWN D5610
Designer: H. Fenton
Size: Large (Red Haired)
Issued: 1937-1942
Price: $2000 £1250

CLOWN D5610
Designer: H. Fenton
Size: Large
        (Brown Haired)
Issued: 1937-1942
Price: $2000 £1250

DICK TURPIN
D5485

CHURCHILL (Natural) D6170

CLARK GABLE D6709

CLOWN D6322
Designer: H. Fenton
Size: Large
        (White Haired)
Issued: 1951-1955
Price: $880 £550

CLOWN D5610
Designer: H. Fenton
Size: Large (Black Haired)
Issued: 1937-1942
Price: $19200 £12000

CLOWN D6834
Designer: S. Taylor
Size: Large
Issued: 1989
Rec. Retail Price

CLOWN D6796 (Kevin Francis)
Limited edition of 5000
Designer: S. Taylor
Size: Large
Issued: 1989
Rec. Retail Price

COLLECTOR D6796 (Kevin Francis) Limited edition of 5000
Designer: S. Taylor
Size: Large
Issued: 1988
Price: $110 £69

COOK and CHESHIRE CAT D6842
Designer: W.K. Harper
Size: Large
Issued: 1990
Rec. Retail Price

D'ARTAGNAN D6691
Designer: S. Taylor
Size: Large
Issued: 1982-
Rec. Retail Price

D'ARTAGNAN D6764
Designer: S. Taylor
Size: Small
Issued: 1988
Rec. Retail Price

D'ARTAGNAN D6765
Designer: S. Taylor
Size: Mini
Issued: 1988
Rec. Retail Price

DAVY CROCKET/SANTA ANNA D6729
Designer: M. Abberley
Size: Large
Issued: 1985-
Price: $104 £65

DICK TURPIN (First version) D5485
Designer: C. Noke & H. Fenton
Size: Large
Issued: 1935-1960
Price: $96 £60

DICK TURPIN (First version) D5618
Designer: C. Noke & H. Fenton
Size: Small
Issued: 1936-1960
Price: $56 £35

D'ARTAGNAN D6691

COLLECTOR D6796

DAVY CROCKET/SANTA ANNA D6729

CHIEF SITTING BULL AND GEORGE ARMSTRONG CUSTER D6712

DICK TURPIN (First version)
D6128
Designer: C. Noke & H. Fenton
Size: Mini
Issued: 1940-1960
Price: $56 £35

DICK TURPIN (Second version)
D6528
Designer: D. Biggs
Size: Large
Issued: 1960-1981
Price: $64 £40

DICK TURPIN (Second version)
D6535
Designer: D. Biggs
Size: Small
Issued: 1960-1981
Price: $56 £35

DICK TURPIN (Second version)
D6542
Designer: D. Biggs
Size: Mini
Issued: 1960-1981
Price: $40 £25

DICK WHITTINGTON
D6375
Designer: G. Blower
Size: Large
Issued: 1953-1960
Price: $256 £160

DICK WHITTINGTON
D6846 (China Guild)
Limited edition of 6000
Designer: W. K. Harper
Size: Large
Issued: 1989
Price: $104 £65

DOC HOLLIDAY D6731
Designer: S. Taylor
Size: Medium
Issued: 1985-1988
Price: $40 £25

DON QUIXOTE D6455
Designer: G. Blower
Size: Large
Issued: 1960-
Rec. Retail Price

DON QUIXOTE D6460
Designer: G. Blower
Size: Small
Issued: 1960-
Rec. Retail Price

DON QUIXOTE D6511
Designer: G. Blower
Size: Mini
Issued: 1960-
Rec. Retail Price

DRAKE D6115
Designer: H. Fenton
Size: Large (Hatless)
Issued: 1940-1941
Price: $2720 £1700

DICK WHITTINGTON D6375

FALCONER D6800

DUKE OF WELLINGTON D6848

DRAKE D6115
Designer: H. Fenton
Size: Large
Issued: 1940-1960
Price: $96 £60

DRAKE D6174
Designer: H. Fenton
Size: Small
Issued: 1941-1960
Price: $56 £35

DUKE OF WELLINGTON
D6848 (U.K. Ceramics)
Limited edition of 5000
Designer: W.K. Harper
Size: Large
Issued: 1989
Price: $120 £75

EARL MOUNTBATTEN OF
BURMA D6851 (Lawleys)
Limited edition of 9500
Designer: S. Taylor
Size: Small
Issued: 1989
Price: $80 £50

ELEPHANT TRAINER D6841
Designer: S. Taylor
Size: Large
Issued: 1990
Rec. Retail Price

ENGINE DRIVER D6823
(Lawleys)
Limited edition of 5000
Designer: S. Taylor
Size: Small
Issued: 1987
Price: $40 £25

FALCONER D6533
Designer: M. Henk
Size: Large
Issued: 1960-
Rec. Retail Price

FALCONER D6540
Designer: M. Henk
Size: Small
Issued: 1960-
Rec. Retail Price

FALCONER D6547
Designer: M. Henk
Size: Mini
Issued: 1960-
Rec. Retail Price

FALCONER D6800 (Peter
Jones) Limited edition of 1000
Designer: M. Henk
Size: Large
Issued: 1987
Price: $72 £45

FALSTAFF D6287
Designer: H. Fenton
Size: Large
Issued: 1950-
Rec. Retail Price

FALSTAFF D6385
Designer: H. Fenton
Size: Small
Issued: 1950-
Rec. Retail Price

DON QUIXOTE D6455

DICK WHITTINGTON D6846

DRAKE D6115 (Hatless)

DRAKE D6115

DOC HOLLIDAY D6731

DICK TURPIN D6528

FALSTAFF D6519
Designer: H. Fenton
Size: Mini
Issued: 1960-
Rec. Retail Price

FALSTAFF D6795 (U.K. Fairs)
Limited edition of 1500
Designer: H. Fenton
Size: Large
Issued: 1987
Price: $80 £50

FARMER JOHN D5788
Designer: C. Noke
Size: Large
Issued: 1938-1960
Price: $112 £70

FARMER JOHN D5789
Designer: C. Noke
Size: Small
Issued: 1938-1960
Price: $72 £45

FAT BOY D5840
Designer: L. Harradine &
H. Fenton
Size: Intermediate
Issued: 1938-1948
Price: $120 £75

FAT BOY D5840
Designer: L. Harradine &
H. Fenton
Size: Small
Issued: 1948-1960
Price: $72 £45

FAT BOY D6139
Designer: L. Harradine &
H. Fenton
Size: Mini
Issued: 1940-1960
Price: $56 £35

FAT BOY D6142
Designer: L. Harradine &
H. Fenton
Size: Tiny
Issued: 1940-1960
Price: $88 £55

FIREMAN D6697
Designer: R. Tabbenor
Size: Large
Issued: 1984-
Rec. Retail Price

FIREMAN D6839 (Lawleys)
Limited edition of 5000
Designer: S. Taylor
Size: Small
Issued: 1987
Price: $40 £25

FORTUNE TELLER D6497
Designer: G. Sharpe
Size: Large
Issued: 1959-1967
Price: $400 £250

FORTUNE TELLER D6503
Designer: G. Sharpe
Size: Small
Issued: 1959-1967
Price: $240 £150

GERONIMO D6733

FALSTAFF D6795

FAT BOY D5840

FORTUNE TELLER D6523
Designer: G. Sharpe
Size: Mini
Issued: 1960-1967
Price: $288 £180

FRIAR TUCK D6321
Designer: H. Fenton
Size: Large
Issued: 1951-1960
Price: $288 £180

GAOLER D6570
Designer: D. Biggs
Size: Large
Issued: 1963-1983
Price: $77 £48

GAOLER D6577
Designer: D. Biggs
Size: Small
Issued: 1963-1983
Price: $48 £30

GAOLER D6584
Designer: D. Biggs
Size: Mini
Issued: 1963-1983
Price: $40 £25

GARDENER D6630
Designer: D. Biggs
Size: Large
Issued: 1973-1981
Price: $144 £90

GARDENER D6634
Designer: D. Biggs
Size: Small
Issued: 1973-1981
Price: $96 £60

GARDENER D6638
Designer: D. Biggs
Size: Mini
Issued: 1973-1981
Price: $61 £38

GEORGE HARRISON D6727
Designer: S. Taylor
Size: Medium
Issued: 1984-
Rec. Retail Price

GEORGE WASHINGTON D6669
Designer: S. Taylor
Size: Large
Issued: 1982-
Rec. Retail Price

GEORGE WASHINGTON/ KING GEORGE III D6749
Limited edition of 9500
Designer: M. Abberley
Size: Large
Issued: 1986
Price: $88 £55

GERONIMO D6733
Designer: S. Taylor
Size: Medium
Issued: 1985-1988
Price: $40 £25

GEORGE WASHINGTON/ KING GEORGE III D6749

FIREMAN D6839

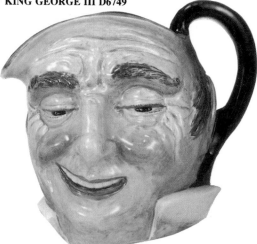

FARMER JOHN D5788

FRIAR TUCK D6321

FORTUNE TELLER D6497

GLADIATOR D6550
Designer: M. Henk
Size: Large
Issued: 1961-1967
Price: $432 £270

GLADIATOR D6553
Designer: M. Henk
Size: Small
Issued: 1961-1967
Price: $288 £180

GLADIATOR D6556
Designer: M. Henk
Size: Mini
Issued: 1961-1967
Price: $224 £140

GOLFER D6623
Designer: D. Biggs
Size: Large
Issued: 1971-
Rec. Retail Price

GOLFER D6756
Designer: D. Biggs
Size: Small
Issued: 1987
Rec. Retail Price

GOLFER D6757
Designer: D. Biggs
Size: Mini
Issued: 1987
Rec. Retail Price

GOLFER D6784 (John Sinclair)
Limited edition of 1000
Designer: D. Biggs
Size: Large
Issued: 1987-
Price: $72 £45

GONDOLIER D6589
Designer: D. Biggs
Size: Large
Issued: 1964-1969
Price: $320 £200

GONDOLIER D6592
Designer: D. Biggs
Size: Small
Issued: 1964-1969
Price: $288 £180

GONDOLIER D6595
Designer: D. Biggs
Size: Mini
Issued: 1964-1969
Price: $272 £170

GONE AWAY D6531
Designer: G. Sharpe
Size: Large
Issued: 1960-1982
Price: $72 £45

GONE AWAY D6538
Designer: G. Sharpe
Size: Small
Issued: 1960-1982
Price: $72 £45

GUARDSMAN D6755

GRANNY D5521

GROUCHO MARX D6710

GONE AWAY D6545
Designer: G. Sharpe
Size: Mini
Issued: 1960-1982
Price: $32 £20

GRANNY D5521
Designer: H. Fenton &
          M. Henk
Size: Large
Issued: 1935-1983
Price: $72 £45

GRANNY (Toothless version) D5521
Designer: H. Fenton &
          M. Henk
Size: Large
Issued: 1935
Price: $720 £450

GRANNY D6384
Designer: H. Fenton &
          M. Henk
Size: Small
Issued: 1953-1983
Price: $48 £30

GRANNY D6520
Designer: H. Fenton &
          M. Henk
Size: Mini
Issued: 1960-1983
Price: $32 £20

GROUCHO MARX D6710
Designer: S. Taylor
Size: Large
Issued: 1984-1987
Price: $64 £40

GUARDSMAN D6568
Designer: M. Henk
Size: Large
Issued: 1963-1983
Price: $72 £45

GUARDSMAN D6755
Designer: S. Taylor
Size: Large
Issued: 1986
Rec. Retail Price

GUARDSMAN D6575
Designer: M. Henk
Size: Small
Issued: 1963-1983
Price: $48 £30

GUARDSMAN D6582
Designer: M. Henk
Size: Mini
Issued: 1963-1983
Price: $40 £25

GUARDSMEN D6771
Designer: S. Taylor
Size: Small
Issued: 1986
Rec. Retail Price

GUARDSMEN D6772
Designer: S. Taylor
Size: Mini
Issued: 1986
Rec. Retail Price

CHARACTER JUGS

GLADIATOR D6550

GUARDSMAN D6568

GONDOLIER D6589

GOLFER D6784

GAOLER D6570

GONE AWAY D6531

GULLIVER D6560
Designer: D. Biggs
Size: Large
Issued: 1962-1967
Price: $384 £240

GULLIVER D6563
Designer: D. Biggs
Size: Small
Issued: 1962-1967
Price: $288 £180

GULLIVER D6566
Designer: D. Biggs
Size: Mini
Issued: 1962-1967
Price: $320 £200

GUNSMITH D6573
Designer: D. Biggs
Size: Large
Issued: 1963-1983
Price: $77 £48

GUNSMITH D6580
Designer: D. Biggs
Size: Small
Issued: 1963-1983
Price: $48 £30

GUNSMITH D6587
Designer: D. Biggs
Size: Mini
Issued: 1963-1983
Price: $40 £25

HAMLET D6672
Designer: M. Abberley
Size: Large
Issued: 1982-1988
Price: $64 £40

HAMPSHIRE CRICKETER
D6739 (H.C.C Club)
Limited edition of 5000
Designer: H. Sales
Size: Medium
Issued: 1985
Price: $61 £38

HENRY V D6671
Designer: R. Tabbenor
Size: Large
Issued: 1982-1988
Price: $61 £38

HENRY VIII D6642
Designer: E. Griffiths
Size: Large
Issued: 1979-
Rec. Retail Price

HENRY VIII D6647
Designer: E. Griffiths
Size: Small
Issued: 1979-
Rec. Retail Price

HENRY VIII D6648
Designer: E. Griffiths
Size: Mini
Issued: 1979-
Rec. Retail Price

GULLIVER D6560

JOHN DOULTON D6656

HAMLET D6672

IZAAC WALTON D6404
Designer: G. Blower
Size: Large
Issued: 1953-1982
Price: $80 £50

JANE SEYMOUR D6646
Designer: M. Abberley
Size: Large
Issued: 1979-
Rec. Retail Price

JANE SEYMOUR D6747
Designer: M. Abberley
Size: Mini
Issued: 1986
Rec. Retail Price

JANE SEYMOUR D6746
Designer: M. Abberley
Size: Small
Issued: 1986
Rec. Retail Price

JARGE D6288
Designer: H. Fenton
Size: Large
Issued: 1950-1960
Price: $232 £145

JARGE D6295
Designer: H. Fenton
Size: Small
Issued: 1950-1960
Price: $144 £90

JESTER D5556
Designer: C. Noke
Size: Small
Issued: 1936-1960
Price: $77 £48

JIMMY DURANTE D6708
Designer: D. Biggs
Size: Large
Issued: 1985-1986
Price: $56 £35

JOCKEY D6625
Designer: D. Biggs
Size: Large
Issued: 1971-1975
Price: $320 £200

JOHN BARLEYCORN D5327
Designer: C. Noke
Size: Large
Issued: 1934-1960
Price: $112 £70

JOHN BARLEYCORN D5735
Designer: C. Noke
Size: Small
Issued: 1937-1960
Price: $72 £45

JOHN BARLEYCORN D6041
Designer: C. Noke
Size: Mini
Issued: 1939-1960
Price: $72 £45

JOHN DOULTON D6656
(Collectors' Club)
Designer: E. Griffiths
Size: Small
Issued: 1980
Price: $57 £38

CHARACTER JUGS

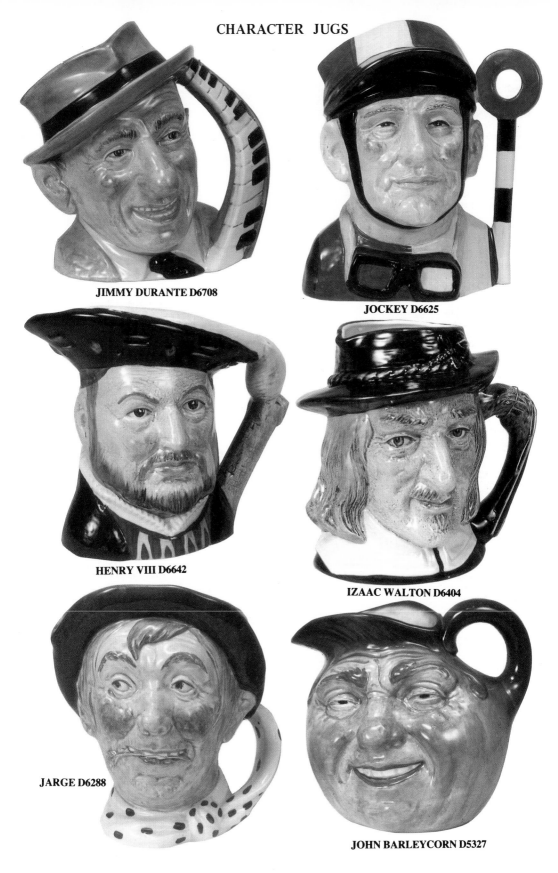

JIMMY DURANTE D6708

JOCKEY D6625

HENRY VIII D6642

IZAAC WALTON D6404

JARGE D6288

JOHN BARLEYCORN D5327

JOHN LENNON D6725
Designer: S. Taylor
Size: Medium
Issued: 1984-
Rec. Retail Price

JOHN LENNON D6797 (John
Sinclair) New colourway,
Limited edition of 1000
Designer: S. Taylor
Size: Medium
Issued: 1987-
Price: $56 £35

JOHN PEEL D5612
Designer: H. Fenton
Size: Large
Issued: 1936-1960
Price: $112 £70

JOHN PEEL D5731
Designer: H. Fenton
Size: Small
Issued: 1937-1960
Price: $64 £40

JOHN PEEL D6130
Designer: H. Fenton
Size: Mini
Issued: 1940-1960
Price: $61 £38

JOHN PEEL D6259
Designer: H. Fenton
Size: Tiny
Issued: 1947-1960
Price: $144 £90

JOHNNY APPLESEED D6372
Designer: H. Fenton
Size: Large
Issued: 1953-1969
Price: $264 £165

JUGGLER D6835
Designer: S. Taylor
Size: Large
Issued: 1989
Rec. Retail Price

**KING ARTHUR and
GUINEVERE D6836**
Limited edition of 9500
Designer: S. Taylor
Size: Large
Issued: 1989-
Price: $104 £65

**KING PHILLIP II of SPAIN
D6822** (Lawleys)
Limited edition of 9500
Designer: W.K. Harper
Size: Small
Issued: 1988
Rec. Retail Price

LAWYER D6498
Designer: M. Henk
Size: Large
Issued: 1959-
Rec. Retail Price

LAWYER D6504
Designer: M. Henk
Size: Small
Issued: 1959-
Rec. Retail Price

JOHN PEEL D6130

LITTLE MESTER D6819

KING PHILLIP II of SPAIN D6822

LAWYER D6524
Designer: M. Henk
Size: Mini
Issued: 1960-
Rec. Retail Price

LEPRECHAUN D6847
Designer: W.K. Harper
Size: Large
Issued: 1990
Rec. Retail Price

LITTLE MESTER D6819 (John
Sinclair) Limited edition of 3500
Designer: S. Taylor
Size: Large
Issued: 1988-
Price: $104 £65

LOBSTER MAN D6617
Designer: D. Biggs
Size: Large
Issued: 1968-
Rec. Retail Price

LOBSTER MAN D6620
Designer: D. Biggs
Size: Small
Issued: 1968-
Rec. Retail Price

LOBSTER MAN D6652
Designer: D. Biggs
Size: Mini
Issued: 1980-
Rec. Retail Price

LOBSTER MAN D6783
New colourway
Designer: D. Biggs
Size: Large
Issued: 1987-1989
Price: $56 £35

LONDON BOBBY D6744
Designer: S. Taylor
Size: Large
Issued: 1986
Rec. Retail Price

LONDON BOBBY D6762
Designer: S. Taylor
Size: Small
Issued: 1986
Rec. Retail Price

LONDON BOBBY D6763
Designer: S. Taylor
Size: Mini
Issued: 1986
Rec. Retail Price

LONG JOHN SILVER D6335
Designer: M. Henk
Size: Large
Issued: 1960-
Rec. Retail Price

LONG JOHN SILVER D6386
Designer: M. Henk
Size: Small
Issued: 1960-
Rec. Retail Price

KING ARTHUR and GUINEVERE D6836

LAWYER D6498   **JOHN LENNON D6725**

JOHNNY APPLESEED D6372   **LOBSTER MAN D6617**

LONG JOHN SILVER D6512
Designer: M. Henk
Size: Mini
Issued: 1960-
Rec. Retail Price

LORD NELSON D6336
Designer: G. Blower
Size: Large
Issued: 1952-1969
Price: $256 £160

LOUIS ARMSTRONG D6707
Designer: D. Biggs
Size: Large
Issued: 1984-1987
Price: $56 £35

LUMBERJACK D6610
Designer: M. Henk
Size: Large
Issued: 1967-1983
Price: $72 £45

LUMBERJACK D6613
Designer: M. Henk
Size: Small
Issued: 1967-1983
Price: $40 £25

MACBETH D6667
Designer: M. Abberley
Size: Large
Issued: 1982-1988
Price: $64 £40

MAD HATTER D6598
Designer: M. Henk
Size: Large
Issued: 1965-1983
Price: $77 £48

MAD HATTER D6602
Designer: M. Henk
Size: Small
Issued: 1965-1983
Price: $52 £32

MAD HATTER D6606
Designer: M. Henk
Size: Mini
Issued: 1965-1983
Price: $56 £35

MAE WEST D6688
Designer: C. Davidson
Size: Large
Issued: 1983-1985
Price: $72 £45

MAORI
Designer: Unknown
Size: Large
Issued: c. 1939
Price: $12000 £7500

MARCH HARE D6776
Designer: W.K. Harper
Size: Large
Issued: 1989
Rec. Retail Price

MARK TWAIN D6654
Designer: E. Griffiths
Size: Large
Issued: 1980-
Rec. Retail Price

MAD HATTER D6598

LORD NELSON D6336

MINE HOST D6468

MARK TWAIN D6694
Designer: E. Griffiths
Size: Small
Issued: 1983-
Rec. Retail Price

MARK TWAIN D6758
Designer: E. Griffiths
Size: Mini
Issued: 1987
Rec. Retail Price

MEPHISTOPHELES D5757
Designer: H. Fenton
Size: Large
Issued: 1937-1948
Price: $1440 £900

MEPHISTOPHELES D5758
Designer: H. Fenton
Size: Small
Issued: 1937-1948
Price: $880 £550

MERLIN D6529
Designer: G. Sharpe
Size: Large
Issued: 1960-
Rec. Retail Price

MERLIN D6536
Designer: G. Sharpe
Size: Small
Issued: 1960-
Rec. Retail Price

MERLIN D6543
Designer: G. Sharpe
Size: Mini
Issued: 1960-
Rec. Retail Price

MICHAEL DOULTON D6808
(Collectors' Club)
Designer: W.K. Harper
Size: Small
Issued: 1988-1989
Price: $56 £35

MIKADO D6501
Designer: M. Henk
Size: Large
Issued: 1959-1969
Price: $336 £210

MIKADO D6507
Designer: M. Henk
Size: Small
Issued: 1959-1969
Price: $240 £150

MIKADO D6525
Designer: M. Henk
Size: Mini
Issued: 1960-1969
Price: $280 £175

MINE HOST D6468
Designer: M. Henk
Size: Large
Issued: 1958-1982
Price: $80 £50

MINE HOST D6470
Designer: M. Henk
Size: Small
Issued: 1958-1982
Price: $56 £35

CHARACTER JUGS

MARK TWAIN D6654

MAE WEST D6688

MICHAEL DOULTON D6808

MACBETH D6667

LUMBERJACK D6610

LOUIS ARMSTRONG D6707

MINE HOST D6513
Designer: M. Henk
Size: Mini
Issued: 1960-1982
Price: $48 £30

MONTY D6202
Designer: H. Fenton
Size: Large
Issued: 1946-
Rec. Retail Price

MR MICAWBER D5843
Designer: L. Harradine and
H. Fenton
Size: Intermediate
Issued: 1938-1948
Price: $120 £75

MR MICAWBER D5843
Designer: L. Harradine and
H. Fenton
Size: Small
Issued: 1948-1960
Price: $64 £40

MR MICAWBER D6138
Designer: L. Harradine and
H. Fenton
Size: Mini
Issued: 1940-1960
Price: $56 £35

MR MICAWBER D6143
Designer: L. Harradine and
H. Fenton
Size: Tiny
Issued: 1940-1960
Price: $96 £60

MR PICKWICK D6060
Designer: L. Harradine and
H. Fenton
Size: Large
Issued: 1940-1960
Price: $136 £85

MR PICKWICK D5839
Designer: L. Harradine and
H. Fenton
Size: Intermediate
Issued: 1938-1948
Price: $136 £85

MR PICKWICK D5839
Designer: L. Harradine and
H. Fenton
Size: Small
Issued: 1948-1960
Price: $64 £40

MR PICKWICK D6245
Designer: L. Harradine and
H. Fenton
Size: Mini
Issued: 1947-1960
Price: $56 £35

MR PICKWICK D6260
Designer: L. Harradine and
H. Fenton
Size: Tiny
Issued: 1947-1960
Price: $136 £85

MR QUAKER D6738 (Quaker
Oats) Limited edition of 3500
Designer: H. Sales
Size: Large
Issued: 1985
Price: $360 £225

MR PICKWICK D6060

NORTH AMERICAN INDIAN D6786

NIGHT WATCHMAN D6569

**NAPOLEON AND JOSEPHINE
D6750**
Designer: M. Abberley
Size: Large
Issued: 1986 Limited edition
Price: $88 £55

NEPTUNE D6548
Designer: M. Henk
Size: Large
Issued: 1961-
Rec. Retail Price

NEPTUNE D6552
Designer: M. Henk
Size: Small
Issued: 1961-
Rec. Retail Price

NEPTUNE D6555
Designer: M. Henk
Size: Mini
Issued: 1961-
Rec. Retail Price

NIGHT WATCHMAN D6569
Designer: M. Henk
Size: Large
Issued: 1963-1983
Price: $77 £48

NIGHT WATCHMAN D6576
Designer: M. Henk
Size: Small
Issued: 1963-1983
Price: $42 £28

NIGHT WATCHMAN D6583
Designer: M. Henk
Size: Mini
Issued: 1963-1983
Price: $32 £20

**NORTH AMERICAN INDIAN
D6611**
Designer: M. Henk
Size: Large
Issued: 1967-
Rec. Retail Price

**NORTH AMERICAN INDIAN
D6611**
Designer: M. Henk
Size: Large
Issued: 1967
Price: $144 £90
(Special Back Stamp Canadian
Centenial)

**NORTH AMERICAN INDIAN
D6614**
Designer: M. Henk
Size: Small
Issued: 1967-
Rec. Retail Price

**NORTH AMERICAN INDIAN
D6665**
Designer: M. Henk
Size: Mini
Issued: 1967-
Rec. Retail Price

**NORTH AMERICAN INDIAN
D6786** (John Sinclair)
Limited edition of 1000
Designer: M. Henk
Size: Large
Issued: 1987-
Price: $64 £40

CHARACTER JUGS

NAPOLEON AND JOSEPHINE D6750

MONTY D6202

NEPTUNE D6548

MR MICAWBER D5843

MR QUAKER D6738

OLD CHARLEY D5420
Designer: C. Noke
Size: Large
Issued: 1934-1983
Price: $77 £48

OLD CHARLEY D5527
Designer: C. Noke
Size: Small
Issued: 1935-1983
Price: $48 £30

OLD CHARLEY D6046
Designer: C. Noke
Size: Mini
Issued: 1939-1982
Price: $40 £25

OLD CHARLEY D6144
Designer: C. Noke
Size: Tiny
Issued: 1940-1960
Price: $93 £58

OLD KING COLE D6036
Designer: H. Fenton
Size: Large
Issued: 1939-1960
Price: $176 £110

OLD KING COLE D6037
Designer: H. Fenton
Size: Small
Issued: 1939-1960
Price: $128 £80

OLD KING COLE (Yellow Crown) D6036
Designer: H. Fenton
Size: Large
Issued: 1939-1940
Price: $1280 £800

OLD KING COLE (Yellow Crown) D6037
Designer: H. Fenton
Size: Small
Issued: 1939-1940
Price: $2240 £1400

OLD SALT D6551
Designer: G. Sharpe
Size: Large
Issued: 1961-
Rec. Retail Price

OLD SALT D6554
Designer: G. Sharpe
Size: Small
Issued: 1961-
Rec. Retail Price

OLD SALT D6557
Designer: P. Gee
Size: Mini
Issued: 1984-
Rec. Retail Price

OLD SALT D6782
New colourway
Designer: G. Sharpe
Size: Large
Issued: 1987
Rec. Retail Price

OTHELLO D6673
Designer: M. Abberley
Size: Large
Issued: 1982-1988
Price: $74 £46

OTHELLO D6673

OLD CHARLEY D5420

PADDY D5753

PADDY D5753
Designer: H. Fenton
Size: Large
Issued: 1937-1960
Price: $88 £55

PADDY D5768
Designer: H. Fenton
Size: Small
Issued: 1937-1960
Price: $56 £35

PADDY D6042
Designer: H. Fenton
Size: Mini
Issued: 1939-1960
Price: $52 £32

PADDY D6145
Designer: H. Fenton
Size: Tiny
Issued: 1940-1960
Price: $88 £55

PARSON BROWN D5486
Designer: C. Noke
Size: Large
Issued: 1935-1960
Price: $96 £60
Price: $160 £100 (White)

PARSON BROWN D5529
Designer: C. Noke
Size: Small
Issued: 1935-1960
Price: $61 £38

PAUL McCARTNEY D6724
Designer: S. Taylor
Size: Medium
Issued: 1984-
Rec. Retail Price

PEARLY BOY (Blue)
Designer: H. Fenton
Size: Large
Issued: 1947-
Price: $3600 £2250

PEARLY BOY (Blue)
Designer: H. Fenton
Size: Small
Issued: 1947-
Price: $1920 £1200

PEARLY BOY (Blue)
Designer: H. Fenton
Size: Mini
Issued: 1947-
Price: $1920 £1200

PEARLY BOY (Brown buttons)
An early version of 'ARRY'
Designer: H. Fenton
Size: Large
Issued: 1947-
Price: $1040 £650

PEARLY BOY (Brown buttons)
An early version of 'ARRY'
Designer: H. Fenton
Size: Small
Issued: 1947-
Price: $720 £450

PEARLY BOY (Brown buttons)
An early version of 'ARRY'
Designer: H. Fenton
Size: Mini
Issued: 1947-
Price: $448 £280

CHARACTER JUGS

OLD KING COLE (Yellow Crown)

OLD KING COLE D6036

PEARLY BOY (Brown buttons)

PARSON BROWN D5486

OLD SALT D6551

PAUL McCARTNEY D6724

89

PEARLY GIRL (Blue)
A very rare version of 'ARRIET
Designer: H. Fenton
Size: Large
Issued: 1947-
Price: $6400 £4000

PEARLY GIRL (Blue)
A very rare version of 'ARRIET
Designer: H. Fenton
Size: Small
Issued: 1947-
Price: $4800 £3000

PEARLY KING D6760
Designer: S. Taylor
Size: Large
Issued: 1987
Rec. Retail Price

PEARLY KING D6844
Designer: S. Taylor
Size: Small
Issued: 1990
Rec. Retail Price

PEARLY QUEEN D6759
Designer: S. Taylor
Size: large
Issued: 1987
Rec. Retail Price

PEARLY QUEEN D6843
Designer: S. Taylor
Size: Small
Issued: 1990
Rec. Retail Price

PENDLE WITCH D6826 (Kevin Francis) Limited edition of 5000
Designer: G. Blower
Size: Large
Issued: 1988
Price: $88 £55

PIED PIPER D6403
Designer: G. Blower
Size: Large
Issued: 1954-1981
Price: $80 £50

PIED PIPER D6462
Designer: G. Blower
Size: Small
Issued: 1957-1981
Price: $56 £35

PIED PIPER D6514
Designer: G. Blower
Size: Mini
Issued: 1960-1981
Price: $53 £32

POACHER D6429
Designer: M. Henk
Size: Large
Issued: 1955-
Rec. Retail Price

POACHER D6464
Designer: M. Henk
Size: Small
Issued: 1957-
Rec. Retail Price

POACHER D6515
Designer: M. Henk
Size: Mini
Issued: 1960-
Rec. Retail Price

PUNCH AND JUDY MAN D6590

POACHER D6429

POSTMAN D6801

POACHER D6781
New colourway
Designer: M. Henk
Size: Large
Issued: 1987
Rec. Retail Price

POLICEMAN D6852 (Lawleys)
Limited edition of 5000
Designer: S. Taylor
Size: Small
Issued: 1990
Price: $40 £25

PORTHOS D6440
Designer: M. Henk
Size: Large
Issued: 1956-
Rec. Retail Price

PORTHOS D6453
Designer: M. Henk
Size: Small
Issued: 1956-
Rec. Retail Price

PORTHOS D6516
Designer: M. Henk
Size: Mini
Issued: 1960-
Rec. Retail Price

PORTHOS D6828 (Peter Jones)
New colourway
Limited edition of 1000
Designer: M. Henk
Size: Large
Issued: 1989
Price: $80 £50

POSTMAN D6801 (Lawleys)
Limited edition of 5000
Designer: S. Taylor
Size: Small
Issued: 1987
Price: $40 £25

PUNCH AND JUDY MAN D6590
Designer: D. Biggs
Size: Large
Issued: 1964-1969
Price: $416 £260

PUNCH AND JUDY MAN D6593
Designer: D. Biggs
Size: Small
Issued: 1964-1969
Price: $288 £180

PUNCH AND JUDY MAN D6596
Designer: D. Biggs
Size: Mini
Issued: 1964-1969
Price: $288 £180

QUEEN ELIZABETH I of ENGLAND D6821 (Lawleys)
Limited edition of 5000
Designer: W.K. Harper
Size: Small
Issued: 1988
Rec. Retail Price

PEARLY QUEEN D6759

PEARLY KING D6760

PENDLE WITCH D6826

QUEEN ELIZABETH I of ENGLAND D6821

PORTHOS D6828

PIED PIPER D6403

QUEEN VICTORIA D6816
Designer: S. Taylor
Size: Large
Issued: 1988
Rec. Retail Price

QUEEN VICTORIA D6788
(China Guild)
Limited edition of 3000
Designer: S. Taylor
Size: Large
Issued: 1988
Price: $104 £65

RED QUEEN D6777
Designer: W.K. Harper
Size: Large
Issued: 1987
Rec. Retail Price

RED QUEEN D6859
Designer: W.K. Harper
Size: Small
Issued: 1990
Rec. Retail Price

RED QUEEN D6860
Designer: W.K. Harper
Size: Mini
Issued: 1990
Rec. Retail Price

REGENCY BEAU D6559
Designer: D. Biggs
Size: Large
Issued: 1962-1967
Price: $720 £450

REGENCY BEAU D6562
Designer: D. Biggs
Size: Small
Issued: 1962-1967
Price: $440 £275

REGENCY BEAU D6565
Designer: D. Biggs
Size: Mini
Issued: 1962-1967
Price: $400 £250

RINGO STARR D6726
Designer: S. Taylor
Size: Medium
Issued: 1984-
Rec. Retail Price

RIP VAN WINKLE D6438
Designer: G. Blower
Size: Large
Issued: 1955-
Rec. Retail Price

RIP VAN WINKLE D6463
Designer: G. Blower
Size: Small
Issued: 1957-
Rec. Retail Price

RIP VAN WINKLE D6517
Designer: G. Blower
Size: Mini
Issued: 1960-
Rec. Retail Price

ROMEO D6670

ROBIN HOOD
D6205

RINGO STARR D6726

RIP VAN WINKLE D6788
(John Sinclair) New colourway
Limited edition of 1000
Designer: G. Blower
Size: Large
Issued: 1987-
Price: $72 £45

ROBIN HOOD (First version)
D6205
Designer: H. Fenton
Size: Large
Issued: 1947-1960
Price: $96 £60

ROBIN HOOD (First version)
D6234
Designer: H. Fenton
Size: Small
Issued: 1947-1960
Price: $56 £35

ROBIN HOOD (First Version)
D6252
Designer: H. Fenton
Size: Mini
Issued: 1947-1960
Price: $56 £35

ROBIN HOOD (Second
version) D6527
Designer: M. Henk
Size: Large
Issued: 1960-
Rec. Retail Price

ROBIN HOOD (Second
version) D6534
Designer: M. Henk
Size: Small
Issued: 1960-
Rec. Retail Price

ROBIN HOOD (Second
version) D6541
Designer: M. Henk
Size: Mini
Issued: 1960-
Rec. Retail Price

ROBINSON CRUSOE D6532
Designer: M. Henk
Size: Large
Issued: 1960-1983
Price: $77 £48

ROBINSON CRUSOE D6539
Designer: M. Henk
Size: Small
Issued: 1960-1983
Price: $48 £30

ROBINSON CRUSOE D6546
Designer: M. Henk
Size: Mini
Issued: 1960-1983
Price: $35 £22

ROMEO D6670
Designer: D. Biggs
Size: Large
Issued: 1983-1988
Price: $64 £40

CHARACTER JUGS

ROBINSON CRUSOE D6532

RIP VAN WINKLE D6438

QUEEN VICTORIA D6816

ROBIN HOOD   D6527

RED QUEEN D6777

RONALD REAGAN D6718
(Republic Committee)
Limited edition of 5000
Designer: E. Griffiths
Size: Large
Issued: 1984
Price: $400 £250

ST. GEORGE D6618
Designer: M. Henk
Size: Large
Issued: 1968-1975
Price: $144 £90

ST. GEORGE D6621
Designer: M. Henk
Size: Small
Issued: 1968-1975
Price: $77 £48

SAIREY GAMP D5451
Designer: L. Harradine and
H. Fenton
Size: Large
Issued: 1935-1986
Price: $67 £42

SAIREY GAMP D5528
Designer: L. Harradine and
H. Fenton
Size: Small
Issued: 1935-1986
Price: $40 £25

SAIREY GAMP D6045
Designer: L. Harradine and
H. Fenton
Size: Mini
Issued: 1939-1986
Price: $45 £28

SAIREY GAMP D6146
Designer: L. Harradine and
H. Fenton
Size: Tiny
Issued: 1940-1960
Price: $80 £50

SAM WELLER D6140
Designer: L. Harradine and
H. Fenton
Size: Mini
Issued: 1940-1960
Price: $61 £38

SAM WELLER D6064
Designer: L. Harradine and
H. Fenton
Size: Large
Issued: 1940-1960
Price: $120 £80

SAM WELLER D5841
Designer: L. Harradine and
H. Fenton
Size: Intermediate
Issued: 1938-1948
Price: $120 £80

SAM WELLER D5841
Designer: L. Harradine and
H. Fenton
Size: Small
Issued: 1948-1960
Price: $64 £40

RONALD REAGAN D6718

SAM WELLER D6140

SANTA CLAUS D6690

SAM WELLER D6147
Designer: L. Harradine and
H. Fenton
Size: Tiny
Issued: 1940-1960
Price: $104 £65

SAMSON and DELILAH D6787
Limited edition of 9500
Designer: S. Taylor
Size: Large
Issued: 1988
Price: $88 £55

SAMUEL JOHNSON D6289
Designer: H. Fenton
Size: Large
Issued: 1950-1960
Price: $256 £160

SAMUEL JOHNSON D6296
Designer: H. Fenton
Size: Small
Issued: 1950-1960
Price: $144 £90

SANCHO PANZA D6456
Designer: G. Blower
Size: Large
Issued: 1957-1983
Price: $77 £48

SANCHO PANZA D6461
Designer: G. Blower
Size: Small
Issued: 1957-1983
Price: $51 £32

SANCHO PANZA D6518
Designer: G. Blower
Size: Mini
Issued: 1960-1983
Price: $35 £22

**SANTA ANNA/DAVY
CROCKET D6729**
Limited edition of 9500
Designer: M. Abberley
Size: Large
Issued: 1985
Price: $104 £65

SANTA CLAUS D6668
Designer: M. Abberley
Size: Large with Peg
Doll Handle
Issued: 1981
Price: $80 £50

SANTA CLAUS D6675
Designer: M. Abberley
Size: Large with Reindeer
Handle
Issued: 1982
Price: $80 £50

SANTA CLAUS D6690
Designer: M. Abberley
Size: Large with Sack of
Toys Handle
Issued: 1983
Price: $72 £45

SAMSON and DELILAH D6787

ST. GEORGE D6618

SAMUEL JOHNSON D6289

SANCHO PANZA D6456

SAIREY GAMP D5451

SANTA CLAUS D6704
Designer: M. Abberley
Size: Large
Issued: 1984-
Rec. Retail Price

SANTA CLAUS D6705
Designer: M. Abberley
Size: Small
Issued: 1984-
Rec. Retail Price

SANTA CLAUS D6706
Designer: M. Abberley
Size: Mini
Issued: 1984-
Rec. Retail Price

SCARAMOUCHE D6558
Designer: M. Henk
Size: Large
Issued: 1962-1967
Price: $640 £400

SCARAMOUCHE D6561
Designer: M. Henk
Size: Small
Issued: 1962-1967
Price: $336 £210

SCARAMOUCHE D6564
Designer: M. Henk
Size: Mini
Issued: 1962-1967
Price: $448 £280

SCARAMOUCHE D6774
(China Guild)
Limited edition of 1500
Designer: S. Taylor
Size: Large
Issued: 1987
Price: $136 £85

SCARAMOUCHE D6814
Designer: S. Taylor
Size: Large
Issued: 1988
Rec. Retail Price

SIMON THE CELLARER D5504
Designer: C. Noke and H. Fenton
Size: Large
Issued: 1935-1960
Price: $96 £60

SIMON THE CELLARER D5616
Designer: C. Noke and H. Fenton
Size: Small
Issued: 1936-1960
Price: $64 £40

SIMPLE SIMON D6374
Designer: G. Blower
Size: Large
Issued: 1953-1960
Price: $416 £260

SIR FRANCIS DRAKE D6805
(China Guild)
Limited edition of 6000
Designer: P. Gee
Size: Large
Issued: 1988
Price: $72 £45

SCARAMOUCHE D6774

SIMON THE CELLARER D5504

SIMPLE SIMON D6374

SIR HENRY DOULTON D6703
Designer: E. Griffiths
Size: Small
Issued: 1984
Price: $61 £38

SIR THOMAS MORE D6792
Designer: S. Taylor
Size: Large
Issued: 1988
Rec. Retail Price

SITTING BULL/GEORGE ARMSTRONG CUSTER D6712
Limited edition of 9500
Designer: M. Abberley
Size: Large
Issued: 1984
Price: $120 £75

SLEUTH D6631
Designer: A. Moore
Size: Large
Issued: 1973-
Rec. Retail Price

SLEUTH D6635
Designer: A. Moore
Size: Small
Issued: 1973-
Rec. Retail Price

SLEUTH D6639
Designer: A. Moore
Size: Mini
Issued: 1973-
Rec. Retail Price

SLEUTH D6773 (Lawleys)
Limited edition of 5000
Designer: S. Taylor
Size: Small
Issued: 1988
Price: $32 £20

SMUGGLER D6616
Designer: D. Biggs
Size: Large
Issued: 1968-1981
Price: $77 £48

SMUGGLER D6619
Designer: D. Biggs
Size: Small
Issued: 1968-1981
Price: $45 £28

SMUTS D6198
Designer: H. Fenton
Size: Large
Issued: 1946-c.1948
Price: $1088 £680

TAM O'SHANTER D6632
Designer: M. Henk
Size: Large
Issued: 1973-1980
Price: $104 £65

TAM O'SHANTER D6636
Designer: M. Henk
Size: Small
Issued: 1973-1980
Price: $61 £38

SIR THOMAS MORE D6792

SMUTS D6198

SLEUTH D6773

SIR FRANCIS DRAKE D6805

SIR HENRY DOULTON D6703

SMUGGLER D6616

CHARACTER JUGS

TAM O'SHANTER D6640
Designer: M. Henk
Size: Mini
Issued: 1973-1980
Price: $51 £32

TOBY GILLETTE D6717
Limited edition of three
Two owned by an American
Collector and the other in the
Sir Henry Doulton Museum
Stoke-on-Trent
Designer: E. Griffiths
Size: Large
Issued: 1984
Price: $25600 £16000

TOBY PHILPOTTS D5736
Designer: C. Noke
Size: Large
Issued: 1937-1969
Price: $96 £60

TOBY PHILPOTTS D5737
Designer: C. Noke
Size: Small
Issued: 1937-1969
Price: $56 £35

TOBY PHILPOTTS D6043
Designer: C. Noke
Size: Mini
Issued: 1939-1969
Price: $45 £28

TONY WELLER D5531
Designer: L. Harradine and
H. Fenton
Size: Extra Large
Issued: c.1936
Price: $192 £120

TONY WELLER D5531
Designer: L. Harradine and
H. Fenton
Size: Large
Issued: c.1936-1960
Price: $96 £60

TONY WELLER D5530
Designer: L. Harradine and
H. Fenton
Size: Small
Issued: 1936-1960
Price: $61 £38

TONY WELLER D6044
Designer: L. Harradine and
H. Fenton
Size: Mini
Issued: 1939-1960
Price: $48 £30

TOUCHSTONE D5613
Designer: C. Noke
Size: Large
Issued: 1936-1960
Price: $144 £90

TOWN CRIER D6530
Designer: D. Biggs
Size: Large
Issued: 1960-1973
Price: $160 £100

TOWN CRIER D6537
Designer: D. Biggs
Size: Small
Issued: 1960-1973
Price: $112 £70

VICAR OF BRAY D5615

UGLY DUCHESS D6599

TOBY PHILPOTTS D5736

TOWN CRIER D6544
Designer: D. Biggs
Size: Mini
Issued: 1960-1973
Price: $120 £75

TRAPPER D6609
Designer: M. Henk and D. Biggs
Size: Large
Issued: 1967-1983
Price: $61 £38

TRAPPER D6609
Designer: M. Henk and D. Biggs
Size: Large (Centenial Back Stamp)
Price: $144 £90

TRAPPER D6612
Designer: M. Henk and D. Biggs
Size: Small
Issued: 1967-1983
Price: $32 £20

UGLY DUCHESS D6599
Designer: M. Henk
Size: Large
Issued: 1965-1973
Price: $368 £230

UGLY DUCHESS D6603
Designer: M. Henk
Size: Small
Issued: 1965-1973
Price: $256 £160

UGLY DUCHESS D6607
Designer: M. Henk
Size: Mini
Issued: 1965-1973
Price: $272 £170

ULYSSES S. GRANT and ROBERT E. LEE D6698
Designer: M. Abberley
Size: Large
Issued: 1983-
Price: $192 £120

UNCLE TOM COBBLEIGH D6337
Designer: M. Henk
Size: Large
Issued: 1952-1960
Price: $272 £170

VETERAN MOTORIST D6633
Designer: D. Biggs
Size: Large
Issued: 1973-1983
Price: $88 £55

VETERAN MOTORIST D6637
Designer: D. Biggs
Size: Small
Issued: 1973-1983
Price: $61 £38

VETERAN MOTORIST D6641
Designer: D. Biggs
Size: Mini
Issued: 1973-1983
Price: $56 £35

VICAR OF BRAY D5615
Designer: C. Noke and H. Fenton
Size: Large
Issued: 1936-1960
Price: $160 £100

VIKING D6496
Designer: M. Henk
Size: Large
Issued: 1959-1975
Price: $120 £75

ULYSSES S. GRANT and ROBERT E. LEE D6698

UNCLE TOM COBBLEIGH D6337

TOUCHSTONE D5613

VIKING D6496

TONY WELLER D5531

TOWN CRIER D6530

VIKING D6502
Designer: M. Henk
Size: Small
Issued: 1959-1975
Price: $104 £65

VIKING D6526
Designer: M. Henk
Size: Mini
Issued: 1959-1975
Price: $120 £75

VISCOUNT MONTGOMERY
of ALAMEIN D6850 (Lawleys)
Limited edition of 9500
Designer: S. Taylor
Size: Small
Issued: 1989
Price: $80 £50

W.C. FIELDS D6674
Designer: D. Biggs
Size: Large
Issued: 1983-1985
Price: $72 £45

W.G. GRACE D6845 (Lawleys)
Limited edition of 9500
Designer: S. Taylor
Size: Small
Issued: 1989
Rec. Retail Price

WALRUS AND CARPENTER D6600
Designer: M. Henk
Size: Large
Issued: 1965-1980
Price: $77 £48

WALRUS AND CARPENTER D6604
Designer: M. Henk
Size: Small
Issued: 1965-1980
Price: $56 £35

WALRUS AND CARPENTER D6608
Designer: M. Henk
Size: Mini
Issued: 1965-1980
Price: $29 £18

WILD BILL HICKOCK D6736
Designer: M. Abberley
Size: Medium
Issued: 1985-1988
Price: $40 £25

WILLIAM SHAKESPEARE
D6689
Designer: M. Abberley
Size: Large
Issued: 1983-
Rec. Retail Price

WYATT EARP D6711
Designer: S. Taylor
Size: Medium
Issued: 1985-1988
Price: $40 £25

YACHTSMAN D6622
Designer: D. Biggs
Size: Large
Issued: 1971-1980
Price: $120 £75

YACHTSMAN D6820
Designer: S. Taylor
Size: Large
Issued: 1988
Rec. Retail Price

W.C. FIELDS D6674

YACHTSMAN D6622

WALRUS AND CARPENTER
D6600

FIGURES

A LA MODE HN2544
Designer: E. J. Griffiths
Height: 12¼in., 31.1cm.
Issued: 1974-1977
Price: $176 £110

A PENNY'S WORTH HN2408
Designer: M. Nicoll
Height: 7in., 20cm.
Issued: 1986
Rec. Retail Price

ABDULLAH HN1410
Designer: L. Harradine
Height: 5¾in., 14.6cm.
Issued: 1930-1938
Price: $672 £420

ABDULLAH HN2104
Designer: L. Harradine
Height: 6in., 15.2cm.
Issued: 1953-1962
    Colour variation
Price: $304 £190

A'COURTING HN2004
Designer: L. Harradine
Height: 7¼in., 18.4cm.
Issued: 1947-1953
Price: $240 £150

ADELE HN2480
Designer: P. Davies
Height: 8in., 20cm.
Issued: 1987
Rec. Retail Price

ADORNMENT HN3015
Designer: P. Parsons
Height: 9½in., 24cm.
Issued: 1989 in a limited
    edition of 750
Price: $640 £400

ADRIENNE HN2152
Designer: M. Davies
Height: 7½in., 19.1cm.
Issued: 1964-1976
Price: $104 £65

ADRIENNE HN2304
Designer: M. Davies
Height: 7½in., 19.1cm.
Issued: 1964-
    Colour variation
Rec. Retail Price

AFFECTION HN2236
Designer: M. Davies
Height: 4½in., 11.4cm.
Issued: 1962-
Rec. Retail Price

AFTERNOON TEA HN1747
Designer: P. Railston
Height: 5¾in., 14.6cm.
Issued: 1935-1981
Price: $216 £135

AFTERNOON TEA HN1748
Designer: P. Railston
Height: 5¼in., 13.3cm.
Issued: 1935-1949
    Colour variation
Price: $280 £175

AILEEN HN1645
Designer: L. Harradine
Height: 6in., 15.2cm.
Issued: 1934-1938
Price: $448 £270

ABDULLAH HN1410

AFTERNOON TEA HN1747

AILEEN HN1664
Designer: L. Harradine
Height: 6in., 15.2cm.
Issued: 1934-1938
Colour variation
Price: $496 £310

AILEEN HN1803
Designer: L. Harradine
Height: 6in., 15.2cm.
Issued: 1937-1949
Colour variation
Price: $400 £250

AJAX HN2908
Designer: S. Keenan
Height: 9¾in., 24.8cm.
Issued: 1980 in a limited
edition of 950
Price: $160 £100

ALCHEMIST HN1259
Designer: L. Harradine
Height: 11½in., 29.2cm.
Issued: 1927-1938
Price: $672 £420

ALCHEMIST HN1282
Designer: L. Harradine
Height: 11¼in., 28.5cm.
Issued: 1928-1938
Colour variation
Price: $672 £420

ALEXANDRA HN2398
Designer: M. Davies
Height: 7¾in., 19.7cm.
Issued: 1970-1976
Price: $136 £85

ALFRED JINGLE HN541
Designer: L. Harradine
Height: 3¾in., 9.5cm.
Issued: 1922-1932
Price: $48 £30

ALFRED JINGLE M52
Designer: L. Harradine
Height: 3¾in., 9.5cm.
Issued: 1932-1982
Price: $48 £30

ALICE HN2158
Designer: M. Davies
Height: 5in., 12.7cm.
Issued: 1960-1980
Price: $72 £45

ALISON HN2336
Designer: M. Davies
Height: 7½in., 19.1cm
Issued: 1966-
Rec. Retail Price

ALISON HN3264
Designer: P. Davies
Height: 7¹/₂in., 19.1cm.
Issued: 1989
Rec. Retail Price

ALL-A-BLOOMING HN1457
Designer: L. Harradine
Height: 6½in., 16.5cm.
Issued: 1931-not known
Price: $400 £250

ALL-A-BLOOMING HN1466
Designer: L. Harradine
Height: 6½in., 16.5cm.
Issued: 1931-1938
Price: $440 £275

ALCHEMIST HN1259

AILEEN HN1803

ALL ABOARD HN2940
Designer: R. Tabbenor
Height: 9¼in., 23.5cm.
Issued: 1982-1986
Price: $104 £65

ALLURE HN3080
Designer: E. Griffiths
Height: 12¼in., 31cm.
Issued: 1987-1989
Price: $88 £55

AMANDA HN2996
Designer: R. Tabbenor
Height: 5¼in., 13.5cm.
Issued: 1986
Rec. Retail Price

AMY HN2958
Designer: Pauline Parsons
Height: 6in., 15cm.
Issued: 1982-1987
Price: $56 £35

AND ONE FOR YOU HN2970
Designer: A. Hughes
Height: 6½in., 16.5cm.
Issued: 1982-1985
Price: $61 £38

AND SO TO BED HN2966
Designer: P. Parsons
Height: 7½in., 19cm.
Issued: 1982-1985
Price: $61 £38

ANDREA HN3058
Designer: A. Hughes
Height: 5¼in., 13cm.
Issued: 1985-
Rec. Retail Price

ANGELA (Style one) HN1204
Designer: L. Harradine
Height: 7¼in., 18.4cm.
Issued: 1926-1938
Price: $600 £375

ANGELA (Style one) HN1303
Designer: L. Harradine
Height: 7¼in., 18.4cm.
Issued: 1928-1938
Colour variation
Price: $640 £400

ANGELA (Style two) HN2389
Designer: P. Davies
Height: 7½in., 19cm.
Issued: 1983-1986
Price: $56 £35

ANGELINA HN2013
Designer: L. Harradine
Height: 6¾in., 17.1cm.
Issued: 1948-1951
Price: $320 £200

ANN HN2739
Designer: D. Tootle
Height: 7¾in., 19.5cm.
Issued: 1983-1986
Price: $48 £30

ANNA HN2802
Designer: M. Davies
Height: 5¾in., 14.6cm.
Issued: 1976-1982
Price: $56 £35

ALL ABOARD HN2940

ALEXANDRA HN2398

ANNABEL HN3273
Designer: R. Tabbenor
Height: 5½in., 14cm.
Issued: 1989
Rec. Retail Price

ANNABELLA HN1871
Designer: L. Harradine
Height: 5¼in., 13.3cm.
Issued: 1938-1949
Price: $320 £200

ANNABELLA HN1872
Designer: L. Harradine
Height: 5¼in., 13.3cm.
Issued: 1938-1949
Colour variation
Price: $320 £200

ANNABELLA HN1875
Designer: L. Harradine
Height: 4¾in., 12.0cm.
Issued: 1938-1949
Colour variation
Price: $320 £200

ANNETTE HN1471
Designer: L. Harradine
Height: 6¼in., 15.9cm.
Issued: 1931-1938
Price: $152 £95

ANNETTE HN1472
Designer: L. Harradine
Height: 6in., 15.2cm.
Issued: 1931-1949
Colour variation
Price: $152 £95

ANNETTE HN1550
Designer: L. Harradine
Height: 6¼in., 15.9cm.
Issued: 1933-1949
Price: $152 £95

ANTHEA HN1526
Designer: L. Harradine
Height: 6½in., 16.5cm.
Issued: 1932-1938
Price: $352 £220

ANTHEA HN1527
Designer: L. Harradine
Height: 6½in., 16.5cm.
Issued: 1932-1949
Colour variation
Price: $280 £175

ANTHEA HN1669
Designer: L. Harradine
Height: 6½in., 16.5cm.
Issued: 1934-1938
Colour variation
Price: $352 £220

ANTOINETTE (Style one) HN1850
Designer: L. Harradine
Height: 8¼in., 21.0cm.
Issued: 1938-1949
Price: $480 £300

ANTOINETTE (Style one) HN1851
Designer: L. Harradine
Height: 8¼in., 21.0cm.
Issued: 1938-1949
Colour variation
Price: $480 £300

ANTOINETTE (Style two)
HN2326
Designer: M. Davies
Height: 6¼in., 15.9cm.
Issued: 1967-1978
Price: $109 £68

APPLE MAID HN2160
Designer: L. Harradine
Height: 6½in., 16.5cm.
Issued: 1957-1962
Price: $256 £160

APRIL HN2708
Designer: P. Davies
Height: 7¾in., 19.7cm.
Issued: 1987
Price: $96 £60

APRIL SHOWER HN3024
Designer: R. Jefferson
Height: 4¾in., 12cm.
Issued: 1983-1986
Price: $56 £35

ARAB HN33
Designer: C. J. Noke
Height: 15¾in., 40.0cm.
Issued: 1913-1938
Price: $640 £400

ARAB HN343
Designer: C. J. Noke
Height: 16½in., 41.9cm.
Issued: 1919-1938
Colour variation
Price: $720 £450

ARAB HN378
Designer: C. J. Noke
Height: 16½in., 41.9cm.
Issued: 1920-1938
Colour variation
Price: $640 £400

ARAGORN HN2916
Designer: H. Sales
Height: 6¼in., 15.9cm.
Issued: 1979-1984
Price: $56 £35

ARTFUL DODGER HN546
Designer: L. Harradine
Height: 3¾in., 9.5cm.
Issued: 1922-1932
Price: $48 £30

ARTFUL DODGER M55
Designer: L. Harradine
Height: 4¼in., 10.8cm.
Issued: 1932-1983
Price: $48 £30

AS GOOD AS NEW HN2971
Designer: A. Hughes
Height: 6½in., 16.5cm.
Issued: 1982-1985
Price: $72 £45

ASCOT HN2356
Designer: M. Davies
Height: 5¾in., 14.6cm.
Issued: 1968-

Rec. Retail Price

AUTUMN BREEZES HN1913

AS GOOD AS NEW HN2971

ASCOT HN2356

ARAGORN HN2916

AT EASE HN2473
Designer: M. Davies
Height: 6in., 15.2cm.
Issued: 1973-1978
Price: $152 £95

AUCTIONEER HN2988
Designer: R. Tabbenor
Height: 8in., 20.3cm.
Issued: 1986
Price: $240 £150

AUGUST HN3165
Designer: P. Davies
Height: 7¾in., 19.7cm.
Issued: 1987
Price: $96 £60

L'AUTOMNE HN3068
Designer: R. Jefferson
Height: 11½in., 29cm.
Issued: 1987 in a limited
edition of 300
Price: $800 £500

AUTUMN (Style one) HN314
Designer: Unknown
Height: 7¼in., 18.4cm.
Issued: 1918-1938
Price: $640 £400

AUTUMN (Style one) HN474
Designer: Unknown
Height: 7½in., 19.1cm.
Issued: 1921-1938
Colour variation
Price: $720 £450

AUTUMN (Style two) HN2087
Designer: M. Davies
Height: 7¼in., 18.4cm.
Issued: 1952-1959
Price: $280 £175

AUTUMN BREEZES HN1911
Designer: L. Harradine
Height: 7½in., 19.1cm.
Issued: 1939-1976
Price: $136 £85

AUTUMN BREEZES HN1913
Designer: L. Harradine
Height: 7½in., 19.1cm.
Issued: 1939-1971
Colour variation
Price: $152 £95

AUTUMN BREEZES HN1934
Designer: L. Harradine
Height: 7½in., 19.1cm.
Issued: 1940-
Colour variation
Rec. Retail Price

AUTUMN BREEZES HN2147
Designer: L. Harradine
Height: 7½in., 19.1cm.
Issued: 1955-1971
Colour variation
Price: $200 £125

AUTUMTIME HN3231
Designer: C. Parsons
Height: 8in., 20.3cm.
Issued: 1989
Price: $128 £80

APRIL SHOWER HN3024

APPLE MAID HN2160

AUCTIONEER HN2988

·GRAND·
ROYAL DOULTON·
AUCTION
·OVER 500 LOTS·
INCLUDING THE RARE
RED HAIRED
CLOWN
CHARACTER JUG
MADE FROM
1937 TO c 1942

AT EASE HN2473

AWAKENING HN1927
Designer: L. Harradine
Height: Unknown
Issued: 1940-1949
Price: $1120 £700

AWAKENING HN2838 (Black)
Designer: P. Davies
Height: 8½in., 22cm.
Issued: 1981
Rec. Retail Price

AWAKENING HN2875 (White)
Designer: P. Davies
Height: 8½in., 22cm.
Issued: 1981-
Rec. Retail Price

B
BABA HN1230
Designer: L. Harradine
Height: 3¼in., 8.3cm.
Issued: 1927-1938
Price: $352 £220

BABA HN1243
Designer: L. Harradine
Height: 3¼in., 8.3cm.
Issued: 1927-1938
Colour variation
Price: $352 £220

BABA HN1244
Designer: L. Harradine
Height: 3¼in., 8.3cm.
Issued: 1927-1938
Colour variation
Price: $352 £220

BABA HN1245
Designer: L. Harradine
Height: 3¼in., 8.3cm.
Issued: 1927-1938
Colour variation
Price: $352 £220

BABA HN1246
Designer: L. Harradine
Height: 3¼in., 8.3cm.
Issued: 1927-1938
Colour variation
Price: $352 £220

BABA HN1247
Designer: L. Harradine
Height: 3¼in., 8.3cm.
Issued: 1927-1938
Colour variation
Price: $352 £220

BABA HN1248
Designer: L. Harradine
Height: 3¼in., 8.3cm.
Issued: 1927-1938
Colour variation
Price: $352 £220

BABETTE HN1423
Designer: L. Harradine
Height: 5in., 12.7cm.
Issued: 1930-1938
Price: $352 £220

BATHER (Style two) HN773

BALLINESE DANCER HN2808

BABETTE HN1424
Designer: L. Harradine
Height: 5in., 12.7cm.
Issued: 1930-1938
Colour variation
Price: $400 £250

BABIE HN1679
Designer: L. Harradine
Height: 4¾in., 12.0cm.
Issued: 1935-
Rec. Retail Price

BABIE HN1842
Designer: L. Harradine
Issued: 1938-1949
Height: 4¾in., 12.0cm.
Colour variation
Price: $104 £65

BABIE HN2121
Designer: L. Harradine
Height: 4¾in., 12.0cm.
Issued: 1983-
Rec. Retail Price

BABY HN12
Designer: C. J. Noke
Height: Unknown
Issued: 1913-1938
Price: $880 £550

BABY BUNTING HN2108
Designer: M. Davies
Height: 5¼in., 13.3cm.
Issued: 1953-1959
Price: $160 £100

BACHELOR HN2319
Designer: M. Nicholl
Height: 7in., 17.8cm.
Issued: 1964-1975
Price: $176 £110

BALLAD SELLER HN2266
Designer: M. Davies
Height: 7½in., 19.1cm.
Issued: 1968-1973
Price: $192 £120

BALLERINA HN2116
Designer: M. Davies
Height: 7¼in., 18.4cm.
Issued: 1953-1973
Price: $208 £130

BALLET CLASS HN3134
Designer: P. Parsons
Height: 6in., 15.5cm.
Issued: 1987
Rec. Retail Price

BALLINESE DANCER HN2808
Designer: P. Davies
Height: 8³⁄₄in., 22.2cm.
Issued: 1982 in a limited edition of 750
Price: $520 £325

BALLOON BOY HN2934
Designer: P. Gee
Height: 7½in., 19cm.
Issued: 1984-
Rec. Retail Price

BALLOON CLOWN HN2894
Designer: W. K. Harper
Height: 9¼in., 23cm.
Issued: 1986
Rec. Retail Price

FIGURES

BALLOON GIRL HN2818
Designer: W. K. Harper
Height: 6½in., 16.5cm.
Issued: 1982-
Rec. Retail Price

BALLOON LADY HN2935
Designer: P. Gee
Height: 8¼in., 21cm.
Issued: 1984-
Rec. Retail Price

BALLOON MAN HN1954
Designer: L. Harradine
Height: 7¼in., 18.4cm.
Issued: 1940-
Rec. Retail Price

BALLOON SELLER HN479
Designer: L. Harradine
Height: 9in., 22.9cm.
Issued: 1921-1938
Price: $680 £425

BALLOON SELLER HN486
Designer: L. Harradine
Height: 9in., 22.9cm.
Issued: 1921-1938
Price: $520 £325

BALLOON SELLER HN548
Designer: L. Harradine
Height: 9in., 22.9cm.
Issued: 1922-1938
         Colour variation
Price: $352 £220

BALLOON SELLER HN583
Designer: L. Harradine
Height: 9in., 22.9cm.
Issued: 1923-1949
         Colour variation
Price: $200 £125

BALLOON SELLER HN697
Designer: L. Harradine
Height: 9in., 22.9cm.
Issued: 1925-1938
         Colour variation
Price: $288 £180

BALLOON SELLER HN2130
Designer: L. Harradine
Height: 4in., 10cm.
Issued: 1989
Rec. Retail Price

BARBARA HN1421
Designer: L. Harradine
Height: 7¾in., 19.7cm.
Issued: 1930-1938
Price: $360 £225

BARBARA HN1432
Designer: L. Harradine
Height: 7¾in., 19.7cm.
Issued: 1930-1938
Price: $360 £225

BARBARA HN1461
Designer: L. Harradine
Height: 7¾in., 19.7cm.
Issued: 1931-1938
         Colour variation
Price: $360 £225

BALLOON GIRL HN2818

BALLOON MAN HN1954

BALLERINA HN2116

BARBARA HN2962
Designer: P. Parsons
Height: 8in., 20cm.
Issued: 1982-1984
Price: $72 £45

BARLIMAN BUTTERBUR HN2923
Designer: D. Lyttleton
Height: 5¼in., 13cm.
Issued: 1982-1984
Price: $56 £35

BASKET WEAVER HN2245
Designer: M. Nicholl
Height: 5¾in., 14.6cm.
Issued: 1959-1962
Price: $320 £200

BATHER (Style one) HN597
Designer: L. Harradine
Height: 7¾in., 19.7cm.
Issued: 1924-1938
Price: $448 £280

BATHER (Style one) HN687
Designer: L. Harradine
Height: 7¾in., 19.7cm.
Issued: 1924-1949
         Colour variation
Price: $448 £280

BATHER (Style one) HN781
Designer: L. Harradine
Height: 7¾in., 19.7cm.
Issued: 1926-1938
         Colour variation
Price: $448 £280

BATHER (Style one) HN782
Designer: L. Harradine
Height: 7¾in., 19.7cm.
Issued: 1926-1938
         Colour variation
Price: $448 £280

BATHER (Style one) HN1238
Designer: L. Harradine
Height: 7¾in., 19.7cm.
Issued: 1927-1938
         Colour variation
Price: $480 £300

BATHER (Style one) HN1708
Designer: L. Harradine
Height: 7¾in., 19.7cm.
Issued: 1935-1938
         Colour variation
Price: $800 £500

BATHER (Style two) HN773
Designer: L. Harradine
Height: 7½in., 19.1cm.
Issued: 1925-1938
Price: $480 £300

BATHER (Style two) HN774
Designer: L. Harradine
Height: 7¾in., 19.7cm.
Issued: 1925-1938
Price: $480 £300

BATHER (Style two) HN1227
Designer: L. Harradine
Height: 7½in., 19.1cm.
Issued: 1927-1938
         Colour variation
Price: $480 £300

BATHING BEAUTY HN3156
Designer: A. Hughes
Height: 9½in., 26cm.
Issued: 1988-1989
Price: $104 £65

BEACHCOMBER HN2487
Designer: M. Nicholl
Height: 6¼in., 15.9cm.
Issued: 1973-1976
Price: $120 £75

BEAT YOU TO IT HN2871
Designer: M. Davies
Height: 6½in., 16.5cm.
Issued: 1980-1987
Price: $72 £45

BEATRICE HN3263
Designer: P. Davies
Height: 7in., 17.8cm.
Issued: 1989
Rec. Retail Price

BECKY HN2740
Designer: D. Tootle
Height: 8in., 20cm.
Issued: 1987
Rec. Retail Price

BEDTIME HN1978
Designer: L. Harradine
Height: 5¾in., 14.6cm.
Issued: 1945-
Rec. Retail Price

BEDTIME STORY HN2059
Designer: L. Harradine
Height: 4¾in., 12.0cm.
Issued: 1950-
Rec. Retail Price

BEETHOVEN HN1778
Designer: R. Garbe
Height: 22in., 55.8cm.
Issued: 1933 in a limited
          edition of 25
Price: $3200 £2000

BEGGAR (Style one) HN526
Designer: L. Harradine
Height: 6½in., 16.5cm.
Issued: 1921-1949
Price: $320 £200

BEGGAR (Style one) HN591
Designer: L. Harradine
Height: 6¾in., 17.2cm.
Issued: 1924-1949
Price: $320 £200

BEGGAR (Style two) HN2175
Designer: L. Harradine
Height: 6¾in., 17.2cm.
Issued: 1956-1972
Price: $288 £180

BELLE HN754
Designer: L. Harradine
Height: 6½in., 16.5cm.
Issued: 1925-1938
Price: $520 £325

BEDTIME HN1978

BEAT YOU TO IT HN2871

BELLE O' THE BALL HN1997

108

BELLE HN776
Designer: L. Harradine
Height: 6½in., 16.5cm.
Issued: 1925-1938
Price: $520 £325

BELLE HN2340
Designer: M. Davies
Height: 4½in., 11.4cm.
Issued: 1968-1988
Price: $40 £25

BELLE O' THE BALL HN1997
Designer: L. Harradine
Height: 6in., 15.2cm.
Issued: 1947-1978
Price: $176 £110

BENMORE HN2909
Designer: S. Keenan
Height: 9¼in., 23.5cm.
 Issued: 1980 in a limited
            edition of 950
Price: $160 £100

BERNICE HN2071
Designer: M. Davies
Height: 7¾in., 19.7cm.
Issued: 1951-1953
Price: $352 £220

BESS HN2002
Designer: L. Harradine
Height: 7¼in., 18.4cm.
Issued: 1947-1969
Price: $176 £110

BESS HN2003
Designer: L. Harradine
Height: 7¼in., 18.4cm.
Issued: 1947-1950
            Colour variation
Price: $240 £150

BETH HN2870
Designer: M. Davies
Height: 5¾in., 14.6cm.
Issued: 1980-1983
Price: $56 £35

BETSY HN2111
Designer: L. Harradine
Height: 7in., 17.8cm.
Issued: 1953-1959
Price: $192 £120

BETTY (Style one) HN402
Designer: L. Harradine
Height: 7½in., 19cm.
Issued: 1920-1938
Price: $1280 £800

BETTY (Style one) HN403
Designer: L. Harradine
Height: 7½in., 19cm.
Issued: 1920-1938
            Colour variation
Price: $1280 £800

BETTY Style one) HN435
Designer: L. Harradine
Height: 7½in., 19cm.
Issued: 1921-1938
            Colour variation
Price: $1280 £800

BEDTIME STORY HN2059

BEACHCOMBER HN2487

BEGGAR HN526

109

BETTY (Style one) HN438
Designer: L. Harradine
Height: 7½in., 19cm.
Issued: 1921-1938
Colour variation
Price: $1280 £800

BETTY (Style one) HN477
Designer: L. Harradine
Height: 7½in., 19cm.
Issued: 1921-1938
Colour variation
Price: $1280 £800

BETTY (Style one) HN478
Designer: L. Harradine
Height: 7½in., 19cm.
Issued: 1921-1938
Colour variation
Price: $1280 £800

BETTY (Style two) HN1404
Designer: L. Harradine
Height: 4½in., 11.4cm.
Issued: 1930-1938
Price: $288 £180

BETTY (Style two) HN1405
Designer: L. Harradine
Height: 4½in., 11.4cm.
Issued: 1930-1938
Colour variation
Price: $288 £180

BETTY (Style two) HN1435
Designer: L. Harradine
Height: 4½in., 11.4cm.
Issued: 1930-1938
Colour variation
Price: $288 £180

BETTY (Style two) HN1436
Designer: L. Harradine
Height: 4½in., 11.4cm.
Issued: 1930-1938
Colour variation
Price: $288 £180

BIDDY HN1445
Designer: L. Harradine
Height: 5½in., 14.0cm.
Issued: 1931-1938
Price: $152 £95

BIDDY HN1500
Designer: L. Harradine
Height: 5½in., 14.0cm.
Issued: 1932-1938
Price: $152 £95

BIDDY HN1513
Designer: L. Harradine
Height: 5½in., 14.0cm.
Issued: 1932-1951
Colour variation
Price: $112 £70

BIDDY PENNY FARTHING
HN1843
Designer: L. Harradine
Height: 9in., 22.9cm.
Issued: 1938-
Rec. Retail Price

BIDDY PENNY FARTHING

BIDDY HN1445   **BLITHE MORNING HN2021**

110

BILBO HN2914
Designer: Harry Sales
Height: 4½in., 11.4cm.
Issued: 1979-1984
Price: $56 £35

BILL SYKES HN537
Designer: L. Harradine
Height: 3¾in., 9.5cm.
Issued: 1922-1932
Price: $48 £30

BILL SYKES M54
Designer: L. Harradine
Height: 4¼in., 10.8cm.
Issued: 1932-1982
Price: $45 £28

BLACKSMITH HN2782
Designer: W. K. Harper
Height: 9in., 22.5cm.
Issued: 1987
Rec. Retail Price

**BLACKSMITH OF
WILLIAMSBURG HN2240**
Designer: M. Davies
Height: 6¾in., 17.2cm.
Issued: 1960-1983
Price: $128 £80

BLIGHTY HN323
Designer: E. W. Light
Height: 11¼in., 28.5cm.
Issued: 1918-1938
Price: $448 £280

BLITHE MORNING HN2021
Designer: L. Harradine
Height: 7¼in., 18.4cm.
Issued: 1949-1971
Price: $160 £100

BLITHE MORNING HN2065
Designer: L. Harradine
Height: 7¼in., 18.4cm.
Issued: 1950-1973
        Colour variation
Price: $160 £100

BLOSSOM HN1667
Designer: L. Harradine
Height: 6¾in., 17.2cm.
Issued: 1934-1949
Price: $432 £270

**BLUE BEARD (Style one)
HN75**
Designer: E. W. Light
Height: Unknown
Issued: 1917-1938
Price: $1040 £650 /

**BLUE BEARD (Style one)
HN410**
Designer: E. W. Light
Height: Unknown
Issued: 1920-1938
        Colour variation
Price: $1040 £650

**BLUEBEARD (Style two)
HN1528**
Designer: L. Harradine
Height: 11½in., 29.2cm.
Issued: 1932-1949
Price: $272 £170

**BLACKSMITH OF
WILLIAMSBURG HN2240**   **BILBO HN2914**

**BLUEBEARD
HN2105**

111

FIGURES

BLUEBEARD (Style two)
HN2105
Designer: L. Harradine
Height: 11in., 27.9cm.
Issued: 1953-
Colour variation
Rec. Retail Price

BLUE BIRD HN1280
Designer: L. Harradine
Height: 4¾in., 12.0cm.
Issued: 1928-1938
Price: $280 £175

BOATMAN HN2417
Designer: M. Nicholl
Height: 6½in., 16.5cm.
Issued: 1971-1987
Price: $120 £75

BOLERO HN3076
Designer: A. Hughes
Height: 13½in., 34.5cm.
Issued: 1987-1989
Price: $80 £50

BON APPETIT HN2444
Designer: M. Nicholl
Height: 6in., 15.2cm.
Issued: 1972-1976
Price: $109 £68

BONJOUR HN1879
Designer: L. Harradine
Height: 6¾in., 17.2cm.
Issued: 1938-1949
Price: $320 £200

BONJOUR HN1888
Designer: L. Harradine
Height: 6¾in., 17.2cm.
Issued: 1938-1949
Colour variation
Price: $320 £200

BONNIE LASSIE HN1626
Designer: L. Harradine
Height: 5¼in., 13.3cm.
Issued: 1934-1953
Price: $192 £120

BONNIE LASSIE HN1626A
Designer: L. Harradine
Height: 5¼in., 13.3cm.
Issued: Unknown
Colour variation
Price: $192 £120

BO-PEEP (Style one) **HN777**
Designer: L. Harradine
Height: 6¾in., 17.2cm.
Issued: 1926-1938
Price: $672 £420

BO-PEEP (Style one) **HN1202**
Designer: L. Harradine
Height: 6¾in., 17.2cm.
Issued: 1926-1938
Colour variation
Price: $640 £400

BO-PEEP (Style one) **HN1327**
Designer: L. Harradine
Height: 6¾in., 17.2cm.
Issued: 1929-1938
Colour variation
Price: $640 £400

BOY FROM WILLIAMSBURG HN2183

BOROMIR HN2918

BOATMAN HN2417

BO-PEEP (Style one) **HN1328**
Designer: L. Harradine
Height: 6¾in., 17.2cm.
Issued: 1929-1938
Colour variation
Price: $640 £400

BO-PEEP (Style two) **HN1810**
Designer: L. Harradine
Height: 5in., 12.7cm.
Issued: 1937-1949
Price: $128 £80

BO-PEEP (Style two) **HN1811**
Designer: L. Harradine
Height: 5in., 12.7cm.
Issued: 1937-
Colour variation
Rec. Retail Price

BO-PEEP M82
Designer: L. Harradine
Height: 4in., 10.1cm.
Issued: 1939-1949
Price: $208 £130

BO-PEEP M83
Designer: L. Harradine
Height: 4in., 10.1cm.
Issued: 1939-1949
Colour variation
Price: $208 £130

BOROMIR HN2918
Designer: Harry Sales
Height: 6¾in., 17.2cm.
Issued: 1980-1984
Price: $56 £35

BOUDOIR HN2542
Designer: E. J. Griffiths
Height: 12¼in., 31.1cm.
Issued: 1974-1977
Price: $128 £80

BOUQUET HN406
Designer: G. Lambert
Height: 9in., 22.9cm.
Issued: 1920-1938
Price: $720 £450

BOUQUET HN414
Designer: G. Lambert
Height: 9in., 22.9cm.
Issued: 1920-1938
Price: $720 £450

BOUQUET HN422
Designer: G. Lambert
Height: 9in., 22.9cm.
Issued: 1920-1938
Colour variation
Price: $720 £450

BOUQUET HN428
Designer: G. Lambert
Height: 9in., 22.9cm.
Issued: 1921-1938
Colour variation
Price: $720 £450

FIGURES

BOY WITH TURBAN HN662

BONNIE LASSIE HN1626

BOY EVACUEE HN3202

BON APPETIT HN2444

BOUQUET HN429
Designer: G. Lambert
Height: 9in., 22.9cm.
Issued: 1921-1938
Colour variation
Price: $720 £450

BOUQUET HN567
Designer: G. Lambert
Height: 9½in., 24.1cm.
Issued: 1923-1938
Colour variation
Price: $720 £450

BOUQUET HN794
Designer: G. Lambert
Height: 9in., 22.9cm.
Issued: 1926-1938
Colour variation
Price: $800 £500

BOY EVACUEE HN3202
Designer: A. Hughes
Height: 8½in., 21.5cm.
Issued: 1989 in a limited
edition of 9500
Rec. Retail Price

**BOY FROM
WILLIAMSBURG HN2183**
Designer: M. Davies
Height: 5½in., 14.0cm.
Issued: 1969-1983
Price: $88 £55

BOY ON CROCODILE HN373
Designer: C. J. Noke
Height: 5in., 12.7cm.
Length: 14½in., 36.8cm.
Issued: 1920-1938
Price: $1920 £1200

BOY ON PIG HN1369
Designer: C. J. Noke
Height: 4in., 10.1cm.
Issued: 1930-1938
Price: $880 £550

BOY WITH TURBAN HN586
Designer: L.Harradine
Height: 3¾in., 9.5cm.
Issued: 1923-1938
Price: $440 £275

BOY WITH TURBAN HN587
Designer: L. Harradine
Height: 3¾in., 9.5cm.
Issued: 1923-1938
Price: $440 £275

BOY WITH TURBAN HN661
Designer: L. Harradine
Height: 3¾in., 9.5cm.
Issued: 1924-1938
Price: $440 £275

BOY WITH TURBAN HN662
Designer: L. Harradine
Height: 3¾in., 9.5cm.
Issued: 1924-1938
Colour variation
Price: $440 £275

BOY WITH TURBAN HN1210
Designer: L. Harradine
Height: 3¾in., 9.5cm.
Issued: 1926-1938
          Colour variation
Price: $440 £275

BOY WITH TURBAN HN1212
Designer: L. Harradine
Height: 3¾in., 9.5cm.
Issued: 1926-1938
Price: $440 £275

BOY WITH TURBAN HN1213
Designer: L. Harradine
Height: 3¾in., 9.5cm.
Issued: 1926-1938
          Colour variation
Price: $440 £275

BOY WITH TURBAN HN1214
Designer: L. Harradine
Height: 3½in., 8.9cm.
Issued: 1926-1938
          Colour variation
Price: $440 £275

BOY WITH TURBAN HN1225
Designer: L. Harradine
Height: 3¾in., 9.5cm.
Issued: 1927-1938
          Colour variation
Price: $440 £275

BREEZY DAYS HN3162
Designer: A. Hughes
Height: 8½in., 21.5cm.
Issued: 1988
Rec. Retail Price

BRETON DANCER HN2383
Designer: P. Davies
Height: 8½in., 21.5cm.
Issued: 1981 in a limited
          edition of 750
Price: $520 £325

BRIDE (Style one) HN1588
Designer: L. Harradine
Height: 8¾in., 22.2cm.
Issued: 1933-1938
Price: $440 £275

BRIDE (Style one) HN1600
Designer: L. Harradine
Height: 8¾in., 22.2cm.
Issued: 1933-1949
          Colour variation
Price: $320 £200

BRIDE (Style one) HN1762
Designer: L. Harradine
Height: 8¾in., 22.2cm.
Issued: 1936-1949
          Colour variation
Price: $320 £200

BRIDE (Style one) HN1841
Designer: L. Harradine
Height: 9½in., 24.1cm.
Issued: 1938-1949
          Colour variation
Price: $400 £250

BRIDE (Style two) HN2166
Designer: M. Davies
Height: 8in., 20.3cm.
Issued: 1956-1976
Price: $136 £85

BOY WITH TURBAN HN1210

BRIDESMAID (Style one) HN1433

BOY WITH TURBAN HN1213

BRETON DANCER HN2383

114

BRIDE (Style three) HN2873
Designer: M. Davies
Height: 8in., 20.3cm.
Issued: 1980-1989
Price: $80 £50

BRIDESMAID (Style one) HN1433
Designer: L. Harradine
Height: 5¼in., 13.3cm.
Issued: 1930-1951
Price: $96 £60

BRIDESMAID (Style one) HN1434
Designer: L. Harradine
Height: 5in., 12.7cm.
Issued: 1930-1949
         Colour variation
Price: $96 £60

BRIDESMAID (Style one) HN1530
Designer: L. Harradine
Height: 5in., 12.7cm.
Issued: 1932-1938
         Colour variation
Price: $96 £60

BRIDESMAID (Style two) HN2148
Designer: M. Davies
Height: 5½in., 14.0cm.
Issued: 1955-1959
Price: $104 £65

BRIDESMAID (Style three) HN2196
Designer: M. Davies
Height: 5¼in., 13.3cm.
Issued: 1960-1976
Price: $64 £40

BRIDESMAID (Style four) HN2874
Designer: M. Davies
Height: 5¼in., 13.3cm.
Issued: 1980-1989
Price: $45 £28

BRIDESMAID M11
Designer: L. Harradine
Height: 3¾in., 9.5cm.
Issued: 1932-1938
Price: $112 £70

BRIDESMAID M12
Designer: L. Harradine
Height: 3¾in., 9.5cm.
Issued: 1932-1945
         Colour variation
Price: $112 £70

BRIDESMAID M30
Designer: L. Harradine
Height: 3¾in., 9.5cm.
Issued: 1932-1945
         Colour variation
Price: $112 £70

BRIDGET HN2070
Designer: L. Harradine
Height: 7¾in., 19.7cm.
Issued: 1951-1973
Price: $192 £120

BRIDE (Style one) HN1841   BRIDE (Style two) HN2166

BRIDGET HN2070

BRIDESMAID   HN2196

BRIGHT WATER HN3529
Designer: R. Jefferson
Height: 8½in., 21.5cm.
Issued: 1983-1986
Price: $48 £30

BROKEN LANCE HN2041
Designer: M. Davies
Height: 8¾in., 22.2cm.
Issued: 1949-1975
Price: $288 £180

BUDDIES HN2546
Designer: E. J. Griffiths
Height: 6in., 15.2cm.
Issued: 1973-1976
Price: $96 £60

BUMBLE M76
Designer: L. Harradine
Height: 4in., 10.1cm.
Issued: 1939-1982
Price: $45 £28

BUNNY HN2214
Designer: M. Davies
Height: 5in., 12.7cm.
Issued: 1960-1975
Price: $64 £40

BUTTERCUP HN2309
Designer: M. Davies
Height: 7in., 17.8cm.
Issued: 1964-

Rec. Retail Price

BUTTERCUP HN2399
Designer: P. Davies
Height: 7½in., 19cm.
Issued: 1983-
Rec. Retail Price

BUTTERFLY HN719
Designer: L. Harradine
Height: 6½in., 16.5cm.
Issued: 1925-1938
Price: $640 £400

BUTTERFLY HN720
Designer: L. Harradine
Height: 6½in., 16.5cm.
Issued: 1925-1938
    Colour variation
Price: $640 £400

BUTTERFLY HN730
Designer: L. Harradine
Height: 6½in., 16.5cm.
Issued: 1925-1938
    Colour variation
Price: $640 £400

BUTTERFLY HN1203
Designer: L. Harradine
Height: 6½in., 16.5cm.
Issued: 1926-1938
    Colour variation
Price: $640 £400

BUTTERFLY HN1456
Designer: L. Harradine
Height: 6½in., 16.5cm.
Issued: 1931-1938
Price: $640 £400

BROKEN LANCE HN2041

CAPTAIN COOK HN2889

BUZ FUZ HN538
Designer: L. Harradine
Height: 3¾in., 9.5cm.
Issued: 1922-1932
Price: $48 £30

BUZ FUZ M53
Designer: L. Harradine
Height: 4in., 10.1cm.
Issued: 1932-1983
Price: $48 £30

C

CALLED LOVE, A LITTLE BOY HN1545
Designer: Unknown
Height: 3½in., 8.9cm.
Issued: 1933-1949
Price: $208 £130

CALUMET HN1428
Designer: C. J. Noke
Height: 6in., 15.2cm.
Issued: 1930-1949
Price: $400 £250

CALUMET HN1689
Designer: C. J. Noke
Height: 6½in., 16.5cm.
Issued: 1935-1949
Colour variation
Price: $400 £250

CALUMET HN2068
Designer: C. J. Noke
Height: 6¼in., 15.9cm.
Issued: 1950-1953
Colour variation
Price: $400 £250

CAMELLIA HN2222
Designer: M. Davies
Height: 7¾in., 19.7cm.
Issued: 1960-1971
Price: $144 £90

CAMILLA HN1710
Designer: L. Harradine
Height: 7in., 17.8cm.
Issued: 1935-1949
Price: $368 £230

CAMILLA HN1711
Designer: L. Harradine
Height: 7in., 17.8cm.
Issued: 1935-1949
Colour variation
Price: $368 £230

CAMILLE HN1586
Designer: L. Harradine
Height: 6½in., 16.5cm.
Issued: 1933-1949
Price: $288 £180

CAMILLE HN1648
Designer: L. Harradine
Height: 6½in., 16.5cm.
Issued: 1934-1949
Colour variation
Price: $288 £180

CAMILLE HN1736
Designer: L. Harradine
Height: 6½in., 16.5cm.
Issued: 1935-1949
Colour variation
Price: $288 £180

CAPTAIN (Style two) HN2260

BUTTERCUP HN2309

CAPTAIN (Style one) HN778
Designer: L. Harradine
Height: 7in., 17.8cm.
Issued: 1926-1938
Price: $720 £450

CAPTAIN (Style two) HN2260
Designer: M. Nicholl
Height: 9½in., 24.1cm.
Issued: 1965-1982
Price: $136 £85

CAPTAIN COOK HN2889
Designer: W. K. Harper
Height: 8in., 20.3cm.
Issued: 1980-1984
Price: $136 £85

CAPTAIN CUTTLE M77
Designer: L. Harradine
Height: 4in., 10.1cm.
Issued: 1939-1982
Price: $48 £30

CAPTAIN MacHEATH HN464
Designer: L. Harradine
Height: 7in., 17.8cm.
Issued: 1921-1949
Price: $600 £375

CAPTAIN MacHEATH HN590
Designer: L. Harradine
Height: 7in., 17.8cm.
Issued: 1924-1949
Price: $600 £375

CAPTAIN MacHEATH HN1256
Designer: L. Harradine
Height: 7in., 17.8cm.
Issued: 1927-1949
Price: $600 £375

CAPTAIN, 2ND NEW YORK REGIMENT 1755 HN2755
Designer: E. J. Griffiths
Height: 10in., 25.4cm.
Issued: 1976 in a limited edition of 350
Price: $560 £350

CAREFREE (Black) HN3029
Designer: R. Jefferson
Height: 12¼in., 31cm.
Issued: 1986
Rec. Retail Price

CAREFREE (White) HN3026
Designer: R. Jefferson
Height: 12¼in., 31cm.
Issued: 1986
Rec. Retail Price

CARMEN (Style one) HN1267
Designer: L. Harradine
Height: 7in., 17.8cm.
Issued: 1928-1938
Price: $640 £400

CARMEN (Style one) HN1300
Designer: L. Harradine
Height: 7in., 17.8cm.
Issued: 1928-1938
Colour variation
Price: $640 £400

CARMEN (Style two) HN2545
Designer: E. J. Griffiths
Height: 11½in., 29.2cm.
Issued: 1974-1977
Price: $152 £95

CARNIVAL HN1260
Designer: L. Harradine
Height: 8¼in., 21.0cm.
Issued: 1927-1938
Price: $880 £550

CARNIVAL HN1278
Designer: L. Harradine
Height: 8½in., 21.6cm.
Issued: 1928-1938
Colour variation
Price: $880 £550

CAROL HN2961
Designer: P. Parsons
Height: 7½in., 19cm.
Issued: 1982-
Rec. Retail Price

CAROLINE HN3170
Designer: P. Davies
Height: 7½in., 19.5cm.
Issued: 1988
Rec. Retail Price

CAROLYN HN2112
Designer: L. Harradine
Height: 7in., 17.8cm.
Issued: 1953-1965
Price: $192 £120

CAROLYN HN2974
Designer: A. Hughes
Height: 5½in., 14cm.
Issued: 1983-1986
Price: $80 £50

CARPENTER HN2678
Designer: M. Nicoll
Height: 8in., 20cm.
Issued: 1986
Rec. Retail price

CARPET SELLER (Style one)
HN1464
Designer: L. Harradine
Height: 9¼in., 23.5cm.
Issued: 1931-?
Price: $192 £120

CARPET SELLER (Style two)
HN1464A
Designer: L. Harradine
Height: 9in., 22.9cm.
Issued: 1924-1969
Price: $192 £120

CARPET VENDOR (Style one)
HN38
Designer: C. J. Noke
Height: Unknown
Issued: 1914-1938
Price: $1600 £1000

CARPET VENDOR (Style one)
HN38A
Designer: C. J. Noke
Height: Unknown
Issued: 1914-1938
Price: $1600 £1000

CARPET SELLER HN1464

CARMEN (Style two) HN2545

CAROLYN HN2112

CARPET VENDOR (Style two) HN76

118

CARPET VENDOR (Style one)
HN348
Designer: C. J. Noke
Height: Unknown
Issued: 1919-1938
Price: $1600 £1000

CARPET VENDOR (Style two)
HN76
Designer: C. J. Noke
Height: 5½in., 14.0cm.
Issued: 1917-1938
Price: $1920 £1200

CARPET VENDOR (Style two)
HN350
Designer: C. J. Noke
Height: 5½in., 14.0cm.
Issued: 1919-1938
Price: $1920 £1200

CARRIE HN2800
Designer: M. Davies
Height: 6in., 15.2cm.
Issued: 1976-1980
Price: $56 £35

CASSIM (Style one) HN1231
Designer: L. Harradine
Height: 3in., 7.6cm.
Issued: 1927-1938
Price: $448 £280

CASSIM (Style one) HN1232
Designer: L. Harradine
Height: 3in., 7.6cm.
Issued: 1927-1938
Colour variation
Price: $448 £280

CASSIM (Style two) HN1311
Designer: L. Harradine
Height: 3¾in., 9.5cm.
Issued: 1929-1938
Price: $448 £280

CASSIM (Style two) HN1312
Designer: L. Harradine
Height: 3¾in., 9.5cm.
Issued: 1929-1938
Price: $448 £280

CATHERINE HN3044
Designer: P. Parsons
Height: 5in., 12.5cm.
Issued: 1985-
Rec. Retail Price

CAVALIER (Style one) HN369
Designer: Unknown
Height: Unknown
Issued: 1920-1938
Price: $900 £600

CAVALIER (Style two) HN2716
Designer: E. J. Griffiths
Height: 9¾in., 24.7cm.
Issued: 1976-1982
Price: $160 £100

CELESTE HN2237
Designer: M. Davies
Height: 6¾in., 17.2cm.
Issued: 1959-1971
Price: $144 £90

CARPENTER HN2678

CAVALIER

119

CELIA HN1726
Designer: L. Harradine
Height: 11½in., 29.2cm.
Issued: 1935-1949
Price: $640 £400

CELIA HN1727
Designer: L. Harradine
Height: 11½in., 29.2cm.
Issued: 1935-1949
Price: $640 £400

CELLIST HN2226
Designer: M. Davies
Height: 8in., 20.3cm.
Issued: 1960-1967
Price: $304 £190

CELLO HN2331
Designer: M. Davies
Height: 6in., 15.2cm.
Issued: 1970 in a limited
edition of 750
Price: $512 £320

CENTURION HN2726
Designer: W. K. Harper
Height: 9¼in., 23.5cm.
Issued: 1982-1984
Price: $120 £75

CERISE HN1607
Designer: L. Harradine
Height: 5¼in., 13.3cm.
Issued: 1933-1949
Price: $128 £80

CHARISMA HN3090
Designer: P. Parsons
Height: 12½in., 31.5cm.
Issued: 1987
Rec. Retail Price

CHARITY HN3087
Designer: E.J. Griffiths
Height: 8½in., 21.5cm.
Issued: 1987 in a limited
edition of 9500
Price: $112 £70

**CHARLEY'S AUNT (Style one)
HN35**
Designer: A. Toft
Height: 6¾in., 17.2cm.
Issued: 1914-1938
Price: $320 £200

CHARLEY'S AUNT HN640
Designer: A. Toft
Height: 7in., 17.8cm.
Issued: 1924-1938
Colour variation
Price: $440 £275

**CHARLEY'S AUNT (Style two)
HN1411**
Designer: H. Fenton
Height: 8in., 20.3cm.
Issued: 1930-1938
Price: $960 £600

**CHARLEY'S AUNT (Style two)
HN1554**
Designer: H. Fenton
Height: 8in., 20.3cm.
Issued: 1933-1938
Price: $960 £600

CHARLOTTE HN2423

CHARLIE CHAPLIN HN2771

CELLIST HN2226

CENTURION HN2726

CHARLEY'S AUNT (Style three) HN1703
Designer: A. Toft
Height: 6in., 15.2cm.
Issued: 1935-1938
Price: $960 £600

CHARLIE CHAPLIN HN2771
Designer: W.K. Harper
Height: 9in., 22.4cm.
Issued: 1989 in a limited edition of 5000
Price: $160 £100

CHARLOTTE HN2421
Designer: J. Bromley
Height: 6½in., 16.5cm.
Issued: 1972-1986
Price: $109 £68

CHARLOTTE HN2423
Designer: J. Bromley
Height: 6¾in., 17cm.
Issued: 1986
Rec. Retail Price

CHARMIAN HN1568
Designer: L. Harradine
Height: 6½in., 16.5cm.
Issued: 1933-1938
Price: $400 £250

CHARMIAN HN1569
Designer: L. Harradine
Height: 6½in., 16.5cm.
Issued: 1933-1938
Colour variation
Price: $400 £250

CHARMIAN HN1651
Designer: L. Harradine
Height: 6½in., 16.5cm.
Issued: 1934-1938
Cololur variation
Price: $400 £250

CHELSEA PAIR (Woman) HN577
Designer: L. Harradine
Height: 6in., 15.2cm.
Issued: 1923-1938
Price: $480 £300

CHELSEA PAIR (Woman) HN578
Designer: L. Harradine
Height: 6in., 15.2cm.
Issued: 1923-1938
Colour variation
Price: $480 £300

CHELSEA PAIR (Man) HN579
Designer: L. Harradine
Height: 6in., 15.2cm.
Issued: 1923-1938
Price: $480 £300

CHELSEA PAIR (Man) HN580
Designer: L. Harradine
Height: 6in., 15.2cm.
Issued: 1923-1938
Colour variation
Price: $480 £300

CHELSEA PENSIONER HN689
Designer: L. Harradine
Height: 5¾in., 14.6cm.
Issued: 1924-1938
Price: $720 £450

CHARITY HN3087

CHARMIAN HN1568

CELLO HN2331

CHERIE HN2341
Designer: M. Davies
Height: 5½in., 14.0cm.
Issued: 1966-
Rec. Retail Price

CHERRY BLOSSOM HN3092
Designer: P. Parsons
Height: 12¼in., 31cm.
Issued: 1987-1989
Price: $80 £50

CHERYL HN3253
Designer: D. Tootle
Height: 7¹/₂in.
Issued: 1989-
Rec. Retail Price

CHIC HN2997
Designer: R. Tabbenor
Height: 13in., 33cm.
Issued: 1987
Rec. Retail Price

CHIEF HN2892
Designer: W. K. Harper
Height: 7in., 17.8cm.
Issued: 1979-1988
Price: $104 £65

CHIEFTAIN HN2929
Designer: S. Keenan
Height: 8¾in., 22.2cm.
Issued: 1982 in a limited
edition of 950
Price: $160 £100

CHILD AND CRAB HN32
Designer: C. J. Noke
Height: 5¼in., 13.3cm.
Issued: 1913-1938
Price: $1200 £750

**CHILD FROM
WILLIAMSBURG HN2154**
Designer: M. Davies
Height: 5½in., 14.0cm.
Issued: 1964-1984
Price: $88 £55

**CHILD STUDY (Style one)
HN603A**
Designer: L. Harradine
Height: 4¾in., 12.0cm.
Issued: 1924-1938
Price: $323 £145

**CHILD STUDY (Style one)
HN603B**
Designer: L. Harradine
Height: 4¾in., 12.0cm.
Issued: 1924-1938
Colour variation
Price: $323 £145

CHILD STUDY HN606A
Designer: L. Harradine
Height: 5in., 12.7cm.
Issued: 1924-1938
Price: $323 £145

CHILD STUDY HN1441
Designer: L. Harradine
Height: 5in., 12.7cm.
Issued: 1931-1938
Price: $296 £185

**CHILD STUDY (Style two)
HN604A**
Designer: L. Harradine
Height: 5½in., 14.0cm.
Issued: 1924-1938
Price: $272 £170

CHIEF HN2892

CHILD FROM
WILLIAMSBURG HN2154

CHITARRONE HN2700

FIGURES

CHILD STUDY (Style two)
HN604B
Designer: L. Harradine
Height: 5½in., 14.0cm.
Issued: 1924-1938
Colour variation
Price: $272 £170

CHILD STUDY (Style two)
HN1442
Designer: L. Harradine
Height: 6¼in., 15.9cm.
Issued: 1931-1938
Price: $296 £185

CHILD STUDY (Style two)
HN1443
Designer: L. Harradine
Issued: 1931-1938
Height: 5in., 12.7cm.
Price: $272 £170

CHILD STUDY (Style three)
HN605A
Designer: L. Harradine
Height: 5½in., 14cm.
Issued: 1924-1938
Price: $232 £145

CHILD STUDY (Style three)
HN605B
Designer: L. Harradine
Height: 5½in., 14cm.
Issued: 1924-1938
Price: $232 £145

CHILD'S GRACE HN62
Designer: L. Perugini
Height: 6¾in., 17.2cm.
Issued: 1916-1938
Price: $880 £550

CHILD'S GRACE HN62A
Designer: L. Perugini
Height: 6¾in., 17.2cm.
Issued: 1916-1938
Colour variation
Price: $880 £550

CHILD'S GRACE HN510
Designer: L. Perugini
Height: 6¾in., 17.1cm.
Issued: 1921-1938
Price: $880 £550

CHINA REPAIRER HN2943
Designer: R. Tabbenor
Height: 6¾in., 17cm.
Issued: 1983-1988
Price: $136 £85

CHINESE DANCER HN2840
Designer: M. Davies
Height: 9in., 22.9cm.
Issued: 1980 in a limited
edition of 750
Price: $480 £300

CHITARRONE HN2700
Designer: M. Davies
Height: 7½in., 19.1cm.
Issued: 1974 in a limited
edition of 750
Price: $520 £325

CHINA REPAIRER HN2943

CHINESE DANCER HN2840

123

CHLOE HN1470
Designer: L. Harradine
Height: 5½in., 14.0cm.
Issued: 1931-1949
Price: $192 £120

CHLOE HN1476
Designer: L. Harradine
Height: 5½in., 14.0cm.
Issued: 1931-1938
Colour variation
Price: $240 £150

CHLOE HN1479
Designer: L. Harradine
Height: 5½in., 14.0cm.
Issued: 1931-1949
Colour variation
Price: $208 £130

CHLOE HN1498
Designer: L. Harradine
Height: 6in., 15.2cm.
Issued: 1932-1938
Colour variation
Price: $240 £150

CHLOE HN1765
Designer: L. Harradine
Height: 6in., 15.2cm.
Issued: 1936-1950
Colour variation
Price: $160 £100

CHLOE HN1956
Designer: L. Harradine
Height: 6in., 15.2cm.
Issued: 1940-1949
Colour variation
Price: $192 £120

CHLOE M9
Designer: L. Harradine
Height: 2¾in., 7.0cm.
Issued: 1932-1945
Price: $160 £100

CHLOE M10
Designer: L. Harradine
Height: 2¾in., 7.0cm.
Issued: 1932-1945
Colour variation
Price: $160 £100

CHLOE M29
Designer: L. Harradine
Height: 2¾in., 7.0cm.
Issued: 1932-1945
Colour variation
Price: $160 £100

CHOICE HN1959
Designer: L. Harradine
Height: 7¼in., 18.4cm.
Issued: 1941-1949
Price: $400 £250

CHOICE HN1960
Designer: L. Harradine
Height: 7¼in., 18.4cm.
Issued: 1941-1949
Colour variation
Price: $400 £250

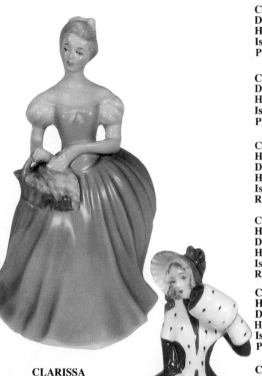

CLARISSA

CHRISTMAS MORN

CHLOE HN1479

CHOIR BOY HN2141
Designer: M. Davies
Height: 4¾in., 12.0cm.
Issued: 1954-1975
Price: $72 £45

CHORUS GIRL HN1401
Designer: L. Harradine
Height: 8½in., 21.6cm.
Issued: 1930-1938
Price: $720 £450

CHRISTENING DAY (Pink) HN3211
Designer: P.A. Northcroft
Height: 8½in., 21.5cm.
Issued: 1988
Rec. Retail Price

CHRISTENING DAY (Blue) HN3210
Designer: P.A. Northcroft
Height: 8½in., 21.5cm.
Issued: 1988
Rec. Retail Price

CHRISTINE (Style one) HN1839
Designer: L. Harradine
Height: 7¾in., 19.7cm.
Issued: 1938-1949
Price: $480 £300

CHRISTINE (Style one) HN1840
Designer: L. Harradine
Height: 7¾in., 19.7cm.
Issued: 1938-1949
Colour variation
Price: $480 £300

CHRISTINE (Style two) HN2792
Designer: M. Davies
Height: 7½in., 19.1cm.
Issued: 1978-
Rec. Retail Price

CHRISTMAS MORN HN1992
Designer: M. Davies
Height: 7in., 17.8cm.
Issued: 1947-
Rec. Retail Price

CHRISTMAS MORN HN3212
Designer: P. Davies
Height: 4in., 10cm.
Issued: 1988
Rec. Retail Price

CHRISTMAS PARCELS HN2851
Designer: W. K. Harper
Height: 8¾in., 22.2cm.
Issued: 1978-1982
Price: $112 £70

CHRISTMAS TIME HN2110
Designer: M. Davies
Height: 6½in., 16.5cm.
Issued: 1953-1967
Price: $208 £130

CHRISTINE
HN2792

CISSIE HN1809

CHRISTMAS PARCELS HN2851

CICELY HN1516
Designer: L. Harradine
Height: 5¾in., 14.6cm.
Issued: 1932-1949
Price: $480 £300

CIRCE HN1249
Designer: L. Harradine
Height: 7¾in., 19.7cm.
Issued: 1927-1938
Price: $768 £480

CIRCE HN1250
Designer: L. Harradine
Height: 7½in., 19.1cm.
Issued: 1927-1938
Price: $768 £480

CIRCE HN1254
Designer: L. Harradine
Height: 7½in., 19.1cm.
Issued: 1927-1938
Colour variation
Price: $768 £480

CIRCE HN1255
Designer: L. Harradine
Height: 7½in., 19.1cm.
Issued: 1927-1938
Colour variation
Price: $768 £480

CISSIE HN1808
Designer: L. Harradine
Height: 5in., 12.7cm.
Issued: 1937-1951
Price: $104 £65

CISSIE HN1809
Designer: L. Harradine
Height: 5in., 12.7cm.
Issued: 1937-
Colour variation
Rec. Retail Price

CLARE HN2793
Designer: M. Davies
Height: 7½in., 19.1cm.
Issued: 1980-1984
Price: $109 £68

CLARIBEL HN1950
Designer: L. Harradine
Issued: 1940-1949
Height: 4¾in., 12.0cm.
Price: $136 £85

CLARIBEL HN1951
Designer: L. Harradine
Height: 4¾in., 12.0cm.
Issued: 1940-1949
Colour variation
Price: $136 £85

CLARINDA HN2724
Designer: W. K. Harper
Height: 8½in., 21.6cm.
Issued: 1975-1980
Price: $104 £65

CLARISSA (Style one) HN1525
Designer: L. Harradine
Height: 10in., 25.4cm.
Issued: 1932-1938
Price: $440 £275

CLARISSA (Style one) HN1687
Designer: L. Harradine
Height: 9¾in., 24.8cm.
Issued: 1935-1949
          Colour variation
Price: $400 £250

CLARISSA (Style two) HN2345
Designer: M. Davies
Height: 7½in., 19.1cm.
Issued: 1968-1982
Price: $109 £68

CLEAR WATER HN3530
Designer: R. Jefferson
Height: 8¼in., 21cm.
Issued: 1983-1986
Price: $72 £45

CLEMENCY HN1633
Designer: L. Harradine
Height: 7in., 17.8cm.
Issued: 1934-1938
Price: $400 £250

CLEMENCY HN1634
Designer: L. Harradine
Height: 7in., 17.8cm.
Issued: 1934-1949
          Colour variation
Price: $320 £200

CLEMENCY HN1643
Designer: L. Harradine
Height: 7in., 17.8cm.
Issued: 1934-1938
          Colour variation
Price: $400 £250

CLEOPATRA HN2868
Designer: M. Davies
Height: 7¼in., 18.4cm.
Issued: 1980 in a limited
          edition of 750
Price: $720 £450

CLOCKMAKER HN2279
Designer: M. Nicoll
Height: 7in., 17.8cm.
Issued: 1961-1975
Price: $192 £120

CLOTHILDE HN1598
Designer: L. Harradine
Height: 7¼in., 18.4cm.
Issued: 1933-1949
Price: $352 £220

CLOTHILDE HN1599
Designer: L. Harradine
Height: 7¼in., 18.4cm.
Issued: 1933-1949
          Colour variation
Price: $352 £220

CLOUD HN1831
Designer: R. Garbe
Height: 23in., 58.4cm.
Issued: 1937-1949
Price: $2000 £1250

CLOTHILDE HN1599

CLOCKMAKER HN2279

CLEOPATRA HN2868

CLOWN HN2890
Designer: W. K. Harper
Height: 9in., 22.9cm.
Issued: 1979-1988
Price: $144 £90

COACHMAN HN2282
Designer: M. Nicoll
Height: 7¼in., 18.4cm.
Issued: 1963-1971
Price: $288 £180

COBBLER (Style one) HN542
Designer: C, J. Noke
Height: 7½in., 19.1cm.
Issued: 1922-1939
Price: $640 £400

COBBLER (Style one) HN543
Designer: C. J. Noke
Height: 7½in., 19.1cm.
Issued: 1922-1938
Colour variation
Price: $680 £425

COBBLER (Style one) HN682
Designer: C. J. Noke
Height: 7½in., 19.1cm.
Issued: 1924-1938
Colour variation
Price: $480 £300

COBBLER (Style two) HN681
Designer: C. J. Noke
Height: 8½in., 21.6cm.
Issued: 1924-1938
Price: $480 £300

COBBLER (Style two) HN1251
Designer: C. J. Noke
Height: 8½in., 21.6cm.
Issued: 1927-1938
Colour variation
Price: $480 £300

COBBLER (Style two) HN1283
Designer: C. J. Noke
Height: 8½in., 21.6cm.
Issued: 1928-1949
Colour variation
Price: $320 £200

COBBLER (Style three) HN1705
Designer: C. J. Noke
Height: 8in., 20.3cm.
Issued: 1935-1949
Price: $320 £200

COBBLER (Style three) HN1706
Designer: C. J. Noke
Height: 8½in., 21.0cm.
Issued: 1935-1969
Colour variation
Price: $160 £100

COCKTAILS HN3070
Designer: A. Hughes
Height: 10¾in., 27.5cm.
Issued: 1987
Rec. Retail Price

COLLINETTE HN1998
Designer: L. Harradine
Height: 7¼in., 18.4cm.
Issued: 1947-1949
Price: $352 £220

COBBLER (Style one) HN542

CLOWN HN2890

COLLINETTE HN1998

COBBLER (Style three) HN1706

COLLINETTE HN1999
Designer: L. Harradine
Height: 7¼in., 18.4cm.
Issued: 1947-1949
           Colour variation
Price: $288 £180

COLONEL FAIRFAX HN2903
Designer: W. K. Harper
Height: 11½in., 29cm.
Issued: 1982-1986
Price: $232 £145

COLUMBINE (Style one) HN1296
Designer: L. Harradine
Height: 6in., 15.2cm.
Issued: 1928-1938
Price: $440 £275

COLUMBINE (Style one) HN1297
Designer: L. Harradine
Height: 6in., 15.2cm.
Issued: 1928-1938
           Colour variation
Price: $440 £275

COLUMBINE (Style one) HN1439
Designer: L. Harradine
Height: 6in., 15.2cm.
Issued: 1930-1938
           Colour variation
Price: $440 £275

COLUMBINE (Style two) HN2185
Designer: M. Davies
Height: 7in., 17.8cm.
Issued: 1957-1969
Price: $144 £90

COLUMBINE HN2738
Designer: D. Tootle
Height: 12½in., 31cm.
Issued: 1982-
Rec. Retail Price

COMING OF SPRING HN1722
Designer: L. Harradine
Height: 12½in., 31.7cm.
Issued: 1935-1949
Price: $1280 £800

COMING OF SPRING HN1723
Designer: L. Harradine
Height: 12½in., 31.7cm.
Issued: 1935-1949
           Colour variation
Price: $1280 £800

CONSTANCE HN1510
Designer: L. Harradine
Height: 6³⁄₄in., 17.1cm.
Issued: 1932-1938
Price: $640 £400

CONSTANCE HN1511
Designer: L. Harradine
Height: Unknown
Issued: 1932-1938
           Colour variation
Price: $640 £400

COLUMBINE HN2738

COLONEL FAIRFAX HN2903

COMING OF SPRING HN1723

CONTEMPLATION HN2213
Designer: P. Davies
Height: 12in., 30cm.
Issued: 1982-1986
Price: $64 £40

CONTEMPLATION HN2241
Designer: P. Davies
Height: 12in., 30cm.
Issued: 1982-1986
　　　　Colour variation
Price: $64 £40

CONTENTMENT HN395
Designer: L. Harradine
Height: 7¼in., 18.4cm.
Issued: 1920-1938
Price: $800 £500

CONTENTMENT HN396
Designer: L. Harradine
Height: 7¼in., 18.4cm.
Issued: 1920-1938
　　　　Colour variation
Price: $800 £500

CONTENTMENT HN421
Designer: L. Harradine
Height: 7¼in., 18.4cm.
Issued: 1920-1938
　　　　Colour variation
Price: $800 £500

CONTENTMENT HN468
Designer: L. Harradine
Height: 7¼in., 18.4cm.
Issued: 1921-1938
　　　　Colour variation
Price: $800 £500

CONTENTMENT HN572
Designer: L. Harradine
Height: 7¼in., 18.4cm.
Issued: 1923-1938
　　　　Colour variation
Price: $800 £500

CONTENTMENT HN685
Designer: L. Harradine
Height: 7¼in., 18.4cm.
Issued: 1923-1938
　　　　Colour variation
Price: $896 £560

CONTENTMENT HN686
Designer: L. Harradine
Height: 7¼in., 18.4cm.
Issued: 1924-1938
　　　　Colour variation
Price: $896 £560

CONTENTMENT HN1323
Designer: L. Harradine
Height: 7¼in., 18.4cm.
Issued: 1929-1938
　　　　Colour variation
Price: $800 £500

COOKIE HN2218
Designer: M. Davies
Height: 4¾in., 12.0cm.
Issued: 1958-1975
Price: $88 £55

COUNTRY LASS HN1991

COMING OF SPRING HN1723

COPPELIA HN2115
Designer: M. Davies
Height: 7¼in., 18.4cm.
Issued: 1953-1959
Price: $440 £275

COQUETTE HN20
Designer: W. White
Height: 9¼in., 23.5cm.
Issued: 1913-1938
Price: $1920 £1200

COQUETTE HN37
Designer: W. White
Height: 9¼in., 23.5cm.
Issued: 1913-1938
Price: $1920 £1200

CORALIE HN2307
Designer: M. Davies
Height: 7¼in., 18.4cm.
Issued: 1964-1988
Price: $104 £65

CORINTHIAN HN1973
Designer: H. Fenton
Height: 7¾in., 19.7cm.
Issued: 1941-1949
Price: $720 £450

**CORPORAL, 1st NEW
HAMPSHIRE REGIMENT
1778 HN2780**
Designer: E. J. Griffiths
Height: 13in., 33.0cm.
Issued: 1975 in a limited
　　　　edition of 350
Price: $560 £350

**COUNTESS MARY HOWE
HN3007**
Designer: P. Gee
Height: 9¼in., 23.5cm.
Issued: 1950 in a limited
　　　　edition of 5000
Rec. Retail Price

COUNTRY GIRL HN3051
Designer: A. Hughes
Height: 7¾in., 19.5cm.
Issued: 1987
Rec. Retail Price

COUNTRY LASS HN1991
Designer: L. Harradine
Height: 7¼in., 18.4cm.
Issued: 1975-1981
Price: $109 £68
Also called MARKET DAY
HN1991

COUNTRY MAID HN3163
Designer: P. Hughes
Height: 8¼in., 21cm.
Issued: 1988
Rec. Retail Price

COUNTRY ROSE HN3221
Designer: P. Davies
Height: 8½in., 21.5cm.
Issued: 1989
Rec. Retail Price

**COURT SHOEMAKER
HN1755**
Designer: L. Harradine
Height: 6¾in., 17.2cm.
Issued: 1936-1949
Price: $1120 £700

COURTIER HN1338
Designer: L. Harradine
Height: 4½in., 11.4cm.
Issued: 1929-1938
Price: $800 £500

COVENT GARDEN HN1339
Designer: L. Harradine
Height: 9in., 22.9cm.
Issued: 1929-1938
Price: $560 £350

COVENT GARDEN HN2857
Designer: W.K. Harper
Height: 10in., 25.5cm.
Issued: 1988
Rec. Retail Price

CRADLE SONG HN2246
Designer: M. Davies
Height: 5½in., 14.0cm.
Issued: 1959-1962
Price: $352 £220

CRAFTSMAN HN2284
Designer: M. Nicoll
Height: 8¼in., 21.0cm.
Issued: 1961-1965
Price: $352 £220

CRINOLINE HN21
Designer: G. Lambert
Height: 6¼in., 15.8cm.
Issued: 1913-1938
        Colour variation
Price: $800 £500

CRINOLINE HN8
Designer: G. Lambert
Height: 6¼in., 15.8cm.
Issued: 1913-1938
Price: $800 £500

CRINOLINE HN9
Designer: G. Lambert
Height: 6¼in., 15.8cm.
Issued: 1913-1938
        Colour variation
Price: $800 £500

CRINOLINE HN9A
Designer: G. Lambert
Height: 6¼in., 15.8cm.
Issued: 1913-1938
        Colour variation
Price: $800 £500

CRINOLINE HN21A
Designer: G. Lambert
Height: 6¼in., 15.8cm.
Issued: 1913-1938
        Colour variation
Price: $800 £500

CRINOLINE HN413
Designer: G. Lambert
Height: 6¼in., 15.9cm.
Issued: 1920-1938
        Colour variation
Price: $800 £500

CRINOLINE HN566
Designer: G. Lambert
Height: 6¼in., 15.9cm.
Issued: 1923-1938
        Colour variation
Price: $800 £500

CUP OF TEA HN2322

COVENT GARDEN HN1339

CRINOLINE HN628
Designer: G. Lambert
Height: 6¼in., 15.9cm.
Issued: 1924-1938
        Colour variation
Price: $800 £500

CRINOLINE LADY HN650
Designer: Unknown
Height: 3in., 7.6cm.
Issued: 1924-1938
Price: $640 £400

CRINOLINE LADY HN651
Designer: Unknown
Height: 3in., 7.6cm.
Issued: 1924-1938
        Colour variation
Price: $640 £400

CRINOLINE LADY HN652
Designer: Unknown
Height: 3in., 7.6cm.
Issued: 1924-1938
        Colour variation
Price: $640 £400

CRINOLINE LADY HN653
Designer: Unknown
Height: 3in., 7.6cm.
Issued: 1924-1938
        Colour variation
Price: $640 £400

CRINOLINE LADY HN654
Designer: Unknown
Height: 3in., 7.6cm.
Issued: 1924-1938
        Colour variation
Price: $800 £500

CRINOLINE LADY HN655
Designer: Unknown
Height: 3in., 7.6cm.
Issued: 1924-1938
        Colour variation
Price: $800 £500

CROUCHING NUDE HN457
Designer: Unknown
Height: 5½in., 14.0cm.
Issued: 1921-1938
Price: $720 £450

CUP OF TEA HN2322
Designer: M. Nicholl
Height: 7in., 17.8cm.
Issued: 1964-1983
Price: $104 £65

CURLY KNOB HN1627
Designer: L. Harradine
Height: 6in., 15.2cm.
Issued: 1934-1949
Price: $296 £185

CURLY LOCKS HN2049
Designer: M. Davies
Height: 4½in., 11.4cm.
Issued: 1949-1953
Price: $256 £160

CURTSEY HN57
Designer: E. W. Light
Height: 11in., 27.9cm.
Issued: 1916-1938
Price: $720 £450

CYMBALS HN2699

CURLY KNOB HN1627

CURTSEY HN57B
Designer: E. W. Light
Height: 11in., 27.9cm.
Issued: 1916-1938
          Colour variation
Price: $720 £450

CURTSEY HN66A
Designer: E. W. Light
Height: 11in., 27.9cm.
Issued: 1916-1938
          Colour variation
Price: $720 £450

CURTSEY HN327
Designer: E. W. Light
Height: 11in., 27.9cm.
Issued: 1918-1938
          Colour variation
Price: $720 £450

CURTSEY HN334
Designer: E. W. Light
Height: 11in., 27.9cm.
Issued: 1918-1938
          Colour variation
Price: $720 £450

CURTSEY HN363
Designer: E. W. Light
Height: 11in., 27.9cm.
Issued: 1919-1938
          Colour variation
Price: $720 £450

CURTSEY HN371
Designer: E. W. Light
Height: 11in., 27.9cm.
Issued: 1920-1938
          Colour variation
Price: $720 £450

CURTSEY HN518
Designer: E. W. Light
Height: 11in., 27.9cm.
Issued: 1921-1938
          Colour variation
Price: $720 £450

CURTSEY HN547
Designer: E. W. Light
Height: 11in., 27.9cm.
Issued: 1922-1938
          Colour variation
Price: $720 £450

CURTSEY HN629
Designer: E. W. Light
Height: 11in., 27.9cm.
Issued: 1924-1938
          Colour variation
Price: $720 £450

CURTSEY HN670
Designer: E. W. Light
Height: 11in., 27.9cm.
Issued: 1924-1938
          Colour variation
Price: $720 £450

CYMBALS HN2699
Designer: M. Davies
Height: 7½in., 19.1cm.
Issued: 1974 in a limited
          edition of 750
Price: $520 £325

CYNTHIA HN1685
Designer: L. Harradine
Height: 5¾in., 14.6cm.
Issued: 1935-1949
Price: $368 £230

CYNTHIA HN1686
Designer: L. Harradine
Height: 5¾in., 14.6cm.
Issued: 1935-1949
            Colour variation
Price: $368 £230

CYNTHIA HN1686A
Designer: L. Harradine
Height: 5¾in., 14.6cm.
Issued: 1935-1949
            Colour variation
Price: $368 £230

CYNTHIA HN2440
Designer: P. Davies
Height: 7¼in., 18cm.
Issued: 1984-
Rec. Retail Price

CYNTHIA HN2440

D

DAFFY-DOWN-DILLY HN1712
Designer: L. Harradine
Height: 7¾in., 19.7cm.
Issued: 1935-1975
Price: $208 £130

DAFFY-DOWN-DILLY HN1713
Designer: L. Harradine
Height: 8¼in., 21.0cm.
Issued: 1935-1949
            Colour variation
Price: $320 £200

DAINTY MAY HN1639
Designer: L. Harradine
Height: 6in., 15.2cm.
Issued: 1934-1949
Price: $192 £120

DAINTY MAY HN1656
Designer: L. Harradine
Height: 6in., 15.2cm.
Issued: 1934-1949
            Colour variation
Price: $192 £120

DAINTY MAY M67
Designer: L. Harradine
Height: 4in., 10.1cm.
Issued: 1935-1949
Price: $192 £120

DAINTY MAY M73
Designer: L. Harradine
Height: 4in., 10.1cm.
Issued: 1936-1949
            Colour variation
Price: $192 £120

DAISY HN1575
Designer: L. Harradine
Height: 3¾in., 9.5cm.
Issued: 1933-1949
Price: $160 £100

DAFFY-DOWN-DILLY HN1712

DAISY HN1961
Designer: L. Harradine
Height: 3½in., 8.9cm.
Issued: 1941-1949
Colour variation
Price: $160 £100

DAMARIS HN2079
Designer: M. Davies
Height: 7¼in., 18.4cm.
Issued: 1951-1952
Price: $480 £300

DANCING DELIGHT HN3078
Designer: A. Hughes
Height: 12¾in., 32cm.
Issued: 1987-1989
Price: $72 £45

"DANCING EYES AND SUNNY HAIR" HN1543
Designer: Unknown
Height: 5in., 12.7cm.
Issued: 1933-1949
Price: $192 £120

DANCING FIGURE HN311
Designer: Unknown
Height: 17¾in., 45.0cm.
Issued: 1918-1938
Price: $2080 £1300

DANCING YEARS HN2235
Designer: M. Davies
Height: 6¾in., 17.2cm.
Issued: 1965-1971
Price: $192 £120

DANDY HN753
Designer: L. Harradine
Height: 6¾in., 17.2cm.
Issued: 1925-1938
Price: $480 £300

DAPHNE HN2268
Designer: M. Davies
Height: 8¼in., 21.0cm.
Issued: 1963-1975
Price: $128 £80

DARBY HN1427
Designer: L. Harradine
Height: 5½in., 14.0cm.
Issued: 1930-1949
Price: $216 £135

DARBY HN2024
Designer: L. Harradine
Height: 5¾in., 14.6cm.
Issued: 1949-1959
Price: $208 £130

DARLING (Style one) HN1
Designer: C. Vyse
Height: 7¾in., 19.5cm.
Issued: 1913-1928
Price: $480 £300

DARLING (Style one) HN1319
Designer: C. Vyse
Height: 7½in., 19.1cm.
Issued: 1929-1959
Colour variation
Price: $104 £65

DARLING (Style one) HN1371
Designer: C. Vyse
Height: 7½in., 19.1cm.
Issued: 1930-1938
Colour variation
Price: $272 £170

DARBY HN1427

133

DARLING (Style one) HN1372
Designer: C. Vyse
Height: 7¾in., 19.7cm.
Issued: 1930-1938
Colour variation
Price: $240 £150

DARLING (Style two) HN1985
Designer: C. Vyse
Height: 5¼in., 13.3cm.
Issued: 1946-
Rec. Retail Price

DAVID COPPERFIELD M88
Designer: L. Harradine
Height: 4¼in., 10.8cm.
Issued: 1949-1983
Price: $48 £30

DAWN HN1858
Designer: L. Harradine
Height: 10in., 25.4cm.
Issued: 1938-?
Price: $800 £500

DAWN HN1858A
Designer: L. Harradine
Height: 9¾in., 24.7cm.
Issued: ??-1949
Colour variation
Price: $800 £500

DAYBREAK HN3107
Designer: R. Jefferson
Height: 11¾in., 30cm.
Issued: 1987-1989
Price: $72 £45

DAYDREAMS HN1731
Designer: L. Harradine
Height: 5¾in., 14.6cm.
Issued: 1935-
Rec. Retail Price

DAYDREAMS HN1732
Designer: L. Harradine
Height: 5½in., 14.0cm.
Issued: 1935-1949
Colour variation
Price: $176 £110

DAYDREAMS HN1944
Designer: L. Harradine
Height: 5½in., 14.0cm.
Issued: 1940-1949
Colour variation
Price: $176 £110

DEAUVILLE HN2344
Designer: P. Davies
Height: 8¼in., 20.9cm.
Issued: 1982 in a limited
edition of 1500
Price: $288 £180

DEBBIE HN2385
Designer: M. Davies
Height: 5½in., 14.0cm.
Issued: 1969-1982
Price: $56 £35

DEBBIE HN2400
Designer: P. Davies
Height: 6in., 15cm.
Issued: 1983-
Rec. Retail Price

DEAUVILLE HN2344

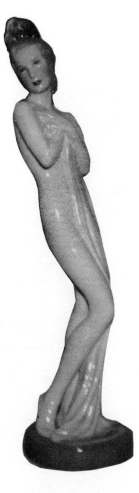

DAWN HN1858

DARLING (Style one) HN1319

DEBUT HN3046
Designer: P. Parsons
Height: 12¼in., 31cm.
Issued: 1987-1989
Price: $80 £50

DEBUTANTE HN2210
Designer: M. Davies
Height: 5in., 12.7cm.
Issued: 1963-1967
Price: $192 £120

DECEMBER HN2696
Designer: P. Davies
Height: 7¾in., 19.7cm.
Issued: 1987
Price: $96 £60

DEIDRE HN2020
Designer: L. Harradine
Height: 7in., 17.8cm.
Issued: 1949-1955
Price: $232 £145

DELICIA HN1662
Designer: L. Harradine
Height: 5¾in., 14.6cm.
Issued: 1934-1938
Price: $416 £260

DELICIA HN1663
Designer: L. Harradine
Height: 5¾in., 14.6cm.
Issued: 1934-1938
Colour variation
Price: $360 £225

DELICIA HN1681
Designer: L. Harradine
Height: 5¾in., 14.6cm.
Issued: 1935-1938
Colour variation
Price: $360 £225

DELIGHT HN1772
Designer: L. Harradine
Height: 7in., 17.8cm.
Issued: 1936-1967
Price: $152 £95

DELIGHT HN1773
Designer: L. Harradine
Height: 6¾in., 17.2cm.
Issued: 1936-1949
Colour variation
Price: $192 £120

DELPHINE HN2136
Designer: M. Davies
Height: 7¼in., 18.4cm.
Issued: 1954-1967
Price: $160 £100

DEMURE HN3045
Designer: P. Parsons
Height: 12½in., 31.5cm.
Issued: 1987-1989
Price: $80 £50

DENISE HN2273
Designer: M. Davies
Height: 7in., 17.8cm.
Issued: 1964-1971
Price: $176 £110

DENISE M34
Designer: Unknown
Height: 4½in., 11.4cm.
Issued: 1933-1945
Price: $256 £160

DENISE HN2273

DELIGHT HN1773

DAYDREAMS HN1731

135

DENISE M35
Designer: Unknown
Height: 4½in., 11.4cm.
Issued: 1933-1945
Colour variation
Price: $256 £160

DENISE HN2477
Designer: P. Davies
Height: 7¾in., 19.5cm.
Issued: 1987
Rec. Retail Price

DERRICK HN1398
Designer: L. Harradine
Height: 8in., 20.3cm.
Issued: 1930-1938
Price: $400 £250

DESPAIR HN596
Designer: Unknown
Height: 4½in., 11.4cm.
Issued: 1924-1938
Price: $480 £300

DETECTIVE HN2359
Designer: E. J. Griffiths
Height: 9¼in., 23.5cm.
Issued: 1977-1983
Price: $109 £68

DEVOTION HN3228
Designer: P. Parsons
Height: 9½in., 24cm.
Issued: 1989
Rec. Retail Price

DIANA HN1716
Designer: L. Harradine
Height: 5¾in., 14.6cm.
Issued: 1935-1949
Price: $96 £60

DIANA HN1717
Designer: L. Harradine
Height: 5¾in., 14.6cm.
Issued: 1935-1949
Colour variation
Price: $96 £60

DIANA HN1986
Designer: L. Harradine
Height: 5¾in., 14.6cm.
Issued: 1946-1975
Colour variation
Price: $72 £45

DIANA HN2468
Designer: P. Davies
Height: 8in., 20cm.
Issued: 1987
Rec. Retail Price

DIANA THE HUNTRESS HN2829
Designer: R. Jefferson
Height: 11¼in., 28.5cm.
Issued: 1986 in a limited edition of 300
Price: $1520 £950

DICK SWIVELLER M90
Designer: L. Harradine
Height: 4¼in., 10.8cm.
Issued: 1949-1982
Price: $48 £30

DERRICK HN1398

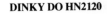

DINKY DO HN2120

DOCTOR HN2858

DETECTIVE HN2359

136

DICK TURPIN HN3272
Designer: G. Tounge
Height: 12in., 30.5cm
Issued: 1989 in a limited
          edition of 5000
Price: $480 £300

DIGGER (Australian) HN322
Designer: E. W. Light
Height: 11¼in., 28.5cm.
Issued: 1918-1938
Price: $640 £400

DIGGER (Australian) HN353
Designer: E. W. Light
Height: 11¼in., 28.5cm.
Issued: 1919-1938
Price: $640 £400

DIGGER (New Zealand) HN321
Designer: E. W. Light
Height: 11¼in., 28.5cm.
Issued: 1918-1938
Price: $640 £400

DILIGENT SCHOLAR HN26
Designer: W. White
Height: 7in., 17.8cm.
Issued: 1913-1938
Price: $1280 £800

DIMITY HN2169
Designer: L. Harradine
Height: 5¾in., 14.6cm.
Issued: 1956-1959
Price: $208 £130

DINKY DO HN1678
Designer: L. Harradine
Height: 4¾in., 12.0cm.
Issued: 1934-
          Colour variation
Rec. Retail Price

DINKY DO HN2120
Designer: L. Harradine
Height: 4¾in., 12.0cm.
Issued: 1983
Rec. Retail Price

"DO YOU WONDER . . ."
HN1544
Designer: Unknown
Height: 5in., 12.7cm.
Issued: 1933-1949
Price: $192 £120

DOCTOR HN2858
Designer: W. K. Harper
Height: 7½in., 19.1cm.
Issued: 1979-
Rec. Retail Price

DOLLY HN355
Designer: C. J. Noke
Height: 7¼in., 18.4cm.
Issued: 1919-1938
Price: $1120 £700

DOLLY VARDON HN1514
Designer: L. Harradine
Height: 8½in., 21.6cm.
Issued: 1932-1938
Price: $560 £350

DOLLY VARDON HN1515
Designer: L. Harradine
Height: 8½in., 21.6cm.
Issued: 1932-1949
Price: $440 £275

DICK TURPIN HN3272

DONNA HN2939
Designer: P. Gee
Height: 7¾in., 19.5cm.
Issued: 1986
Rec. Retail Price

DORCAS HN1490
Designer: L. Harradine
Height: 7in., 17.8cm.
Issued: 1932-1938
Price: $240 £150

DORCAS HN1491
Designer: L. Harradine
Height: 6¾in., 17.2cm.
Issued: 1932-1938
Price: $264 £165

DORCAS HN1558
Designer: L. Harradine
Height: 6¾in., 17.2cm.
Issued: 1933-1952
Colour variation
Price: $160 £100

DOREEN HN1363
Designer: L. Harradine
Height: 5¼in., 13.3cm.
Issued: 1929-1938
Price: $600 £375

DOREEN HN1389
Designer: L. Harradine
Height: 5¼in., 13.3cm.
Issued: 1930-1938
Colour variation
Price: $600 £375

DOREEN HN1390
Designer: L. Harradine
Height: 5¾in., 14.6cm.
Issued: 1929-1938
Colour variation
Price: $600 £375

DORIS KEENE as CAVALLINI (Style one) HN90
Designer: C. J. Noke
Height: 11in., 27.9cm.
Issued: 1918-1936
Price: $1600 £1000

DORIS KEENE as CAVALLINI (Style one) HN467
Designer: C. J. Noke
Height: 11in., 27.9cm.
Issued: 1921-1936
Colour variation
Price: $1600 £1000

DORIS KEENE as CAVALLINI (Style two) HN96
Designer: C. J. Noke
Height: 10¾in., 27.8cm.
Issued: 1918-1938
Price: $1600 £1000

DORIS KEENE as CAVALLINI (Style two) HN345
Designer: C. J. Noke
Height: 10½in., 26.6cm.
Issued: 1919-1949
Colour variation
Price: $1600 £1000

DOROTHY HN3098
Designer: P. Parsons
Height: 7in., 18cm.
Issued: 1987
Rec. Retail Price

DREAMLAND HN1473

DRUMMER BOY HN2679

DREAM WEAVER HN2283

DOUBLE JESTER HN365
Designer: C. J. Noke
Height: Unknown
Issued: 1920-1938
Price: $2720 £1700

DREAM WEAVER HN2283
Designer: M. Nicoll
Height: 8¼in., 21.0cm.
Issued: 1972-1976
Price: $120 £75

DREAMING HN3133
Designer: P. Parsons
Height: 9in., 22.5cm.
Issued: 1987
Rec. Retail Price

DREAMLAND HN1473
Designer: L. Harradine
Height: 4¾in., 12.0cm.
Issued: 1931-1938
Price: $1600 £1000

DREAMLAND HN1481
Designer: L. Harradine
Height: 4¾in., 12.0cm.
Issued: 1931-1938
    Colour variation
Price: $1440 £900

DRESSING UP HN2964
Designer: P. Parsons
Height: 7½in., 19cm.
Issued: 1982-1986
Price: $80 £50

DRUMMER BOY HN2679
Designer: M. Nicoll
Height: 8½in., 21.6cm.
Issued: 1976-1982
Price: $256 £160

**DRYAD OF THE PINES
HN1869**
Designer: R. Garbe
Height: 23in., 58.4cm.
Issued: 1938-1949
Price: $1920 £1200

DUCHESS OF YORK HN3086
Designer: E.J. Griffiths
Height: 8½in., 21.5cm.
Issued: 1986 in a limited
    edition of 1500
Price: $240 £150

DULCIE HN2305
Designer: M. Davies
Height: 7¼in., 18.4cm.
Issued: 1981-1984
Price: $112 £70

DULCIMER HN2798
Designer: M. Davies
Height: 6½in., 16.5cm.
Issued: 1975 in a limited
    edition of 750
Price: $400 £250

DULCINEA HN1343
Designer: L. Harradine
Height: 5½in., 14.0cm.
Issued: 1929-1938
Price: $1120 £700

DULCIMER HN2798

DUCHESS OF YORK HN3086

DULCINEA HN1419
Designer: L. Harradine
Height: 5½in., 14.0cm.
Issued: 1930-1938
         Colour variation
Price: $1120 £700

DUNCE HN6
Designer: C. J. Noke
Height: 10½in., 26.6cm.
Issued: 1913-1938
Price: $1440 £900

DUNCE HN310
Designer: C. J. Noke
Height: 10½in., 26.7cm.
Issued: 1918-1938
         Colour variation
Price: $1440 £900

DUNCE HN357
Designer: C. J. Noke
Height: 10½in., 26.7cm.
Issued: 1919-1938
         Colour variation
Price: $1440 £900

E

EASTER DAY HN1976
Designer: M. Davies
Height: 7¼in., 18.4cm.
Issued: 1945-1951
Price: $352 £220

EASTER DAY HN2039
Designer: M. Davies
Height: 7¼in., 18.4cm.
Issued: 1949-1969
         Colour variation
Price: $224 £140

EASTERN GRACE HN3138
Designer: P. Parsons
Height: 12in., 30.5cm.
Issued: 1988-1989
Price: $88 £55

EDITH HN2957
Designer: P. Parsons
Height: 5¾in., 14.5cm.
Issued: 1982-1985
Price: $80 £50

ELAINE HN2791
Designer: M. Davies
Height: 7½in., 19.1cm.
Issued: 1980
Rec. Retail Price

ELAINE HN3214
Designer: P. Davies
Height: 3³/₄in., 9.5cm.
Issued: 1988
Rec. Retail Price

ELEANOR OF PROVINCE
HN2009
Designer: M. Davies
Height: 9½in., 24.1cm.
Issued: 1948-1953
Price: $520 £325

DULCINEA HN1343

ELIZA HN2543   ELAINE HN2791

FIGURES

ELEANORE HN1753
Designer: L. Harradine
Height: 7in., 17.8cm.
Issued: 1936-1949
Price: $560 £350

ELEANORE HN1754
Designer: L. Harradine
Height: 7in., 17.8cm.
Issued: 1936-1949
  Colour variation
Price: $560 £350

ELEGANCE HN2264
Designer: M. Davies
Height: 7¼in., 18.4cm.
Issued: 1961-1985
Price: $112 £70

ELFREDA HN2078
Designer: L. Harradine
Height: 7¼in., 18.4cm.
Issued: 1951-1955
Price: $440 £275

ELIZA HN2543
Designer: E. J. Griffiths
Height: 11¼in., 28.6cm.
Issued: 1974-1975
Price: $176 £110

ELIZA HN2543A
Designer: E. J. Griffiths
Height: 11¾in., 29.8cm.
Issued: 1975-1977
  Colour variation
Price: $176 £110

ELIZA HN3179
Designer: D. Tootle
Height: 7½in., 19cm.
Issued: 1988
Rec. Retail Price

ELIZABETH HN2946
Designer: B. Franks
Height: 8in., 20cm.
Issued: 1982-1986
Price: $109 £68

ELIZABETH FRY HN2
Designer: C. Vyse
Height: 17in., 43.2cm.
Issued: 1913-1938
Price: $2400 £1500

ELIZABETH FRY HN2A
Designer: C. Vyse
Height: 17in., 43.2cm.
Issued: 1913-1938
Price: $2400 £1500

ELLEN HN3020
Designer: P. Parsons
Height: 3½in., 9cm.
Issued: 1984-1987
Price: $56 £35

ELLEN TERRY as QUEEN CATHERINE HN379
Designer: C. J. Noke
Height: 12½in., 31.7cm.
Issued: 1920-1949
Price: $880 £550

ELSIE MAYNARD HN639
Designer: C. J. Noke
Height: 7in., 17.8cm.
Issued: 1924-1949
Price: $480 £300

EASTER DAY HN2039

ELFREDA HN2078

ELEANOR OF PROVINCE HN2009

ELIZABETH HN2946

141

ELSIE MAYNARD HN2902
Designer: W. K. Harper
Height: 11¼in., 28.5cm.
Issued: 1982-1986
Price: $192 £120

ELYSE HN2429
Designer: M. Davies
Height: 5¾in., 14.6cm.
Issued: 1972-
Rec. Retail Price

ELYSE (Green) HN2474
Designer: P. Davies
Height: 6¾in., 17cm.
Issued: 1987
Rec. Retail Price

EMBROIDERING HN2855
Designer: W. K. Harper
Height: 7¼in., 18.4cm.
Issued: 1980-
Rec. Retail Price

EMIR HN1604
Designer: C. J. Noke
Height: 7½in., 19.1cm.
Issued: 1933-1949
Price: $400 £250

EMIR HN1605
Designer: C. J. Noke
Height: 7¼in., 18.4cm.
Issued: 1933-1949
Price: $400 £250
(Also called Ibrahim HN2095)

EMMA HN2834
Designer: M. Davies
Height: 5¾in., 14.6cm.
Issued: 1977-1982
Price: $56 £35

ENCHANTING EVENING HN3108
Designer: R. Jefferson
Height: 11¾in., 30cm.
Issued: 1987
Rec. Retail Price

ENCHANTMENT HN2178
Designer: M. Davies
Height: 7½in., 19.1cm.
Issued: 1957-1982
Price: $109 £68

ENCORE HN2751
Designer: D. Tootle
Height: 10in., 25.5cm.
Issued: 1988-1989
Price: $77 £48

ENIGMA HN3110
Designer: R. Jefferson
Height: 12¾in., 32cm.
Issued: 1987
Rec. Retail Price

ENTRANCED HN3186
Designer: E.J. Griffiths
Height: 7¼in., 18.5cm.
Issued: 1988-1989
Price: $77 £48

ERMINE COAT HN1981
Designer: L. Harradine
Height: 6¾in., 17.2cm.
Issued: 1945-1967
Price: $176 £110

EMBROIDERING HN2855

ESMERALDA HN2168

ENCHANTMENT HN2178

ELSIE MAYNARD HN2902

ERMINE MUFF HN54
Designer: C. J. Noke
Height: 8½in., 21.6cm.
Issued: 1916-1938
Price: $720 £450

ERMINE MUFF HN332
Designer: C. J. Noke
Height: 8½in., 21.6cm.
Issued: 1918-1938
Colour variation
Price: $720 £450

ERMINE MUFF HN671
Designer: C. J. Noke
Height: 8½in., 21.6cm.
Issued: 1924-1938
Colour variation
Price: $720 £450

ERMINIE M40
Designer: Unknown
Height: 4in., 10.1cm.
Issued: 1933-1945
Price: $272 £170

ESMERALDA HN2168
Designer: M. Davies
Height: 5½in., 14.0cm.
Issued: 1956-1959
Price: $208 £130

ESTELLE HN1566
Designer: L. Harradine
Height: 8in., 20.3cm
Issued: 1933-1938
Price: $600 £375

ESTELLE HN1802
Designer: L. Harradine
Height: 8in., 20.3cm.
Issued: 1937-1949
Colour variation
Price: $480 £300

ETE HN3067
Designer: R. Jefferson
Height: 11½in., 29cm.
Issued: 1989 in a limited
edition of 300
Price: $800 £500

EUGENE HN1520
Designer: L. Harradine
Height: 5¾in., 14.6cm.
Issued: 1932-1938
Price: $440 £275

EUGENE HN1521
Designer: L. Harradine
Height: 5in., 12.7cm.
Issued: 1932-1938
Colour variation
Price: $440 £275

EUROPA AND THE BULL HN95
Designer: H. Tittensor
Height: 9¾in., 24.7cm.
Issued: 1918-1938
Price: $1920 £1200

EUROPA AND THE BULL HN2828
Designer: R. Jefferson
Height: 10½in., 26.5cm.
Issued: 1985 in a limited
edition of 300
Price: $1520 £950

ESTELLE HN1802   EUGENE HN1520

EUROPA AND THE BULL HN2828

EVE HN2466
Designer: P. Davies
Height: 9¼in., 23.5cm.
Issued: 1984 in a limited
         edition of 750
Price: $720 £450

EVELYN HN1622
Designer: L. Harradine
Height: 6¼in., 15.9cm.
Issued: 1934-1949
Price: $480 £300

EVELYN HN1637
Designer: L. Harradine
Height: 6in., 15.2cm.
Issued: 1934-1938
         Colour variation
Price: $480 £300

EVENTIDE HN2814
Designer: W. K. Harper
Height: 7¾in., 19.7cm.
Issued: 1977-
Rec. Retail Price

F

FAGIN HN534
Designer: L. Harradine
Height: 4in., 10.1cm.
Issued: 1922-1932
Price: $45 £30

FAGIN M49
Designer: L. Harradine
Height: 4in., 10.1cm.
Issued: 1932-1983
Price: $48 £28

FAIR LADY HN2193
Designer: M. Davies
Height: 7¼in., 18.4cm.
Issued: 1963-
Rec. Retail Price

FAIR LADY HN2832
Designer: M. Davies
Height: 7¼in., 18.4cm.
Issued: 1977-
         Colour variation
Rec. Retail Price

FAIR LADY HN2835
Designer: M. Davies
Height: 7¼in., 18.4cm.
Issued: 1977
         Colour variation
Rec. Retail Price

FAIR LADY HN3216
Designer: P. Davies
Height: 3¾in., 9.5cm.
Issued: 1988
Rec. Retail Price

FAIR MAIDEN HN2211
Designer: M. Davies
Height: 5¼in., 13.3cm.
Issued: 1967
Rec. Retail Price

FAIRY (Style one) HN1324

EVENTIDE HN2814

EVE HN2466

FIGURES

FAIR MAIDEN HN2434
Designer: P. Davies
Height: 5¼in., 13.3cm.
Issued: 1983-
Colour variation
Rec. Retail Price

FAIRY (Style one) HN1324
Designer: L. Harradine
Height: 6½in., 16.5cm.
Issued: 1929-1938
Price: $400 £250

FAIRY (Style two) HN1374
Designer: L. Harradine
Height: 4in., 10.1cm.
Issued: 1930-1938
Price: $400 £250

FAIRY (Style two) HN1380
Designer: L. Harradine
Height: 4in., 10.1cm.
Issued: 1930-1938
Colour variation
Price: $400 £250

FAIRY (Style two) HN1532
Designer: L. Harradine
Height: 4in., 10.1cm.
Issued: 1932-1938
Price: $440 £275

FAIRY (Style three) HN1375
Designer: L. Harradine
Height: 3in., 7.6cm.
Issued: 1930-1938
Price: $400 £250

FAIRY (Style three) HN1395
Designer: L. Harradine
Height: 3in., 7.6cm.
Issued: 1930-1938
Colour variation
Price: $400 £250

FAIRY (Style three) HN1533
Designer: L. Harradine
Height: 3in., 7.6cm.
Issued: 1932-1938
Price: $440 £275

FAIRY (Style four) HN1376
Designer: L. Harradine
Height: 2½in., 6.3cm.
Issued: 1930-1938
Price: $400 £250

FAIRY (Style four) HN1536
Designer: L. Harradine
Height: 2½in., 6.3cm.
Issued: 1932-1938
Price: $440 £275

FAIRY (Style five) HN1378
Designer: L. Harradine
Height: 2½in., 6.3cm.
Issued: 1930-1938
Price: $400 £250

FAIRY (Style five) HN1396
Designer: L. Harradine
Height: 2½in., 6.3cm.
Issued: 1930-1938
Colour variation
Price: $400 £250

FAIRY (Style two) HN1380　　**FAIRY (Style three) HN1395**

FAIR LADY HN2193

FAIRY (Style five) HN1535
Designer: L. Harradine
Height: 2½in., 6.3cm.
Issued: 1932-1938
Colour variation
Price: $440 £275

FAIRY (Style six) HN1379
Designer: L. Harradine
Height: 2½in., 6.3cm
Issued: 1930-1938
Price: $400 £250

FAIRY (Style six) HN1394
Designer: L. Harradine
Height: 2½in., 6.3cm.
Issued: 1930-1938
Colour variation
Price: $400 £250

FAIRY (Style six) HN1534
Designer: L. Harradine
Height: 2½in., 6.3cm.
Issued: 1932-1938
Price: $440 £275

FAIRY (Style seven) HN1393
Designer: L. Harradine
Height: 2½in., 6.3cm.
Issued: 1930-1938
Price: $400 £250

FAIRY SPELL HN2979
Designer: A. Hughes
Height: 5¼in., 13cm.
Issued: 1983-1986
Price: $61 £38

FAITH HN3082
Designer: E.J. Griffiths
Height: 8½in., 21.5cm.
Issued: 1986 in a limited
edition of 9500
Price: $112 £70

FALSTAFF (Style one) HN571
Designer: C. J. Noke
Height: 7in., 17.8cm.
Issued: 1923-1938
Price: $400 £250

FALSTAFF (Style one) HN575
Designer: C. J. Noke
Height: 7in., 17.8cm.
Issued: 1923-1938
Price: $400 £250

FALSTAFF (Style one) HN608
Designer: C.J. Noke
Height: 7in., 17.8cm.
Issued: 1924-1938
Colour variation
Price: $400 £250

FALSTAFF (Style one) HN609
Designer: C. J. Noke
Height: 7in., 17.8cm.
Issued: 1924-1938
Colour variation
Price: $400 £250

FAIRY SPELL HN2979

FAITH HN3082

146

FALSTAFF (Style one) HN 619
Designer: C. J. Noke
Height: 7in., 17.8cm.
Issued: 1924-1938
         Colour variation
Price: $400 £250

FALSTAFF (Style one) HN638
Designer: C. J. Noke
Height: 7in., 17.8cm.
Issued: 1924-1938
         Colour variation
Price: $400 £250

FALSTAFF (Style one) HN1216
Designer: C. J. Noke
Height: 7in., 17.8cm.
Issued: 1926-1949
         Colour variation
Price: $280 £175

FALSTAFF (Style one) HN1606
Designer: C. J. Noke
Height: 7in., 17.8cm.
Issued: 1933-1949
         Colour variation
Price: $280 £175

FALSTAFF (Style two) HN618
Designer: C. J. Noke
Height: 7in., 17.8cm.
Issued: 1924-1938
Price: $280 £175

FALSTAFF (Style two) HN2054
Designer: C. J. Noke
Height: 7in., 17.8cm.
Issued: 1950-
         Colour variation
Rec. Retail Price

FALSTAFF HN3236
Designer: C.J. Noke
Height: 4in., 10cm.
Issued: 1989
Rec. Retail Price

FAMILY HN2720 (White)
Designer: E. Griffiths
Height: 12in., 30.5cm.
Issued: 1981
Rec. Retail Price

FAMILY HN2721 (Black)
Designer: E. Griffiths
Height: 12in., 30.5cm.
Issued: 1981
Rec. Retail Price

FAMILY ALBUM HN2321
Designer: M. Nicoll
Height: 6¼in., 15.9cm.
Issued: 1966-1973
Price: $208 £130

FARAWAY HN2133
Designer: M. Davies
Height: 2½in., 6.3cm.
Issued: 1958-1962
Price: $256 £160

FARMER HN3195
Designer: A. Hughes
Height: 9in., 23cm.
Issued: 1988
Rec. Retail Price

FAMILY ALBUM HN2321

FALSTAFF HN2054

FARMER'S BOY HN2520
Designer: W. M. Chance
Height: 8½in., 21.6cm.
Issued: 1938-1960
Price: $800 £500

FARMER'S WIFE HN2069
Designer: L. Harradine
Height: 9in., 22.9cm.
Issued: 1951-1955
Price: $304 £190

FARMER'S WIFE HN3164
Designer: A. Hughes
Height: 8¾in., 22cm.
Issued: 1988
Rec. Retail Price

FAT BOY (Style one) HN530
Designer: L. Harradine
Height: 3½in., 8.9cm.
Issued: 1922-1932
Price: $61 £38

FAT BOY (Style two) HN555
Designer: L. Harradine
Height: 7in., 17.8cm.
Issued: 1923-1939
Price: $352 £220

FAT BOY (Style two) HN1893
Designer: L. Harradine
Height: 7in., 17.8cm.
Issued: 1938-1952
Colour variation
Price: $320 £200

FAT BOY (Style three) HN2096
Designer: L. Harradine
Height: 7¼in., 18.4cm.
Issued: 1952-1967
Price: $192 £120

FAT BOY M44
Designer: L. Harradine
Height: 4¼in., 10.8cm.
Issued: 1932-1982
Price: $48 £30

FAVOURITE HN2249
Designer: M. Nicoll
Height: 7¾in., 19.7cm.
Issued: 1960-
Rec. Retail Price

FEBRUARY HN2703
Designer: P. Davies
Height: 7¾in., 19.7cm.
Issued: 1987
Price: $96 £60

FIDDLER HN2171
Designer: M. Nicoll
Height: 8¾in., 22.2cm.
Issued: 1956-1962
Price: $400 £250

FIONA (Style one) HN1924
Designer: L. Harradine
Height: 5¾in., 14.6cm.
Issued: 1940-1949
Price: $480 £300

FIRST DANCE HN2803

FARMER'S BOY HN2520

148

FIONA (Style one) HN1925
Designer: L. Harradine
Height: 5¾in., 14.6cm.
Issued: 1940-1949
Colour variation
Price: $480 £300

FIONA (Style one) HN1933
Designer: L. Harradine
Height: 5¾in., 14.6cm.
Issued: 1940-1949
Colour variation
Price: $480 £300

FIONA (Style two) HN2694
Designer: M. Davies
Height: 7½in., 19.1cm.
Issued: 1974-1980
Price: $75 £50

FIONA HN3252
Designer: D. Tootle
Height: 7in., 17.8cm.
Issued: 1989
Rec. Retail Price

FIRST DANCE HN2803
Designer: M. Davies
Height: 7¼in., 18.4cm.
Issued: 1977-
Price: $109 £68

FIRST LOVE (White) HN2747
Designer: D. Tootle
Height; 13in., 33cm.
Issued: 1987
Rec. Retail Price

FIRST STEPS HN2242
Designer: M. Davies
Height: 6½in., 16.5cm.
Issued: 1959-1965
Price: $256 £160

FIRST WALTZ HN2862
Designer: M. Davies
Height: 7¼in., 18.4cm.
Issued: 1979-1983
Price: $120 £75

FISHERWOMEN HN80
Designer: Unknown
Height: Unknown
Issued: 1917-1938
Price: $1920 £1200

FISHERWOMEN HN349
Designer: Unknown
Height: Unknown
Issued: 1919-1938
Colour variation
Price: $1920 £1200

FISHERWOMEN HN359
Designer: Unknown
Height: Unknown
Issued: 1919-1938
Colour variation
Price: $1920 £1200

FISHERWOMEN HN631
Designer: Unknown
Height: Unknown
Issued: 1924-1938
Colour variation
Price: $1920 £1200

FIDDLER HN2171

FAVOURITE HN2249

FIRST STEPS HN2242

FIONA (Style one) HN1924

FITZHERBERT, MRS HN2007
Designer: M. Davies
Height: 9¼in., 23.5cm.
Issued: 1948-1953
Price: $560 £350

FLEUR HN2368
Designer: J. Bromley
Height: 7¼in., 18.4cm.
Issued: 1968-
Rec. Retail Price

FLEUR (Red) HN2369
Designer: J. Bromley
Height: 7¾in., 19.5cm.
Issued: 1983-1986
        Colour variation
Price: $109 £68

FLEURETTE HN1587
Designer: L. Harradine
Height: 6½in., 16.5cm.
Issued: 1933-1949
Price: $280 £175

FLIRTATION HN3071
Designer: A. Hughes
Height: 10in., 25.5cm.
Issued: 1987
Rec. Retail Price

FLORA HN2349
Designer: M. Nicoll
Height: 7¾in., 19.7cm.
Issued: 1966-1973
Price: $144 £90

FLORENCE HN2745
Designer: D. Tootle
Height: 8in., 20cm.
Issued: 1988
Rec. Retail Price

FLORENCE NIGHTINGALE HN3144
Designer: P. Parsons
Height: 8¼in., 21cm.
Issued: 1988 in a limited
        edition of 500
Price: $256 £160

FLOUNCED SKIRT HN57A
Designer: E. W. Light
Height: 9¾in., 24.7cm.
Issued: 1916-1938
Price: $720 £450

FLOUNCED SKIRT HN66
Designer: E. W. Light
Height: 9¾in., 24.7cm.
Issued: 1916-1938
        Colour variation
Price: $720 £450

FLOUNCED SKIRT HN77
Designer: E. W. Light
Height: 9¾in., 24.7cm.
Issued: 1917-1938
        Colour variation
Price: $720 £450

FLOUNCED SKIRT HN78
Designer: E. W. Light
Height: 9¾in., 24.7cm.
Issued: 1917-1938
        Colour variation
Price: $720 £450

FLOWER ARRANGING HN3040

FLOWER SELLER'S CHILDREN HN1342

150

FLOUNCED SKIRT HN333
Designer: E. W. Light
Height: 9¾in., 24.7cm.
Issued: 1918-1938
Colour variation
Price: $720 £450

FLOWER ARRANGING HN3040
Designer: P. Parsons
Height: 8¾in., 22cm.
Issued: 1988 in a limited edition of 750
Price: $640 £400

FLOWER SELLER HN789
Designer: L. Harradine
Height: 8¾in., 22.2cm.
Issued: 1926-1938
Price: $720 £450

FLOWER SELLER'S CHILDREN HN525
Designer: L. Harradine
Height: 8¼in. 21.0cm.
Issued: 1921-1949
Price: $400 £250

FLOWER SELLER'S CHILDREN HN551
Designer: L. Harradine
Height: 8¼in. 21.0cm.
Issued: 1922-1949
Colour variation
Price: $400 £250

FLOWER SELLER'S CHILDREN HN1206
Designer: L. Harradine
Height: 8¼in. 21.0cm.
Issued: 1926-1949
Colour variation
Price: $400 £250

FLOWER SELLER'S CHILDREN HN1342
Designer: L. Harradine
Height: 8in., 20.3cm.
Issued: 1929-
Colour variation
Rec. Retail Price

FLOWER SELLER'S CHILDREN HN1406
Designer: L. Harradine
Height: 8¼in., 21.0cm.
Issued: 1930-1938
Colour variation
Price: $560 £350

FLUTE HN2483
Designer: M. Davies
Height: 6in., 15.2cm.
Issued: 1973 in a limited edition of 750
Price: $512 £320

FOAMING QUART HN2162
Designer: M. Davies
Height: 6in., 15.2cm.
Issued: 1955-
Rec. Retail Price

FLUTE HN2483

FLOWER SELLER HN789

FOAMING QUART HN2162

FOLLY HN1335
Designer: L. Harradine
Height: 9in., 22.9cm.
Issued: 1929-1938
Price: $960 £600

FOLLY HN1750
Designer: L. Harradine
Height: 9½in., 24.1cm.
Issued: 1936-1949
Colour variation
Price: $720 £450

FORGET-ME-NOT HN1812
Designer: L. Harradine
Height: 6in., 15.2cm.
Issued: 1937-1949
Price: $240 £150

FORGET-ME-NOT HN1813
Designer: L. Harradine
Height: 6in., 15.2cm.
Issued: 1937-1949
Colour variation
Price: $240 £150

FORTUNE TELLER HN2159
Designer: L. Harradine
Height: 6½in., 16.5cm.
Issued: 1955-1967
Price: $296 £185

FORTY WINKS HN1974
Designer: H. Fenton
Height: 6¾in., 14.2cm.
Issued: 1945-1973
Price: $136 £85

FOUR O'CLOCK HN1760
Designer: L. Harradine
Height: 6in., 15.2cm.
Issued: 1936-1949
Price: $320 £200

FRAGRANCE HN2334
Designer: M. Davies
Height: 7¼in., 18.4cm.
Issued: 1966-
Rec. Retail Price

FRAGRANCE HN3220
Designer: P. Davies
Height: 3½in., 9cm.
Issued: 1988
Rec. Retail Price

FRANCINE HN2422
Designer: J. Bromley
Height: 5in., 12.7cm.
Issued: 1972-1980
Price: $120 £75

FRANGCON HN1720
Designer: L. Harradine
Height: 7½in., 19.1cm.
Issued: 1935-1949
Price: $400 £250

FRANGÇON HN1721
Designer: L. Harradine
Height 7¼in., 18.4cm.
Issued: 1935-1949
Colour variation
Price: $400 £250

FORTY WINKS HN1974

FOLLY HN1335

FOLLY HN1750

FRENCH HORN HN2795

FREE SPIRIT (White) HN3157
Designer: A. Hughes
Height: 10½in., 26.5cm.
Issued: 1987
Rec. Retail Price

FREE SPIRIT (Black) HN3159
Designer: A. Hughes
Height: 10½in., 26.5cm.
Issued; 1987
Rec. Retail Price

FREE AS THE WIND HN3139
Designer: P. Parsons
Height: 9½in., 24cm.
Issued: 1989
Rec. Retail Price

FREEDOM HN3528
Designer: R. Jefferson
Height: 8½in., 22cm.
Issued: 1983-1986
Price: $72 £45

FRENCH HORN HN2795
Designer: M. Davies
Height: 6in., 15.2cm.
Issued: 1976 in a limited
edition of 750
Price: $520 £325

FRENCH PEASANT HN2075
Designer: L. Harradine
Height: 9¼in., 23.5cm.
Issued: 1951-1955
Price: $320 £200

FRIAR TUCK HN2143
Designer: M. Davies
Height: 7½in., 19.1cm.
Issued: 1954-1965
Price: $320 £200

FRODO HN2912
Designer: H. Sales
Height: 4½in., 11.4cm.
Issued: 1979-1984
Price: $56 £35

FRUIT GATHERING HN449
Designer: L. Harradine
Height: 7¾in., 19.7cm.
Issued: 1921-1938
Price: $1200 £750
FRUIT GATHERING HN476
Designer: L. Harradine
Height: 7¾in., 19.7cm.
Issued: 1921-1938
Colour variation
Price: $1200 £750

FRUIT GATHERING HN503
Designer: L. Harradine
Height: 7¾in., 19.7cm.
Issued: 1921-1938
Colour variation
Price: $1200 £750
FRUIT GATHERING HN561
Designer: L. Harradine
Height: 7¾in., 19.7cm.
Issued: 1923-1938
Colour variation
Price: $1200 £750

FRUIT GATHERING HN562
Designer: L. Harradine
Height: 7¾in., 19.7cm.
Issued: 1923-1938
Colour variation
Price: $1200 £750

FRIAR TUCK HN2143

FRAGRANCE HN2334

FRODO HN2912

FORTUNE TELLER HN2159

153

FRUIT GATHERING HN707
Designer: L. Harradine
Height: 7¼in., 18.4cm.
Issued: 1925-1938
          Colour variation
Price: $1200 £750

FRUIT GATHERING HN706
Designer: L. Harradine
Height: 7¼in., 18.4cm.
Issued: 1925-1938
          Colour variation
Price: $1200 £750

G

GAFFER HN2053
Designer: L. Harradine
Height: 7¾in., 19.7cm.
Issued: 1950-1959
Price: $224 £140

GAIETY HN3140
Designer: P. Parsons
Height: 10¼in., 26cm.
Issued: 1988
Rec. Retail Price

GAIL HN2937
Designer: P. Gee
Height: 7½in., 19cm.
Issued: 1986
Rec. Retail Price

GAINSBOROUGH HAT HN46
Designer: H. Tittensor
Height: 8¾in., 22.2cm.
Issued: 1915-1938
Price: $640 £400

GAINSBOROUGH HAT HN46A
Designer: H. Tittensor
Height: 8¾in., 22.2cm
Issued: 1915-1938
          Colour variation
Price: $640 £400

GAINSBOROUGH HAT HN47
Designer: H. Tittensor
Height: 8¾in., 22.2cm.
Issued: 1915-1938
          Colour variation
Price: $640 £400

GAINSBOROUGH HAT HN329
Designer: H. Tittensor
Height: 8¾in., 22.2cm.
Issued: 1918-1938
          Colour variation
Price: $640 £400

GAINSBOROUGH HAT HN352
Designer: H. Tittensor
Height: 8¾in., 22.2cm.
Issued: 1919-1938
          Colour variation
Price: $640 £400

GAINSBOROUGH HAT HN383
Designer: H. Tittensor
Height: 8¾in., 22.2cm.
Issued: 1920-1938
          Colour variation
Price: $640 £400

GANDALF HN2911

FRUIT GATHERING HN707

GALADRIEL HN2915

FIGURES

**GAINSBOROUGH HAT
HN453**
Designer: H. Tittensor
Height: 8¾in., 22.2cm.
Issued: 1921-1938
Colour variation
Price: $640 £400

**GAINSBOROUGH HAT
HN675**
Designer: H. Tittensor
Height: 8¾in., 22.2cm.
Issued: 1924-1938
Colour variation
Price: $640 £400

**GAINSBOROUGH HAT
HN705**
Designer: H. Tittensor
Height: 9in., 22.9cm.
Issued: 1925-1938
Colour variation
Price: $640 £400

GALADRIEL HN2915
Designer: H. Sales
Height: 5½in., 14.0cm.
Issued: 1979-1984
Price: $56 £35

GAMEKEEPER HN2879
Designer: E. Griffiths
Height: 7in., 17.8cm.
Issued: 1984-
Rec. Retail Price

GANDALF HN2911
Designer: H. Sales
Height: 7in., 17.8cm.
Issued: 1979-1984
Price: $61 £38

GARDENER HN3161
Designer: A. Hughes
Height: 8¼in., 21cm.
Issued: 1989
Rec. Retail Price

GAY MORNING HN2135
Designer: M. Davies
Height: 7in., 17.8cm.
Issued: 1954-1967
Price: $192 £120

GEISHA (Style one) HN354
Designer: H. Tittensor
Height: 10¾in., 27.3cm.
Issued: 1919-1938
Price: $920 £575

GEISHA (Style one) HN376
Designer: H. Tittensor
Height: 10¾in., 27.3cm.
Issued: 1920-1938
Colour variation
Price: $920 £575

GEISHA (Style one) HN387
Designer: H. Tittensor
Height: 10¾in., 27.3cm.
Issued: 1920-1938
Colour variation
Price: $920 £575

**GAINSBOROUGH HAT
HN705**

GAFFER HN2053

GAMEKEEPER HN2879

155

GEISHA (Style one) HN634
Designer: H. Tittensor
Height: 10¾in., 27.3cm.
Issued: 1924-1938
Colour variation
Price: $920 £575

GEISHA (Style one) HN741
Designer: H. Tittensor
Height: 10¾in., 27.3cm.
Issued: 1925-1938
Colour variation
Price: $920 £575

GEISHA (Style one) HN779
Designer: H. Tittensor
Height: 10¾in., 27.3cm.
Issued: 1926-1938
Colour variation
Price: $920 £575

GEISHA (Style one) HN1321
Designer: H. Tittensor
Height: 10¾in., 27.3cm.
Issued: 1929-1938
Colour variation
Price: $920 £575

GEISHA (Style one) HN1322
Designer: H. Tittensor
Height: 10¾in., 27.3cm.
Issued: 1929-1938
Colour variation
Price: $920 £575

GEISHA (Style two) HN1223
Designer: C. J. Noke
Height: 6¾in., 17.2cm.
Issued: 1927-1938
Price: $640 £400

GEISHA (Style two) HN1234
Designer: C. J. Noke
Height: 6¾in., 17.2cm.
Issued: 1927-1938
Colur variation
Price: $640 £400

GEISHA (Style two) HN1292
Designer: C. J. Noke
Height: 6¾in., 17.2cm.
Issued: 1928-1938
Colour variation
Price: $640 £400

GEISHA (Style two) HN1310
Designer: C. J. Noke
Height: 6¾in., 17.2cm.
Issued: 1929-1938
Colour variation
Price: $640 £400

GEISHA (Flambe) HN3229
Designer: P. Parsons
Height: 9½in., 24cm.
Issued: 1989
Rec. Retail Price

GENEVIEVE HN1962
Designer: L. Harradine
Height: 7in., 17.8cm.
Issued: 1941-1975
Price: $144 £90

GEISHA (Style two) HN1234   **GENEVIEVE HN1962**

GIMLI HN2922   **GEISHA HN1223**

GENIE HN2989
Designer: R. Tabbenor
Height: 9¾in., 24.5cm.
Issued: 1983-
Rec. Retail Price

GENIE (Flambe) HN2999
Designer: R. Tabbenor
Height: 9³/₄in., 24.5cm.
Issued: 1989
Rec. Retail Price

**GENTLEMAN FROM
WILLIAMSBURG HN2227**
Designer: M. Davies
Height: 6¼in., 15.9cm.
Issued: 1960-1983
Price: $128 £80

GENTLEWOMAN HN1632
Designer: L. Harradine
Height: 7½in., 19.1cm.
Issued: 1934-1949
Price: $304 £190

**GEORGE WASHINGTON
AT PRAYER HN2861**
Designer: L. Ispanky
Height: 12½in., 31.7cm.
Issued: 1977 in a limited
edition of 750
Price: $400 £250

GEORGIANA HN2093
Designer: M. Davies
Height: 8¼in., 21.0cm.
Issued: 1952-1955
Price: $400 £250

GEORGINA HN2377
Designer: M. Davies
Height: 5¾in., 14.6cm.
Issued: 1981-1986
Price: $64 £40

GERALDINE HN2348
Designer: M. Davies
Height: 7¼in., 18.4cm.
Issued: 1972-1976
Price: $104 £65

GILLIAN HN1670
Designer: L. Harradine
Height: 7¾in., 19.7cm.
Issued: 1934-1949
Price: $240 £150

GILLIAN HN1670A
Designer: L. Harradine
Height: 7¾in., 19.7cm.
Issued: Unknown
Colour variation
Price: $280 £175

GILLIAN HN3042
Designer: P. Parsons
Height: 8¼in., 21.0cm.
Issued: 1985-
Rec. Retail Price

GIMLI HN2922
Designer: H. Sales
Height: 5½in., 14.0cm.
Issued: 1980-1984
Price: $56 £35

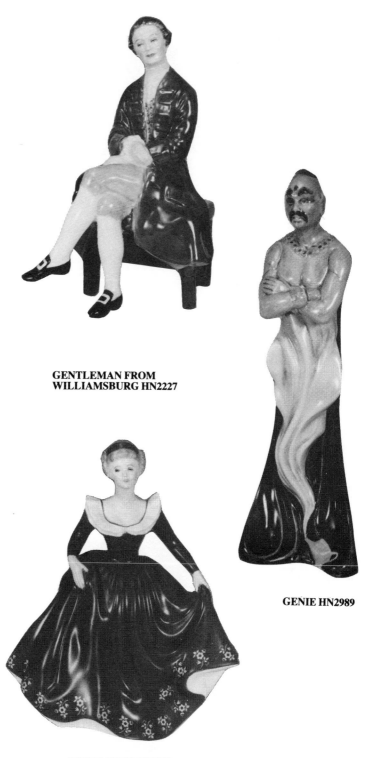

GENTLEMAN FROM
WILLIAMSBURG HN2227

GENIE HN2989

GERALDINE HN2348

GIRL EVACUEE HN3023
Designer: A. Hughes
Height: 8in., 20.3cm.
Issued: 1989 in a limited
edition of 9500
Price: $160 £100

**GIRL WITH YELLOW
FROCK HN588**
Designer: Unknown
Height: 6¼in., 15.9cm.
Issued: 1923-1938
Price: $1200 £750

GISELLE HN2139
Designer: M. Davies
Height: 6in., 15.2cm.
Issued: 1954-1969
Price: $208 £130

**GISELLE, THE FOREST
GLADE HN2140**
Designer: M. Davies
Height: 7in., 17.8cm.
Issued: 1954-1965
Price: $216 £135

GLADYS HN1740
Designer: L. Harradine
Height: 5¼in., 13.3cm.
Issued: 1935-1949
Price: $480 £300

GLADYS HN1741
Designer: L. Harradine
Height: 5in., 12.7cm.
Issued: 1935-1938
Colour variation
Price: $480 £300

GLEANER HN1302
Designer: Unknown
Height: 14½in., 36.8cm.
Issued: 1928-1938
Price: $2400 £1500

GLORIA HN1488
Designer: L. Harradine
Height: 7¼in., 18.4cm.
Issued: 1932-1938
Price: $640 £400

GLORIA HN1700
Designer: L. Harradine
Height: 7in., 17.8cm.
Issued: 1935-1938
Colour variation
Price: $640 £400

GLORIA HN3200
Designer: A. Hughes
Height: 9in., 23cm.
Issued: 1989
Rec. Retail Price

GNOME HN319
Designer: H. Tittensor
Height: 6¼in., 15.9cm.
Issued: 1918-1938
Price: $448 £280

GNOME HN380
Designer: H. Tittensor
Height: 6¼in., 15.9cm.
Issued: 1920-1938
Colour variation
Price: $448 £280

GOOD CATCH HN2258   **GOOD MORNING HN2671**

GISELLE HN2139   **GLEANER HN1302**

GNOME HN381
Designer: H. Tittensor
Height: 6¼in., 15.9cm.
Issued: 1920-1938
Colour variation
Price: $448 £280

GOLDEN DAYS HN2274
Designer: M. Davies
Height: 3¾in., 9.5cm.
Issued: 1964-1973
Price: $72 £45

GOLFER HN2992
Designer: R. Tabbenor
Height: 9½in., 24cm.
Issued: 1988
Rec. Retail Price

GOLLUM HN2913
Designer: H. Sales
Height: 3¼in., 8.3cm.
Issued: 1979-1984
Price: $56 £35

GOLLYWOG HN1979
Designer: L. Harradine
Height: 5¼in., 13.3cm.
Issued: 1945-1959
Price: $224 £140

GOLLYWOG HN2040
Designer: L. Harradine
Height: 5¼in., 13.3cm.
Issued: 1949-1959
Colour variation
Price: $224 £140

GOOD CATCH HN2258
Designer: M. Nicoll
Height: 7¼in., 18.4cm.
Issued: 1966-1986
Price: $120 £75

GOOD DAY SIR HN2896
Designer: W. K. Harper
Height: 8½in., 21.5cm.
Issued: 1986-1989
Price: $96 £60

GOOD FRIENDS HN2783
Designer: W. K. Harper
Height: 9in., 23cm.
Issued: 1985-
Rec. Retail Price

GOOD KING WENCESLAS HN2118
Designer: M. Davies
Height: 8½in., 21.6cm.
Issued: 1953-1976
Price: $200 £125

GOOD KING WENCESLAS HN3262
Designer: P. Davies
Height: 4¼in., 11cm.
Issued: 1989
Rec. Retail Price

GOOD MORNING HN2671
Designer: M. Nicoll
Height: 8in., 20.3cm.
Issued: 1974-1976
Price: $96 £60

GOOD PALS HN3132
Designer: P. Parsons
Height: 6¼in., 15.5cm.
Issued: 1987
Rec. Retail Price

GOOD DAY SIR HN2896

GOLLUM HN2913

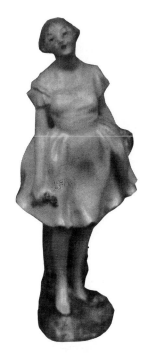

GIRL WITH YELLOW FROCK HN588

GIRL EVACUEE HN3023

159

GOODY TWO SHOES
HN1889
Designer: L. Harradine
Height: 4¾in., 12.0cm.
Issued: 1938-1949
Price: $136 £85

GOODY TWO SHOES
HN1905
Designer: L. Harradine
Height: 4¾in., 12.0cm.
Issued: 1939-1949
Colour variation
Price: $136 £85

GOODY TWO SHOES
HN2037
Designer: L. Harradine
Height: 5in., 12.7cm.
Issued: 1949-1989
Colour variation
Price: $64 £40

GOODY TWO SHOES M80
Designer: L. Harradine
Height: 4in., 10.1cm.
Issued: 1939-1949
Price: $192 £120

GOODY TWO SHOES M81
Designer: L. Harradine
Height: 4in., 10.1cm.
Issued: 1939-1949
Colour variation
Price: $192 £120

GOOSEGIRL HN425
Designer: L. Harradine
Height: 8in., 20.3cm.
Issued: 1921-1938
Price: $1280 £800

GOOSEGIRL HN436
Designer: L. Harradine
Height: 8in., 20.3cm.
Issued: 1921-1938
Colour variation
Price: $1280 £800

GOOSEGIRL HN437
Designer: L. Harradine
Height: 8in., 20.3cm.
Issued: 1921-1938
Colour variation
Price: $1280 £800

GOOSEGIRL HN448
Designer: L. Harradine
Height: 8in., 20.3cm.
Issued: 1921-1938
Colour variation
Price: $1280 £800

GOOSEGIRL HN559
Designer: L. Harradine
Height: 8in., 20.3cm.
Issued: 1923-1938
Colour variation
Price: $1280 £800

GOOSEGIRL HN560
Designer; L. Harradine
Height: 8in., 20.3cm.
Issued: 1923-1938
Colour variation
Price: $1280 £800

GOODY TWO SHOES HN2037

GRADUATE (The Female)
HN3016

GRADUATE (The Male)
HN3017

GOSSIPS HN1426
Designer: L. Harradine
Height: 5¾in., 14.6cm.
Issued: 1930-1949
Price: $352 £220

GOSSIPS HN1429
Designer: L. Harradine
Height: 5¾in., 14.6cm.
Issued: 1930-1949
Colour variation
Price: $352 £220

GOSSIPS HN2025
Designer: L. Harradine
Height: 5½in., 14.0cm.
Issued: 1949-1967
Colour variation
Price: $240 £150

GRACE HN2318
Designer: M. Nicoll
Height: 7¾in., 19.7cm.
Issued: 1966-1980
Price: $109 £68

GRACE DARLING HN3089
Designer: E.J. Griffiths
Height: 9in., 22.5cm.
Issued: 1987 in a limited
edition of 9500
Price: $200 £125

GRADUATE (The Female)
HN3016
Designer: P. Parsons
Height: 8¾in., 22.0cm.
Issued: 1984
Rec. Retail Price

GRADUATE (The Male)
HN3017
Designer: P. Parsons
Height: 9¼in., 23.5cm.
Issued: 1984-
Rec. Retail Price

GRAND MANNER HN2723
Designer: W. K. Harper
Height: 7¾in., 19.7cm.
Issued: 1975-1982
Price: $136 £85

GRANDMA HN2052
Designer: L. Harradine
Height: 6¾in., 17.2cm.
Issued: 1950-1959
Price: $216 £135

GRANDMA HN2052A
Designer: L. Harradine
Height: 6¾in., 17.2cm.
Issued: 1950-1959
Colour variation
Price: $200 £125

GRANNY HN1804
Designer: L. Harradine
Height: 7in., 17.8cm.
Issued: 1937-1949
Price: $360 £225

GRAND MANNER HN2723

GRACE DARLING HN3089

GRACE HN2318

GRANDMA HN2052

GRANNY HN1832
Designer: L. Harradine
Height: 6¾in., 17.1cm.
Issued: 1937-1949
Colour variation
Price: $360 £225

GRANNY'S HERITAGE HN1873
Designer: L. Harradine
Height: 6¾in., 17.1cm.
Issued: 1938-1949
Price: $560 £350

GRANNY'S HERITAGE HN1874
Designer: L. Harradine
Height: 6¼in., 15.9cm.
Issued: 1938-1949
Colour variation
Price: $560 £350

GRANNY'S HERITAGE HN2031
Designer: L. Harradine
Height: 6¾in., 17.2cm.
Issued: 1949-1969
Colour variation
Price: $240 £150

GRANNY'S SHAWL HN1642
Designer: L. Harradine
Height: 5¾in., 14.6cm.
Issued: 1934-1949
Price: $192 £120

GRETCHEN HN1397   GWENDOLEN HN1494

GRANNY'S SHAWL HN1647
Designer: L. Harradine
Height: 5¾in., 14.6cm.
Issued: 1934-1949
Colour variation
Price: $192 £120

GRETA HN1485
Designer: L. Harradine
Height: 5½in., 14.0cm.
Issued: 1931-1953
Price: $120 £75

GRETCHEN HN1397
Designer: L. Harradine
Height: 7¾in., 19.7cm.
Issued: 1930-1938
Price: $560 £350

GRETCHEN HN1562
Designer: L. Harradine
Height: 7¾in., 19.7cm.
Issued: 1933-1938
Colour variation
Price: $560 £350

GRIEF HN595
Designer: Unknown
Height: 2in., 5.1cm.
Issued: 1924-1938
Price: $600 £375

GRISELDA HN1993
Designer: L. Harradine
Height: 5¾in., 14.6cm.
Issued: 1947-1953
Price: $320 £200

GWENDOLEN HN1503   GROSSMITH'S TSANG IHANG HN582

GRIZEL HN1629
Designer: L. Harradine
Height: 6¾in., 17.2cm.
Issued: 1934-1938
Price: $440 £275

GROSSMITH'S TSANG IHANG HN582
Designer: Unknown
Height: 11½in., 29.2cm.
Issued: 1923-?
Price: $720 £450

GUY FAWKES HN98
Designer: C. J. Noke
Height: 10½in., 26.7cm.
Issued: 1918-1949
Price: $800 £500

GUY FAWKES HN347
Designer: C. J. Noke
Height: 10½in., 26.7cm.
Issued: 1919-1938
Colour variation
Price: $800 £500

GUY FAWKES HN445
Designer: C. J. Nokes
Height: 10½in., 26.7cm.
Issued: 1921-1938
Colour variation
Price: $800 £500

GUY FAWKES HN3271
Designer: C.J. Noke
Height: 4¼in., 11cm.
Issued: 1989
Rec. Retail Price

GWENDOLEN HN1494
Designer: L. Harradine
Height: 6in., 15.2cm.
Issued: 1932-1938
Price: $352 £220

GWENDOLEN HN1503
Designer: L. Harradine
Height: 6in., 15.2cm.
Issued: 1932-1949
Colour variation
Price: $352 £220

GWENDOLEN HN1570
Designer: L. Harradine
Height: 6in., 15.2cm.
Issued: 1933-1949
Colour variation
Price: $352 £220

GWYNNETH HN1980
Designer: L. Harradine
Height: 7in., 17.8cm.
Issued: 1934-1952
Price: $280 £175

GYPSY DANCE (Style one) HN2157
Designer: M. Davies
Height: 7in., 17.8cm.
Issued: 1955-1957
Price: $208 £130

GUY FAWKES HN98   GWYNNETH HN1980

GYPSY DANCE (Style one) HN2157

GYPSY DANCE (Style two)
HN2230
Designer: M. Davies
Height: 7in., 17.8cm.
Issued: 1959-1971
Price: $192 £120

GYPSY WOMAN WITH
CHILD HN1301
Designer: Unknown
Height: 14¼in., 36.2cm.
Issued: 1928-1938
Price: $2000 £1250

H

HAPPY ANNIVERSARY HN3097
Designer: P. Parsons
Height: 6½in., 16.5cm.
Issued: 1987
Rec. Retail Price

HAPPY ANNIVERSARY
HN3254
Designer: D. Tootle
Height: 12in., 30.5cm.
Issued: 1989
Rec. Retail Price

HAPPY BIRTHDAY HN3095
Designer: P. Parsons
Height: 7½in., 19.5cm.
Issued: 1987
Rec. Retail Price

"HAPPY JOY BABY BOY . . ."
HN1541
Designer: Unknown
Height: 6¼in., 15.9cm.
Issued: 1933-1949
Price: $224 £140

HARLEQUIN HN2186
Designer: M. Davies
Height: 7¼in., 18.4cm.
Issued: 1957-1969
Price: $160 £100

HARLEQUIN HN2737
Designer: D. Tootle
Height 12½in., 31.0cm.
Issued: 1982-
Rec. Retail Price

HARLEQUINADE HN585
Designer: L. Harradine
Height: 6½in., 16.5cm.
Issued: 1923-1938
Price: $720 £450

HARLEQUINADE HN635
Designer: L. Harradine
Height: 6½in., 16.5cm.
Issued: 1924-1938
Colour variation
Price: $896 £560

HARLEQUINADE HN711
Designer: L. Harradine
Height: 6½in., 16.5cm.
Issued: 1925-1938
Colour variation
Price: $720 £450

HARLEQUINADE HN780
Designer: L. Harradine
Height: 6½in., 16.5cm.
Issued: 1926-1939
Colour variation
Price: $720 £450

HARLEQUINADE MASKED HN1304

GYPSY DANCE HN2230

HARLEQUINADE HN585

HARLEQUIN HN2737

HARLEQUINADE MASKED
HN768
Designer: L. Harradine
Height: 6½in., 16.5cm.
Issued: 1925-1938
Price: $800 £500

HARLEQUINADE MASKED
HN769
Designer: L. Harradine
Height: 6½in., 16.5cm.
Issued: 1925-1938
        Colour variation
Price: $800 £500

HARLEQUINADE MASKED
HN1274
Designer: L. Harradine
Height: 6½in., 16.5cm.
Issued: 1928-1938
        Colour variation
Price: $800 £500

HARLEQUINADE MASKED
HN1304
Designer: L. Harradine
Height: 6½in., 16.5cm.
Issued: 1928-1938
        Colour variation
Price: $800 £500

HARMONY HN2824
Designer: R. Jefferson
Height: 8in., 20.3cm.
Issued: 1978-1984
Price: $112 £70

HARP HN2482
Designer: M. Davies
Height: 8¾in., 22.2cm.
Issued: 1973 in a limited
        edition of 750
Price: $512 £320

HARRIET HN3177
Designer: D. Tootle
Height: 7¼in., 18.5cm.
Issued: 1988
Rec. Retail Price

HARVESTIME HN3084
Designer: E.J. Griffiths
Height: 8in., 20cm.
Issued: 1988
Rec. Retail Price

HAZEL HN1797
Designer: L. Harradine
Height: 5¼in., 13.3cm.
Issued: 1936-1949
        Colour variation
Price: $208 £130

HAZEL HN1797
Designer: L. Harradine
Height: 5¼in., 13.3cm.
Issued: 1936-1949
        Colour variation
Price: $208 £130

HAZEL HN3167
Designer: P. Davies
Height: 8in., 20cm.
Issued: 1988
Rec. Retail Price

HARMONY HN2824

HARLEQUIN HN2186

HARP HN2482

HE LOVES ME HN2046
Designer: L. Harradine
Height: 5½in., 14.0cm.
Issued: 1949-1962
Price: $120 £75

HEART TO HEART HN2276
Designer: M. Davies
Height: 5½in., 14.0cm.
Issued: 1961-1971
Price: $208 £130

HEATHER HN2956
Designer: P. Parsons
Height: 6in., 15.0cm.
Issued: 1982-
Rec. Retail Price

HEIDI HN2975
Designer: A. Hughes
Height: 4½in., 11.5cm.
Issued: 1983-1986
Price: $61 £38

HELEN HN1508
Designer: L. Harradine
Height: 8in., 20.3cm.
Issued: 1932-1938
Price: $472 £295

HELEN HN1509
Designer: L. Harradine
Height: 8in., 20.3cm.
Issued: 1932-1938
        Colour variation
Price: $472 £295

HELEN HN1572
Designer: L. Harradine
Height: 8in., 20.3cm.
Issued: 1933-1938
        Colour variation
Price: $472 £295

HELEN HN2994
Designer: R. Tabbenor
Height: 5in., 12.5cm.
Issued: 1985-1987
Price: $48 £30

HELEN OF TROY HN2387
Designer: P. Davies
Height: 9¼in., 23.4cm.
Issued: 1981 as a limited
        edition of 750
Price: $880 £550

HELMSMAN HN2499
Designer: M. Nicoll
Height: 9in., 22.9cm.
Issued: 1974-1986
Price: $104 £65

HENRIETTA MARIA HN2005
Designer: M. Davies
Height: 9½in., 24.1cm.
Issued: 1948-1953
Price: $600 £375

HENRY VIII (Style one) HN370
Designer: C. J. Noke
Height: Unknown
Issued: 1920-1938
Price: $1600 £1000

HEIDI HN2975

HER LADYSHIP HN1977

HENRIETTA MARIA HN2005

HELEN HN1572

HENRY VIII (Style one) HN673
Designer: C. J. Noke
Height: Unknown
Issued: 1924-1938
Colour variation
Price: $1600 £1000

HENRY VIII (Style two) HN1792
Designer: C. J. Noke
Height: 11½in., 29.2cm.
Issued: 1933 in a limited edition of 200
Price: $1400 £875

HENRY IRVING AS CARDINAL WOLSEY HN344
Designer: C. J. Noke
Height: 13¼in., 33.7cm.
Issued: 1919-1949
Price: $960 £600

HENRY LYTTON AS JACK POINT HN610
Designer: C. J. Noke
Height: 6½in., 16.5cm.
Issued: 1924-1949
Price: $640 £400

HER LADYSHIP HN1977
Designer: L. Harradine
Height: 7¼in., 18.4cm.
Issued: 1945-1959
Price: $256 £160

HER MAJESTY QUEEN ELIZABETH II HN2878
Designer: E. Griffiths
Height: 10½in., 27.0cm.
Issued: 1983 in a limited edition of 2500
Price: $360 £225

HER MAJESTY QUEEN ELIZABETH, THE QUEEN MOTHER HN2882
Designer: E.J. Griffiths
Height: 11¾in., 29.8cm.
Issued: 1980 in a limited edition of 1500
Price: $560 £350

"HERE A LITTLE CHILD I STAND" HN1546
Designer: Unknown
Height: 6¼in., 15.9cm.
Issued: 1933-1949
Price: $192 £120

HERMINIA HN1644
Designer: L. Harradine
Height; 6½in., 16.5cm.
Issued: 1934-1938
Price: $560 £350

HERMINIA HN1646
Designer: L. Harradine
Height: 6½in., 16.5cm.
Issued: 1934-1938
Colour variation
Price: $608 £380

HENRY VIII (Style two) HN1792

HELMSMAN HN2499

HELEN OF TROY HN2387

HERMINIA HN1704
Designer: L. Harradine
Height: 6¾in., 17.2cm.
Issued: 1935-1938
Colour variation
Price: $560 £350

HERMIONE HN2058
Designer: M. Davies
Height: 7¾in., 19.7cm.
Issued: 1950-1952
Price: $480 £300

HIBERNIA HN2932
Designer: S. Keenan
Height: 9in., 23cm.
Issued: 1983 in a limited
edition of 950
Price: $192 £120

HIGHWAYMAN HN527
Designer: L. Harradine
Height: 6½in., 16.5cm.
Issued: 1921-1949
Price: $480 £300

HIGHWAYMAN HN592
Designer: L. Harradine
Height: 6½in., 16.5cm.
Issued: 1924-1949
Price: $480 £300

HIGHWAYMAN HN1257
Designer: L. Harradine
Height: 6½in., 16.5cm.
Issued: 1927-1949
Price: $480 £300

HILARY HN2335
Designer: M. Davies
Height: 7¼in., 18.4cm.
Issued: 1967-1980
Price: $104 £65

HINGED PARASOL HN1578
Designer: L. Harradine
Height: 6½in., 16.5cm.
Issued: 1933-1949
Price: $400 £250

HINGED PARASOL HN1579
Designer: L. Harradine
Height: 6½in., 16.5cm.
Issued: 1933-1949
Colour variation
Price: $400 £250

**HIS ROYAL HIGHNESS
PRINCE PHILIP DUKE OF
EDINBURGH HN2386**
Designer: P. Davies
Height: 8¼in., 21.0cm.
Issued: 1981 in a limited
edition of 1500
Price: $360 £225

HIVER HN3069
Designer: R. Jefferson
Height: 11¹/²in., 29cm.
Issued: 1988 in a limited
edition of 300
Price: $800 £500

HOME AGAIN HN2167
Designer: M. Davies
Height: 3¼in., 8.3cm.
Issued: 1956-
Rec. Retail Price

HINGED PARASOL HN1578

**HUCKLEBERRY FINN
HN2927**

**HIS ROYAL HIGHNESS
PRINCE PHILIP DUKE OF
EDINBURGH HN2386**

FIGURES

HOMECOMING HN3532
Designer: R. Willis
Height: 14¾in., 37.5cm.
Issued: 1987
Rec. Retail Price

HONEY HN1909
Designer: L. Harradine
Height: 7in., 17.8cm.
Issued: 1939-1949
Price: $280 £175

HONEY HN1910
Designer: L. Harradine
Height: 6¾in., 17.2cm.
Issued: 1939-1949
Colour variation
Price: $280 £175

HONEY HN1963
Designer: L. Harradine
Height: 6¾in., 17.2cm.
Issued: 1941-1949
Colour variation
Price: $280 £175

HOPE HN3061
Designer: E.J. Griffiths
Height: 8½in., 21.5cm.
Issued: 1984 in a limited
edition of 9500
Price: $240 £150

HORNPIPE HN2161
Designer: M. Nicoll
Height: 9¼in., 23.5cm.
Issued: 1955-1962
Price: $512 £320

**HOSTESS OF
WILLIAMSBURG HN2209**
Designer: M. Davies
Height: 7¼in., 18.4cm.
Issued: 1960-1983
Price: $112 £70

**HUCKLEBERRY FINN
HN2927**
Designer: D. Lyttleton
Height: 7in., 17.5cm.
Issued: 1982-1985
Price: $61 £38

HUNTING SQUIRE HN1409
Designer: Unknown
Height: 9¾in., 24.7cm.
Issued: 1930-1938
Price: $1600 £1000

HUNTS LADY HN1201
Designer: L Harradine
Height: 8¼in., 21.0cm.
Issued: 1926-1938
Price: $1440 £900

HUNTSMAN (Style one) HN1226
Designer: L. Harradine
Height: 8¾in., 22.2cm.
Issued: 1927-1938
Price: $1440 £900

HUNTSMAN (Style two) HN1815
Designer: Unknown
Height: 9½in., 24.1cm.
Issued: 1937-1949
Price: $1600 £1000
Also called John Peel

HOSTESS OF WILLIAMSBURG HN2209

HILARY HN2335

HUNTSMAN HN2492

HOPE HN3061

HUNTSMAN (Style three)
HN2492
Designer: M. Nicoll
Height: 7½in., 19.1cm.
Issued: 1974-1978
Price: $136 £85

HURDY GURDY HN2796
Designer: M. Davies
Height: 6in., 15.2cm.
Issued: 1975 in a limited
        edition of 750
Price: $560 £350

I

IBRAHIM HN2095
Designer: C. J. Noke
Height: 7¾in., 19.7cm.
Issued: 1952-1955
Price: $400 £250
Also called Emir

IDLE HOURS HN3115
Designer: A. Maslankowski
Height: 12¼in., 31cm.
Issued: 1987-1989
Price: $77 £48

I'M NEARLY READY HN2976
Designer: A. Hughes
Height: 7½in., 19.0cm.
Issued: 1984-1986
Price: $64 £40

IN GRANDMA'S DAYS HN339
Designer: C. J. Noke
Height: 8¾in., 22.2cm.
Issued: 1919-1938
Price: $640 £400

IN GRANDMA'S DAYS HN340
Designer: C. J. Noke
Height: 8¾in., 22.2cm.
Issued: 1919-1938
        Colour variation
Price: $640 £400

IN GRANDMA'S DAYS HN388
Designer: C. J. Noke
Height: 8¾in., 22.2cm.
Issued: 1920-1938
        Colour variation
Price: $640 £400

IN GRANDMA'S DAYS HN442
Designer: C. J. Noke
Height: 8¾in., 22.2cm.
Issued: 1921-1938
        Colour variation
Price: $640 £400
Also called Lilac Shawl and
Poke Bonnet

IN THE STOCKS (Style one)
HN1474
Designer: L. Harradine
Height: 5in., 12.7cm.
Issued: 1931-1938
Price: $1280 £800

HURDY GURDY HN2796

IN THE STOCKS   HN1475

FIGURES

IN THE STOCKS (Style one)
HN1475
Designer: L. Harradine
Height: 5¼in., 13.3cm.
Issued: 1931-1938
Colour variation
Price: $1280 £800

IN THE STOCKS (Style two)
HN2163
Designer: M. Nicoll
Height: 5¾in., 14.6cm.
Issued: 1955-1959
Price: $480 £300

INDIAN BRAVE HN2376
Designer: M. Davies
Height: 16in., 40.6cm.
Issued: 1967 in a limited
edition of 500
Price: $3200 £2000

INDIAN TEMPLE DANCER
HN2830
Designer: M. Davies
Height: 9¼in., 23.5cm.
Issued: 1977 in a limited
edition of 750
Price: $520 £325

INDIAN MAIDEN HN3117
Designer: A. Maslankowski
Height: 12in., 30.5cm.
Issued: 1988
Rec. Retail Price

INNOCENCE HN2842
Designer: E. J. Griffiths
Height: 7½in., 19.1cm.
Issued: 1979-1983
Price: $120 £75

INNOCENCE HN3226
Designer: P. Parsons
Height: 7¾in., 19.7cm.
Issued: 1988 in a limited
edition of 9500
Rec. Retail Price

INVITATION HN2170
Designer: M. Davies
Height: 5½in., 14.0cm.
Issued: 1956-1975
Price: $112 £70

IONA HN1346
Designer: L. Harradine
Height: 7½in., 19.1cm.
Issued: 1929-1938
Price: $1600 £1000

IRENE HN1621
Designer: L. Harradine
Height: 6½in., 16.5cm.
Issued: 1934-1951
Price: $256 £160

IRENE HN1697
Designer: L. Harradine
Height: 7in., 17.8cm.
Issued: 1935-1949
Colour variation
Price: $288 £180

IRENE HN1952
Designer: L. Harradine
Height: 6¾in., 17.2cm.
Issued: 1940-1950
Colour variation
Price: $288 £180

INDIAN BRAVE HN2376

INVITATION HN2170

INDIAN TEMPLE DANCER
HN2830

171

IRISH COLLEEN HN766
Designer: L. Harradine
Height: 6½in., 16.5cm.
Issued: 1925-1938
Price: $1040 £650

IRISH COLLEEN HN767
Designer: L. Harradine
Height: 6½in., 16.5cm.
Issued: 1925-1938
Price: $1040 £650

IRISHMAN HN1307
Designer: H. Fenton
Height: 6¾in., 17.2cm.
Issued: 1928-1938
Price: $640 £400

ISADORA HN2938
Designer: P. Gee
Height: 8in., 20cm.
Issued: 1986
Rec. Retail Price

IT WON'T HURT HN2963
Designer: P. Parsons
Height: 7½in., 19.0cm.
Issued: 1982-1986
Price: $72 £45

IVY HN1768
Designer: L. Harradine
Height: 4¾in., 12.0cm.
Issued: 1936-1979
Price: $64 £40

IVY HN1769
Designer: L. Harradine
Height: 4¾in., 12.0cm.
Issued: 1936-1979
         Colour variation
Price: $64 £40

J

JACK HN2060
Designer: L. Harradine
Height: 5½in., 14.0cm.
Issued: 1950-1971
Price: $104 £65

JACK POINT HN85
Designer: C. J. Noke
Height: 16¼in., 41.2cm.
Issued: 1918-1938
Price: $1280 £800

JACK POINT HN91
Designer: C. J. Noke
Height: 16¼in., 41.2cm.
Issued: 1918-1938
         Colour variation
Price: $1280 £800

JACK POINT HN99
Designer: C. J. Noke
Height: 16¼in., 41.2cm.
Issued: 1918-1938
         Colour variation
Price: $1280 £800

ISADORA HN2938

IT WON'T HURT HN2963

JANE HN2806

FIGURES

JACK POINT HN2080
Designer: C. J. Noke
Height: 16in., 40.6cm.
Issued: 1952-
           Colour variation
Rec. Retail Price

JACQUELINE HN2000
Designer: L. Harradine
Height: 7¼in., 18.4cm.
Issued: 1947-1951
Price: $280 £175

JACQUELINE HN2333
Designer: P. Davies
Height: 7½in., 19.0cm.
Issued: 1983-
Rec. Retail Price

JACQUELINE HN2001
Designer: L. Harradine
Height: 7¼in., 18.4cm.
Issued: 1947-1951
           Colour variation
Price: $280 £175

JAMES HN3013
Designer: P. Parsons
Height: 6in., 15cm.
Issued: 1983-1987
Price: $56 £35

JANE HN2014
Designer: L. Harradine
Height: 6¼in., 15.9cm.
Issued: 1948-1951
Price: $224 £140

JANE HN2806
Designer: P. Davies
Height: 8in., 20.0cm.
Issued: 1983-1986
Price: $88 £55

JANET (Style one) HN1537
Designer: L. Harradine
Height: 6¼in., 15.9cm.
Issued: 1932-
Price: $75 £47

JANET (Style one) HN1538
Designer: L. Harradine
Height: 6¼in., 15.9cm.
Issued: 1932-1949
           Colour variation
Price: $136 £85

JANET (Style one) HN1652
Designer: L. Harradine
Height: 6½in., 16.5cm.
Issued: 1934-1949
           Colour variation
Price: $136 £85

JANET (Style one) HN1737
Designer: L. Harradine
Height: 6¼in., 15.9cm.
Issued: 1935-1949
           Colour variation
Price: $136 £85

JANET (Style two) HN1916
Designer: L. Harradine
Height: 5¼in., 13.3cm.
Issued: 1939-1949
Price: $128 £80

JACQUELINE HN2000

IRISH COLLEEN HN766

JANET HN1537

JACQUELINE HN2333

173

JANET (Style two) HN1964
Designer: L. Harradine
Height: 5in., 12.7cm.
Issued: 1941-1949
Colour variation
Price: $128 £80

JANET M69
Designer: L. Harradine
Height: 4in., 10.1cm.
Issued: 1936-1949
Price: $160 £100

JANET M75
Designer: L. Harradine
Height: 4in., 10.1cm.
Issued: 1936-1949
Colour variation
Price: $160 £100

JANICE HN2022
Designer: M. Davies
Height: 7¼in., 18.4cm.
Issued: 1949-1955
Price: $256 £160

JANICE HN2165
Designer: M. Davies
Height: 7¼in., 18.4cm.
Issued: 1955-1965
Colour variation
Price: $256 £160

JANINE HN2461
Designer: J. Bromley
Height: 7½in., 19.1cm.
Issued: 1971-
Rec. Retail Price

JANUARY HN2697
Designer: P. Davies
Height: 7¾in., 19.7cm.
Issued: 1987
Price: $96 £60

JAPANESE FAN HN399
Designer: H. Tittensor
Height: 4¾in., 12.1cm.
Issued: 1920-1938
Price: $720 £450

JAPANESE FAN HN405
Designer: H. Tittensor
Height: 4¾in., 12.1cm.
Issued: 1920-1938
Colour variation
Price: $720 £450

JAPANESE FAN HN439
Designer: H. Tittensor
Height: 4½in., 12.1cm.
Issued: 1921-1938
Colour variation
Price: $720 £450

JAPANESE FAN HN440
Designer: H. Tittensor
Height: 4¾in., 12.1cm.
Issued: 1921-1938
Colour variation
Price: $720 £450

JANINE HN2461

JASMINE HN1862   JEAN HN2032

174

JASMINE HN1862
Designer: L. Harradine
Height: 7¼in., 18.4cm.
Issued: 1938-1949
Price: $312 £195

JASMINE HN1863
Designer: L. Harradine
Height: 7½in., 19.1cm.
Issued: 1938-1949
Colour variation
Price: $312 £195

JASMINE HN1876
Designer: L. Harradine
Height: 7½in., 19.1cm.
Issued: 1938-1949
Colour variation
Price: $312 £195

JEAN HN1877
Designer: L. Harradine
Height: 7½in., 19.1cm.
Issued: 1938-1949
Price: $216 £135

JEAN HN1878
Designer: L. Harradine
Height: 7½in., 19.1cm.
Issued: 1938-1949
Colour variation
Price: $216 £135

JEAN HN2032
Designer: L. Harradine
Height: 7½in., 19.1cm.
Issued: 1949-1959
Colour variation
Price: $224 £140

JEAN HN2710
Designer: P. Davies
Height: 5¾in., 14.5cm.
Issued: 1983-1986
Price: $72 £45

JEMMA HN3168
Designer; P. Davies
Height: 8¹/₂in., 21cm.
Issued: 1988
Rec. Retail Price

JENNIFER HN1484
Designer: L. Harradine
Height: 6½in., 16.5cm.
Issued: 1931-1949
Price: $288 £180

JENNIFER HN2392
Designer: P. Davies
Height: 7in., 17.5cm.
Issued: 1982-
Rec. Retail Price

JERSEY MILKMAID HN2057
Designer: L. Harradine
Height: 6½in., 16.5cm
Issued: 1950-1959
Price: $112 £70
Also called The Milkmaid

JESSICA HN3169
Designer: P. Davies
Height: 7in., 18cm.
Issued: 1988
Rec. Retail Price

JESTER (Style one)

JESTER (Style two)

JESTER (Style one) HN45
Designer: C. J. Noke
Height: 9½in., 24.1cm.
Issued: 1915-1938
Price: $800 £500

JESTER (Style one) HN71
Designer: C. J. Noke
Height: 9½in., 24.1cm.
Issued: 1917-1938
Colour variation
Price: $800 £500

JESTER (Style one) HN71A
Designer: C. J. Noke
Height: 9½in., 24.1cm.
Issued: 1917-1938
Colour variation
Price: $800 £500

JESTER (Style one) HN320
Designer: C. J. Noke
Height: 10in., 25.4cm.
Issued: 1918-1938
Colour variation
Price: $800 £500

JESTER (Style one) HN367
Designer: C. J. Noke
Height: 10in., 25.4cm.
Issued: 1920-1938
Colour variation
Price: $800 £500

JESTER (Style one) HN412
Designer: C. J. Noke
Height: 10in., 25.4cm.
Issued: 1920-1938
Colour variation
Price: $800 £500

JESTER (Style one) HN426
Designer: C. J. Noke
Height: 10in., 25.4cm.
Issued: 1921-1938
Colour variation
Price: $800 £500

JESTER (Style one) HN446
Designer: C. J. Noke
Height: 10in., 25.4cm.
Issued: 1921-1938
Colour variation
Price: $800 £500

JESTER (Style one) HN552
Designer: C. J. Noke
Height: 10in., 25.4cm.
Issued: 1922-1938
Colour variation
Price: $800 £500

JESTER (Style one) HN616
Designer: C. J. Noke
Height: 10in., 25.4cm.
Issued: 1924-1938
Colour variation
Price: $800 £500

JESTER (Style one) HN627
Designer: C. J. Noke
Height: 10in., 25.4cm.
Issued: 1924-1938
Colour variation
Price: $800 £500

JESTER (Style one) HN1295
Designer: C. J. Noke
Height: 10in., 25.4cm.
Issued: 1928-1949
Colour variation
Price: $640 £400

JESTER (Style one) HN1702
Designer: C. J. Noke
Height: 10in., 25.4cm.
Issued: 1935-1949
Colour variation
Price: $560 £350

JESTER (Style one) HN2016
Designer: C. J. Noke
Height: 10in., 25.4cm.
Issued: 1949-
Colour variation
Rec. Retail Price

JESTER (Style two) HN45A
Designer: C. J. Noke
Height: 10¼in., 26.0cm.
Issued: 1915-1938
Price: $800 £500

JESTER (Style two) HN45B
Designer: C. J. Noke
Height: 10¼in., 26.0cm.
Issued: 1915-1938
Colour variation
Price: $800 £500

JESTER (Style two) HN55
Designer: C. J. Noke
Height: 10¼in., 26.0cm.
Issued: 1916-1938
Colour variation
Price: $800 £500

JESTER (Style two) HN308
Designer: C. J. Noke
Height: 10¼in., 26.0cm.
Issued: 1918-1938
Colour variation
Price: $800 £500

JESTER (Style two) HN630
Designer: C. J. Noke
Height: 10¼in., 26.0cm.
Issued: 1924-1938
Colour variation
Price: $800 £500

JESTER (Style two) HN1333
Designer: C. J. Noke
Height: 10¼in., 26.0cm.
Issued: 1929-1949
Colour variation
Price: $800 £500

JILL HN2061
Designer: L. Harradine
Height: 5½in., 14.0cm.
Issued: 1950-1971
Price: $109 £68

JOAN HN1422
Designer: L. Harradine
Height: 5½in., 14.0cm.
Issued: 1930-1949
Price: $232 £145

JOAN HN2023
Designer: L. Harradine
Height: 5¾in., 14.6cm.
Issued 1949-1959
Colour variation
Price: $216 £135

JOAN HN2023

JESTER HN2016

JOAN HN3217
Designer: P. Davies
Height: 7½in., 19cm.
Issued: 1988 in a limited
edition of 2000
Price: $112 £70

JOANNE HN2373
Designer: J. Bromley
Height: 5¼in., 13.0cm.
Issued: 1982-1988
Price: $61 £38

JOHN PEEL HN1408
Designer: Unknown
Height: 8¾in., 22.2cm.
Issued: 1930-1937
Price: $1600 £1000
Also called Huntsman

JOKER HN3196
Designer: A. Hughes
Height: 9¾in., 23.5cm.
Issued: 1988
Rec. Retail Price

JOLLY SAILOR HN2172
Designer: M. Nicoll
Height: 6½in., 16.5cm.
Issued: 1956-1965
Price: $400 £250

JOVIAL MONK HN2144
Designer: M. Davies
Height: 7¾in., 19.7cm.
Issued: 1954-1976
Price: $176 £110

JOY HN3184
Designer: D. Tootle
Height: 6¾in., 17cm.
Issued: 1988
Rec. Retail Price

JUDGE HN2443
Designer: M. Nicoll
Height: 6½in., 16.5cm.
Issued: 1972-1976
Matte
Price: $128 £80

JUDGE HN2443A
Designer: M. Nicoll
Height: 6½in., 16.5cm.
Issued: 1976
Gloss
Rec. Retail Price

JUDGE AND JURY HN1264
Designer: J. G. Hughes
Height: 6in., 15.2cm.
Issued: 1927-1938
Price: $1920 £1200

JUDITH HN2089
Designer: L. Harradine
Height: 7in., 17.8cm.
Issued: 1952-1959
Price: $200 £125

JUDITH HN2278
Designer: M. Nicoll
Height: 6¾in., 17cm.
Issued: 1987-1989
Price: $96 £60

JULIA HN2705
Designer: M. Davies
Height: 7½in., 19.1cm.
Issued: 1975-
Rec. Retail Price

JULIA HN2705

JUDGE HN2443

JUNO AND THE PEACOCK HN2827

JULIA HN2706
Designer: P. Davies
Height: 7½in., 19.1cm.
Issued: 1985-
           Colour variation
Rec. Retail Price

JULIE HN2995
Designer: R. Tabbenor
Height: 5in., 12.5cm.
Issued: 1985-
Rec. Retail Price

JULY HN2794
Designer: P. Davies
Height: 7¾in., 19.7cm.
Issued: 1987
Price: $96 £60

JUNE HN1690
Designer: L. Harradine
Height: 7¼in., 18.4cm.
Issued: 1935-1949
Price: $312 £195

JUNE HN1691
Designer: L. Harradine·
Height: 7¼in., 18.4cm.
Issued: 1935-1949
           Colour variation
Price: $256 £160

JUNE HN1947
Designer: L. Harradine
Height: 7¼in., 18.4cm.
Issued: 1940-1949
           Colour variation
Price: $312 £195

JUNE HN2027
Designer: L. Harradine
Height: 7¼in., 18.4cm.
Issued: 1949-1952
           Colour variation
Price: $256 £160

JUNE M65
Designer: L. Harradine
Height: 4¼in., 10.8cm.
Issued: 1935-1949
Price: $192 £120

JUNE M71
Designer: L. Harradine
Height: 4¼in., 10.8cm.
Issued: 1936-1949
           Colour variation
Price: $192 £120

JUNE HN2790
Designer: P. Davies
Height: 7¾in., 19.7cm.
Issued: 1987
Price: $96 £60

JUNE HN2991
Designer: R. Tabbenor
Height: 9in., 22.5cm.
Issued: 1988
Rec. Retail Price

JUNO AND THE PEACOCK HN2827
Designer: R. Jefferson
Height: 11in., 27.9cm.
Issued: 1984 in a limited
           edition of 300
Price: $1520 £950

JUST ONE MORE HN2980
Designer: A. Hughes
Height: 7in., 17.5cm.
Issued: 1984-1986
Price: $64 £40

K

KAREN HN1994
Designer: L. Harradine
Height: 8in., 20.3cm.
Issued: 1947-1955
Price: $272 £170

KAREN HN2388
Designer: P. Davies
Height: 8in., 20.0cm.
Issued: 1982-
Rec. Retail Price

KATE HN2789
Designer: M. Davies
Height: 7½in., 19.1cm.
Issued: 1978-1987
Price: $96 £60

KATE HANNIGAN HN3088
Designer: E.J. Griffiths
Height: 9in., 27.5cm.
Issued: 1987
Price: $144 £90

KATE HARDCASTLE HN1718
Designer: L. Harradine
Height: 8in., 20.3cm.
Issued: 1935-1949
Price: $296 £185

KATE HARDCASTLE HN1719
Designer: L. Harradine
Height: 8in., 20.3cm.
Issued: 1935-1949
    Colour variation
Price: $277 £185

KATE HARDCASTLE HN1734
Designer: L. Harradine
Height: 8¼in., 21.0cm.
Issued: 1935-1949
    Colour variation
Price: $400 £250

KATE HARDCASTLE HN1861
Designer: L. Harradine
Height: 8in., 20.3cm.
Issued: 1938-1949
    Colour variation
Price: $480 £300

KATE HARDCASTLE HN1919
Designer: L. Harradine
Height: 8¼in., 21.0cm.
Issued: 1939-1949
    Colour variation
Price: $480 £300

KATE HARDCASTLE HN2028
Designer: L. Harradine
Height: 7¾in., 19.7cm.
Issued: 1949-1952
    Colour variation
Price: $296 £185

KAREN HN2388

KATE HARDCASTLE HN1719

KATHARINE HN61
Designer: C. J. Noke
Height: 5¾in., 14.6cm.
Issued: 1916-1938
Price: $880 £550

KATHARINE HN74
Designer: C. J. Noke
Height: 5¾in., 14.6cm.
Issued: 1917-1938
        Colour variation
Price: $880 £550

KATHARINE HN341
Designer: C. J. Noke
Height: 5¾in., 14.6cm.
Issued: 1919-1938
        Colour variation
Price: $928 £580

KATHARINE HN471
Designer: C. J. Noke
Height: 5¾in., 14.6cm.
Issued: 1921-1938
        Colour variation
Price: $880 £550

KATHARINE HN615
Designer: C. J. Noke
Height: 5¾in., 14.6cm.
Issued: 1924-1938
        Colour variation
Price: $880 £550

KATHARINE HN793
Designer: C. J. Noke
Height: 5¾in., 14.6cm.
Issued: 1926-1938
        Colour variation
Price: $880 £550

KATHLEEN HN1252
Designer: L. Harradine
Height: 7¾in., 19.7cm.
Issued: 1927-1938
Price: $432 £270

KATHLEEN HN1253
Designer: L. Harradine
Height: 7½in., 19.1cm.
Issued: 1927-1938
        Colour variation
Price: $432 £270

KATHLEEN HN1275
Designer: L. Harradine
Height: 7½in., 19.1cm.
Issued: 1928-1939
        Colour variation
Price: $432 £270

KATHLEEN HN1279
Designer: L. Harradine
Height: 7¾in., 19.7cm.
Issued: 1928-1938
        Colour variation
Price: $400 £250

KATHLEEN HN1291
Designer: L. Harradine
Height: 7½in., 19.1cm.
Issued: 1928-1938
        Colour variation
Price: $464 £290

KATE HARDCASTLE HN1718

KATHLEEN HN1252

179

KATHLEEN HN1357
Designer: L. Harradine
Height: 7½in., 19.1cm.
Issued: 1929-1938
Colour variation
Price: $400 £250

KATHLEEN HN1512
Designer: L. Harradine
Height: 7½in., 19.1cm.
Issued: 1932-1938
Colour variation
Price: $400 £250

KATHLEEN HN2933
Designer: S. Keenan
Height: 6½in., 16.5cm.
Issued: 1984-1987
Price: $96 £60

KATHLEEN HN3100
Designer: S. Keenan
Height: 6¹/₂in., 16.5cm.
Issued: 1986
Rec. Retail Price

KATHY HN2346
Designer: M. Davies
Height: 4¾in., 12.0cm.
Issued: 1981-1987
Price: $56 £35

KATRINA HN2327
Designer: M. Davies
Height: 7½in., 19.1cm.
Issued: 1965-1969
Price: $160 £100

KELLY HN2478
Designer: P. Davies
Height: 7½in., 19.0cm.
Issued: 1985-
Rec. Retail Price

KERRY HN3036
Designer: A. Hughes
Height: 5¼in., 13.5cm.
Issued: 1986
Rec. Retail Price

KING CHARLES HN404
Designer: C. J. Noke and
H. Tittensor
Height: 16¾in., 42.5cm.
Issued: 1920-1951
Price: $1600 £1000

KING CHARLES HN2084
Designer: C. J. Noke
Height: 16in., 40.6cm.
Issued: 1952-
Rec. Retail Price

KIRSTY HN2381
Designer: M. Davies
Height: 7½in., 19.1cm.
Issued: 1971-
Rec. Retail Price

KIRSTY HN3213
Designer: P. Davies
Height: 3³/₄in., 9.5cm.
Issued: 1989
Rec. Retail Price

KITTY HN1367
Designer: Unknown
Height: 4in., 10.1cm.
Issued: 1930-1938
Price: $720 £450

KIRSTY HN2381

KO-KO HN2898

KATHLEEN HN3100

FIGURES

KO-KO (Style one) HN1266
Designer: L. Harradine
Height: 5in., 12.7cm.
Issued: 1928-1949
Price: $400 £250

KO-KO (Style one) HN1286
Designer: L. Harradine
Height: 5in., 12.7cm.
Issued: 1938-1949
Colour variation
Price: $400 £250

KO-KO (Style two) HN2898
Designer: W. K. Harper
Height: 11½in., 29.2cm.
Issued: 1980-1986
Price: $224 £140

KURDISH DANCER HN2867
Designer: M. Davies
Height: 8¼in., 21.0cm.
Issued: 1979 in a limited
edition of 750
Price: $520 £325

L

LA SYLPHIDE HN2138
Designer: M. Davies
Height: 7in., 17.8cm.
Issued: 1956-1965
Price: $216 £135

LADY AND BLACKAMOOR
(Style one) HN374
Designer: H. Tittensor
Height: Unknown
Issued: 1920-1938
Price: $1920 £1200

LADY AND BLACKAMOOR
(Style two) HN375
Designer: H. Tittensor
Height: Unknown
Issued: 1920-1938
Price: $1920 £1200

LADY AND BLACKAMOOR
(Style two) HN377
Designer: H. Tittensor
Height: Unknown
Issued: 1920-1938
Colour variation
Price: $1920 £1200

LADY AND BLACKAMOOR
(Style two) HN470
Designer: H. Tittensor
Height: Unknown
Issued: 1921-1938
Colour variation
Price: $1920 £1200

LADY AND THE UNICORN
HN2825
Designer: R. Jefferson
Height: 8¾in., 22.2cm.
Issued: 1982 in a limited
edition of 300
Price: $1520 £950

LA SYLPHIDE HN2138

KURDISH DANCER HN2867

LADY AND THE UNICORN HN2825

181

FIGURES

LADY ANNE HN83
Designer: E. W. Light
Height: Unknown
Issued: 1918-1938
Price: $1600 £1000

LADY ANNE HN87
Designer: E. W. Light
Height: Unknown
Issued: 1918-1938
Colour variation
Price: $1600 £1000

LADY ANNE HN93
Designer: E. W. Light
Height: Unknown
Issued: 1918-1938
Colour variation
Price: $1600 £1000

LADY ANNE NEVILL HN2006
Designer: M. Davies
Height: 9¾in., 24.7cm.
Issued: 1948-1953
Price: $640 £400

LADY APRIL HN1958
Designer: L. Harradine
Height: 7in., 17.8cm.
Issued: 1940-1959
Price: $224 £140

LADY APRIL HN1965
Designer: L. Harradine
Height: 7in., 17.8cm.
Issued: 1941-1949
Colour variation
Price: $224 £140

LADY BETTY HN1967
Designer: L. Harradine
Height: 6½in., 16.5cm.
Issued: 1941-1951
Price: $224 £140

LADY CHARMIAN HN1948
Designer: L. Harradine
Height: 8in., 20.3cm.
Issued: 1940-1973
Price: $176 £110

LADY CHARMIAN HN1949
Designer: L. Harradine
Height: 8in., 20.3cm.
Issued: 1940-1975
Colour variation
Price: $176 £110

LADY CLARE HN1465
Designer: L. Harradine
Height: 7¾in., 19.7cm.
Issued: 1931-1938
Price: $448 £280

LADY CLOWN HN717
Designer: L. Harradine
Height: 7½in., 19.1cm.
Issued: 1925-1938
Price: $960 £600

LADY CLOWN HN718
Designer: L. Harradine
Height: 7½in., 19.1cm.
Issued: 1925-1938
Colour variation
Price: $960 £600

LADY JESTER HN1285

LADY ANNE NEVILL HN2006

LADY CLOWN HN738
Designer: L. Harradine
Height: 7½in., 19.1cm.
Issued: 1925-1938
Colour variation
Price: $960 £600

LADY CLOWN HN770
Designer: L. Harradine
Height: 7½in., 19.1cm.
Issued: 1925-1938
Colour variation
Price: $960 £600

LADY CLOWN HN1263
Designer: L. Harradine
Height: 7¼in., 18.4cm.
Issued: 1927-1938
Colour variation
Price: $960 £600
Also called CLOWNETTE

**LADY DIANA SPENCER
HN2885**
Designer: E. Griffiths
Height: 7¾in., 19.6cm.
Issued: 1982 as a limited
edition of 1500
Price: $240 £150

LADY FAYRE HN1265
Designer: L. Harradine
Height: 5¼in., 13.3cm.
Issued: 1928-1938
Price: $360 £225

LADY FAYRE HN1557
Designer: L. Harradine
Height: 5¾in., 14.6cm.
Issued: 1933-1938
Colour variation
Price: $400 £250

**LADY FROM
WILLIAMSBURG HN2228**
Height: 6in., 15.2cm.
Designer: M. Davies
Issued: 1960-1983
Price: $112 £70

**LADY JESTER (Style one)
HN1221**
Designer: L. Harradine
Height: 7in., 17.8cm.
Issued: 1927-1938
Price: $1200 £750

**LADY JESTER (Style one)
HN1222**
Designer: L. Harradine
Height: 7in., 17.8cm.
Issued: 1927-1938
Colour variation
Price: $1200 £750

**LADY JESTER (Style one)
HN1332**
Designer: L. Harradine
Height: 7in., 17.8cm.
Issued: 1929-1938
Colour variation
Price: $1200 £750

LADY JESTER (Style two)
HN1284
Designer: L. Harradine
Height: 4¼in., 10.8cm.
Issued: 1928-1938
Price: $1200 £750

LADY JESTER (Style two)
HN1285
Designer: L. Harradine
Height: 4¼in., 10.8cm.
Issued: 1928-1938
Colour variation
Price: $1200 £750

LADY OF THE ELIZABETHAN
PERIOD (Style one) HN40
Designer: E. W. Light
Height; 9½in., 24.1cm.
Issued: 1914-1938
Price: $1280 £800

LADY OF THE ELIZABETHAN
PERIOD (Style one) HN40A
Designer: E. W. Light
Height: 9½in., 24.1cm.
Issued: 1914-1938
Price: $1280 £800

LADY OF THE ELIZABETHAN
PERIOD (Style one) HN73
Designer: E. W. Light
Height: 9½in., 24.1cm.
Issued: 1917-1938
Colour variation
Price: $1280 £800

LADY OF THE ELIZABETHAN
PERIOD (Style one) HN411
Designer: E. W. Light
Height: 9¾in., 24.7cm.
Issued 1920-1938
Colour variation
Price: $1280 £800

LADY OF THE ELIZABETHAN
PERIOD (Style two) HN309
Designer: E. W. Light
Height: 9½in., 24.1cm.
Issued: 1918-1938
Price: $1280 £800

LADY OF THE FAN HN48
Designer: E. W. Light
Height: 9½in., 24.1cm.
Issued: 1916-1938
Price: $1120 £700

LADY OF THE FAN HN52
Designer: E. W. Light
Height: 9½in., 24.1cm.
Issued: 1916-1938
Colour variation
Price: $1120 £700

LADY OF THE FAN HN335
Designer: E. W. Light
Height: 9½in., 24.1cm
Issued: 1919-1938
Colour variation
Price: $1120 £700

LADY DIANA SPENCER
HN2885

LADY FROM WILLIAMSBURG HN2228

LADY OF THE FAN HN509
Designer: E. W. Light
Height: 9½in., 24.1cm.
Issued: 1921-1938
Colour variation
Price: $1120 £700

LADY OF THE FAN HN53A
Designer: E. W. Light
Height: 9in., 22.9cm.
Issued: 1916-1938
Colour variation
Price: $1120 £700

LADY OF THE FAN HN53
Designer: E. W. Light
Height: 9½in., 24.1cm.
Issued: 1916-1938
Colour variation
Price: $1120 £700

LADY OF THE GEORGIAN
PERIOD HN41
Designer: E. W. Light
Height; 10¼in., 26.0cm.
Issued: 1914-1938
Price: $1280 £800

LADY OF THE GEORGIAN
PERIOD HN331
Designer: E. W. Light
Height: 10¼in., 26.0cm.
Issued: 1918-1938
Colour variation
Price: $1280 £800

LADY OF THE GEORGIAN
PERIOD HN444
Designer: E. W. Light
Height: 10¼in., 26.0cm.
Issued: 1921-1938
Colour variation
Price: $1280 £800

LADY OF THE GEORGIAN
PERIOD HN690
Designer: E. W. Light
Height: 10¼in., 26.0cm.
Issued: 1925-1938
Price: $1280 £800

LADY OF THE GEORGIAN
PERIOD HN702
Designer: E. W. Light
Height: 10¼in., 26.0cm.
Issued: 1925-1938
Colour variation
Price: $1280 £800

LADY OF THE SNOWS
HN1780
Designer: R. Garbe
Height: Unknown
Issued: 1933-?
Price: $1920 £1200

LADY OF THE SNOWS
HN1830
Designer: R. Garbe
Height: Unknown
Issued: 1937-1949
Price: $1920 £1200

LADY OF THE TIME OF HENRY VI HN43
Designer: E. W. Light
Height: 9¼in., 23.5cm.
Issued: 1914-1938
Price: $1600 £1000

LADY PAMELA HN2718
Designer: D. V. Tootle
Height: 8in., 23.0cm.
Issued: 1974-1980
Price: $112 £70

LADY WITH ERMINE MUFF HN82
Designer: E. W. Light
Height: 6¾in., 17.2cm.
Issued: 1918-1938
Price: $1600 £1000
Also known as 'The Afternoon Call'

LADY WITH ROSE HN48A
Designer: E. W. Light
Height: 9½in., 24.1cm.
Issued: 1916-1938
Price: $1280 £800

LADY WITH ROSE HN52A
Designer: E. W. Light
Height: 9½in., 24.1cm.
Issued: 1916-1938
        Colour variation
Price: $1280 £800

LADY WITH ROSE HN68
Designer: E. W. Light
Height: 9½in., 24.1cm.
Issued: 1916-1938
        Colour variation
Price: $1280 £800

LADY WITH ROSE HN304
Designer: E. W. Light
Height: 9½in., 24.1cm.
Issued: 1918-1938
        Colour variation
Price: $1280 £800

LADY WITH ROSE HN336
Designer: E. W. Light
Height: 9½in., 24.1cm.
Issued: 1919-1938
        Colour variation
Price: $1280 £800

LADY WITH ROSE HN515
Designer: E. W. Light
Height: 9½in., 24.1cm.
Issued: 1921-1938
        Colour variation
Price: $1360 £850

LADY WITH ROSE HN517
Designer: E. W. Light
Height: 9½in., 24.1cm.
Issued: 1921-1938
        Colour variation
Price: $1360 £850

LADY WITH ROSE HN584
Designer: E. W. Light
Height: 9½in., 24.1cm.
Issued: 1923-1938
        Colour variation
Price: $1360 £850

LAIRD HN2361

LADY PAMELA HN2718

LADY WITH ROSE HN624
Designer: E. W. Light
Height: 9½in., 24.1cm.
Issued: 1924-1938
        Colour variation
Price: $1360 £850

LADY WITH SHAWL HN447
Designer: L. Harradine
Height: 13¼in., 33.7cm.
Issued: 1921-1938
Price: $1920 £1200

LADY WITH SHAWL HN458
Designer: L. Harradine
Height: 13¼in., 33.7cm.
Issued: 1921-1938
        Colour variation
Price: $1920 £1200

LADY WITH SHAWL HN626
Designer: L. Harradine
Height: 13¼in., 33.7cm.
Issued: 1924-1938
        Colour variation
Price: $1920 £1200

LADY WITH SHAWL HN678
Designer: L. Harradine
Height: 13¼in., 33.7cm.
Issued: 1924-1938
        Colour variation
Price: $1920 £1200

LADY WITH SHAWL HN679
Designer: L. Harradine
Height: 13¼in., 33.7cm.
Issued: 1924-1938
        Colour variation
Price: $1920 £1200

LADY WITHOUT BOUQUET HN393
Designer: G. Lambert
Height: 9in., 22.9cm.
Issued: 1920-1938
Price: $1600 £1000

LADY WITHOUT BOUQUET HN394
Designer: G. Lambert
Height: 9in., 22.9cm.
Issued: 1920-1938
        Colour variation
Price: $1600 £1000

LADYBIRD HN1638
Designer: L. Harradine
Height: 7¾in., 19.7cm.
Issued: 1934-1949
Price: $720 £450

LADYBIRD HN1640
Designer: L. Harradine
Height: 7¾in., 19.7cm.
Issued: 1934-1938
        Colour variation
Price: $880 £550

LAIRD HN2361
Designer: M. Nicoll
Height: 8in., 20.3cm.
Issued: 1969-
Rec. Retail Price

LADYBIRD HN1638

LAST WALTZ HN2315

LAURIANNE HN2719

LALLA ROOKH HN2910
Designer: S. Keenan
Height: 9in., 22.8cm.
Issued: 1981 in a limited
edition of 950
Price: $160 £100

LAMBETH WALK HN1880
Designer: L. Harradine
Height: 10in., 25.4cm.
Issued: 1938-1949
Price: $1200 £750

LAMBETH WALK HN1881
Designer: L. Harradine
Height: 10in., 25.4cm.
Issued: 1938-1949
Colour variation
Price: $1200 £750

LAMBING TIME HN1890
Designer: L. Harradine
Height: 9¼in., 23.5cm.
Issued: 1938-1980
Price: $152 £95

LAND OF NOD HN56
Designer: H. Tittensor
Height: 9½in., 24.1cm.
Issued: 1916-1938
Price: $1280 £800

LAND OF NOD HN56A
Designer: H. Tittensor
Height: 9½in., 24.1cm.
Issued: 1916-1938
Price: $1280 £800

LAND OF NOD HN56B
Designer: H. Tittensor
Height: 9½in., 24.1cm.
Issued: 1916-1938
Colour variation
Price: $1280 £800

LAST WALTZ HN2315
Designer: M. Davies
Height: 7¾in., 19.7cm.
Issued: 1967-
Rec. Retail Price

LAURA HN2960
Designer: P. Parsons
Height: 7¼in., 18.0cm
Issued: 1983-
Rec. Retail Price

LAURA HN3136
Designer: P. Parsons
Height: 7¹/₄in., 18.4cm.
Issued: 1988-1989
Price: $96 £60

LAURIANNE HN2719
Designer: D. V. Tootle
Height: 6¼in., 15.9cm.
Issued: 1974-1978
Price: $109 £68

LAVENDER WOMAN HN22
Designer: P. Stabler
Height: 8¼in., 21.0cm.
Issued: 1913-1938
Price: $1360 £850

LAVENDER WOMAN HN23
Designer: P. Stabler
Height: 8¼in., 21.0cm.
Issued: 1913-1938
Colour variation
Price: $1360 £850

LAVENDER WOMAN HN23A
Designer: P. Stabler
Height: 8¼in., 21.0cm.
Issued: 1913-1938
Colour variation
Price: $1360 £850

LAVENDER WOMAN HN342
Designer: P. Stabler
Height: 8¼in., 21.0cm.
Issued: 1919-1938
Colour variation
Price: $1360 £850

LAVENDER WOMAN HN569
Designer: P. Stabler
Height: 8¼in., 21.0cm.
Issued: 1924-1938
Colour variation
Price: $1360 £850

LAVENDER WOMAN HN744
Designer: P. Stadler
Height: 8¼in., 21.0cm.
Issued: 1925-1938
Colour variation
Price: $1360 £850

LAVINIA HN1955
Designer: L. Harradine
Height: 5in., 12.7cm.
Issued: 1940-1978
Price: $72 £45

LAWYER HN3041
Designer: P. Parsons
Height: 9in., 23.0cm.
Issued: 1985-
Rec. Retail Price

LEADING LADY HN2269
Designer: M. Davies
Height: 7¾in., 19.7cm.
Issued: 1965-1976
Price: $112 £70

LEDA AND THE SWAN HN2826
Designer: R. Jefferson
Height: 9¾in., 25.0cm.
Issued: 1983 — in a limited edition of 300
Price: $1520 £950

LEGOLAS HN2917
Designer: H. Sales
Height: 6¼in., 15.9cm.
Issued: 1980-1984
Price: $56 £35

LEISURE HOUR HN2055
Designer: M. Davies
Height: 7in., 17.8cm.
Issued: 1950-1965
Price: $280 £175

LESLEY HN2410
Designer: M. Nicoll
Height: 8in., 20cm.
Issued: 1986
Rec. Retail Price

LEGOLAS HN2917

LEDA AND THE SWAN HN2826

FIGURES

LIBERTY HN3201
Designer: A. Hughes
Height: 9¹/₂in., 23.5cm.
Issued: 1989
Rec. Retail Price

LIDO LADY HN1220
Designer: L. Harradine
Height: 6¾in., 17.2cm.
Issued: 1927-1938
Price: $720 £450

LIDO LADY HN1229
Designer: L. Harradine
Height: 6¾in., 17.2cm.
Issued: 1927-1938
Colour variation
Price: $720 £450

LIFEBOAT MAN HN2764
Designer: W.K. Harper
Height: 9¹/₂in., 24cm.
Issued: 1987
Rec. Retail Price

LIGHTS OUT HN2262
Designer: M. Davies
Height: 5in., 12.7cm.
Issued: 1965-1969
Price: $224 £140

LILAC SHAWL HN44
Designer: C. J. Noke
Height: 8¾in., 22.2cm.
Issued: 1915-1938
Price: $640 £400

LILAC SHAWL HN44A
Designer: C. J. Noke
Height: 8¾in., 22.2cm.
Issued: 1915-1938
Colour variation
Price: $640 £400
Also called In Grandma's Days
and Poke Bonnet

LILAC TIME HN2137
Designer: M. Davies
Height: 7¼in., 18.4cm.
Issued: 1954-1969
Price: $224 £140

LILY HN1798
Designer: L. Harradine
Height: 5in., 12.7cm.
Issued: 1936-1949
Price: $96 £60

LILY HN1799
Designer: L. Harradine
Height: 5in., 12.7cm.
Issued: 1936-1949
Colour variation
Price: $104 £65

LINDA HN2106
Designer: L. Harradine
Height: 4¾in., 12.0cm.
Issued: 1953-1976
Price: $88 £55

LINDA HN2758
Designer: E. Griffiths
Height: 7¾in., 19.5cm.
Issued: 1984-1988
Price: $80 £50

LILAC TIME HN2137

LIDO LADY HN1220

LEISURE HOUR HN2055

187

LISA HN2310
Designer: M. Davies
Height: 7¼in., 18.4cm.
Issued: 1969-1982
Price: $96 £60

LISA HN2394
Designer: P. Davies
Height: 7¾in., 19.5cm.
Issued: 1983-
Rec. Retail Price

LISA HN3265
Designer: P. Davies
Height: 7¾in., 19.7cm.
Issued: 1989
Rec. Retail Price

LISETTE HN1523
Designer: L. Harradine
Height: 5¼in., 13.3cm.
Issued: 1932-1938
Price: $360 £225

LISETTE HN1524
Designer: L. Harradine
Height: 5¼in., 13.3cm.
Issued: 1932-1938
          Colour variation
Price: $360 £225

LISETTE HN1684
Designer: L. Harradine
Height: 6½in., 16.5cm.
Issued: 1935-1938
          Colour variation
Price: $360 £225

LITTLE BO-PEEP HN3030
Designer: A. Hughes
Height: 8in., 20.0cm.
Issued: 1984-1987
Price: $61 £38

LITTLE BOY BLUE HN2062
Designer: L. Harradine
Height: 5½in., 14.0cm.
Issued: 1950-1973
Price: $128 £80

LITTLE BOY BLUE HN3035
Designer: A. Hughes
Height: 7¾in., 19.5cm.
Issued: 1984-1987
Price: $61 £38

**"LITTLE CHILD SO RARE
AND SWEET" (Style One)
HN1540**
Designer: Unknown
Height: 5in., 12.7cm.
Issued: 1933-1949
Price: $208 £130

**"LITTLE CHILD SO RARE
AND SWEET" (Style two)
HN1542**
Designer: Unknown
Height: 5in., 12.7cm.
Issued: 1933-1949
Price: $208 £130

**LITTLE LORD
FAUNTLEROY HN2972**

LISA HN2310

LITTLE BOY BLUE HN2062

LITTLE JACK HORNER
HN2063
Designer: L. Harradine
Height: 4½in., 11.4cm.
Issued: 1950-1953
Price: $208 £130

LITTLE JACK HORNER
HN3034
Designer: A. Hughes
Height: 7in., 17.5cm.
Issued: 1984-1987
Price: $61 £38

LITTLE LADY MAKE
BELIEVE HN1870
Designer: L. Harradine
Height: 6¼in., 15.9cm.
Issued: 1938-1949
Price: $224 £140

LITTLE LAND HN63
Designer: H. TIttensor
Height: 7½in., 19.1cm.
Issued: 1916-1938
Price: $1440 £900

LITTLE LAND HN67
Designer: H. Tittensor
Height: 7½in., 19cm.
Issued: 1916-1938
Price: $1440 £900

LITTLE LORD
FAUNTLEROY HN2972
Designer: A. Hughes
Height: 6¼in., 16.0cm
Issued: 1982-1986
Price: $64 £40

LITTLE MISS MUFFET
HN2727
Designer: W. K. Harper
Height: 6¼in., 16.0cm.
Issued: 1984-1987
Price: $61 £38

LITTLE MISTRESS HN1449
Designer; L. Harradine
Height: 5¾in., 14.6cm.
Issued: 1931-1949
Price: $224 £140

LITTLE MOTHER (Style one)
HN389
Designer: H. Tittensor
Height: Unknown
Issued: 1920-1938
Price: $2000 £1250

LITTLE MOTHER (Style one)
HN390
Designer: H. Tittensor
Height: Unknown
Issued: 1920-1938
Colour variation
Price: $2000 £1250

LITTLE MOTHER (Style one)
HN469
Designer: H. Tittensor
Height: Unknown
Issued: 1921-1938
Colour variation
Price: $1600 £1000

LITTLE MISS MUFFET   HN2727

LITTLE MOTHER (Style two)
HN1418
Designer: L. Harradine
Height: 8in., 20.3cm.
Issued: 1930-1938
Price: $1280 £800

LITTLE MOTHER (Style two)
HN1641
Designer: L. Harradine
Height: 8in., 20.3cm.
Issued: 1934-1949
Price: $960 £600
Also called Young Widow

LITTLE NELL HN540
Designer: L. Harradine
Height: 4in., 10.1cm.
Issued: 1922-1932
Price: $61 £38

LITTLE NELL M51
Designer: L. Harradine
Height: 4¼in., 10.8cm.
Issued: 1932-1982
Price: $48 £30

LIZANA HN1756
Designer: L. Harradine
Height: 8½in., 21.6cm
Issued: 1936-1949
Price: $320 £200

LIZANA HN1761
Designer: L. Harradine
Height: 8½in., 21.6cm.
Issued: 1936-1938
Price: $368 £230

LIZZIE HN2749
Designer: D. Tootle
Height: 8½in., 22cm.
Issued: 1988
Rec. Retail Price

LOBSTER MAN HN2317
Designer: M. Nicoll
Height: 7¼in., 18.4cm.
Issued: 1964-
Rec. Retail Price

LOBSTER MAN HN2323
Designer: M. Nicoll
Height: 7½in., 19cm.
Issued: 1987
Rec. Retail Price

LONDON CRY,
STRAWBERRIES HN749
Designer: L. Harradine
Height: 6¾in., 17.2cm.
Issued: 1925-1938
Price: $640 £400

LONDON CRY,
STRAWBERRIES HN772
Designer: L. Harradine
Height: 6¾in., 17.2cm.
Issued: 1925-1938
Colour variation
Price: $640 £400

LONDON CRY, TURNIPS
AND CARROTS HN752
Designer: L. Harradine
Height: 6¾in., 17.2cm.
Issued: 1925-1938
Price: $640 £400

LOBSTER MAN HN2317   LONG JOHN SILVER HN2204

LOVE LETTER HN2149

190

FIGURES

**LONDON CRY, TURNIPS
AND CARROTS HN771**
Designer: L. Harradine
Height: 6¾in., 17.2cm.
Issued: 1925-1938
Price: $640 £400

LONG JOHN SILVER HN2204
Designer: M. Nicoll
Height: 9in., 22.9cm.
Issued: 1957-1965
Price: $288 £180

**LORD OLIVIER AS
RICHARD III HN2881**
Designer: E. Griffiths
Height: 11¼in., 28.5cm
Issued: 1985 in a limited
edition of 750
Price: $400 £250

LORETTA HN2337
Designer: M. Davies
Height: 7¾in., 19.7cm.
Issued: 1966-1980
Price: $104 £65

LORI HN2801
Designer: M. Davies
Height: 5¾in., 14.6cm.
Issued: 1976-1987
Price: $48 £30

LORNA HN2311
Designer: M. Davies
Height: 8¼in., 21.0cm.
Issued: 1965-1985
Price: $96 £60

LORRAINE HN3118
Designer: A. Maslankowski
Height: 8in., 20cm.
Issued: 1988
Rec. Retail Price

LOUISE HN2869
Designer: M. Davies
Height: 6in., 15.2cm.
Issued: 1980-1986
Price: $48 £30

LOVE LETTER HN2149
Designer: M. Davies
Height: 5½in., 14.0cm.
Issued: 1958-1976
Price: $264 £165

LOVE LETTER, THE HN3105
Designer: R. Jefferson
Height: 12in., 30.5cm.
Issued: 1987-1989
Price: $64 £40

LOVERS HN2762 (White)
Designer: D. Tootle
Height: 12 in., 30.5cm.
Issued: 1981
Rec. Retail Price

LOVERS HN2763 (Black)
Designer: D. Tootle
Height: 12in., 30.5cm.
Issued: 1981
Rec. Retail Price

LUCREZIA BORGIA HN2342
Designer: P. Davies
Height: 8in., 20.0cm.
Issued: 1985 in a limited
edition of 750
Price: $752 £470

LORETTA HN2337 **LORNA HN2311**

LUCREZIA BORGIA HN2342

LUCY HN2863
Designer: M. Davies
Height: 6in., 15.2cm.
Issued: 1980-1984
Price: $56 £35

LUCY ANN HN1502
Designer: L. Harradine
Height: 5¼in., 13.3cm.
Issued: 1932-1951
Price: $112 £70

LUCY ANN HN1565
Designer: L. Harradine
Height: 5¼in., 13.3cm.
Issued: 1933-1938
           Colour variation
Price: $144 £90

**LUCY LOCKETT (Style one)
HN485**
Designer: L. Harradine
Height: 6in., 15.2cm.
Issued: 1921-1949
Price: $480 £300

**LUCY LOCKETT (Style one)
HN524**
Designer: L. Harradine
Height: 6in., 15.2cm.
Issued: 1921-1949
           Colour variation
Price: $480 £300

**LUCY LOCKETT (Style two)
HN695**
Designer: L. Harradine
Height: 6in., 15.2cm.
Issued: 1925-1949
Price: $320 £200

**LUCY LOCKETT (Style two)
HN696**
Designer: L. Harradine
Height: 6in., 15.2cm.
Issued: 1925-1949
           Colour variation
Price: $320 £200

LUNCHTIME HN2485
Designer: M. Nicoll
Height: 8in., 20.3cm.
Issued: 1973-1980
Price: $109 £68

LUTE HN2431
Designer: M. Davies
Height: 6¼in., 15.9cm.
Issued: 1972 in a limited
           edition of 750
Price: $512 £320

LYDIA HN1906
Designer: L. Harradine
Height: 4¼in., 10.8cm.
Issued: 1939-1949
Price: $120 £75

LYDIA HN1907
Designer: L. Harradine
Height: 4¾in., 12.0cm.
Issued: 1939-1949
           Colour variation
Price: $120 £75

LUNCHTIME HN2485

LUCY ANN HN1502

LUTE HN2431

FIGURES

LYDIA HN1908
Designer: L. Harradine
Height: 4¾in., 12.0cm.
Issued: 1939-
Colour variation
Rec. Retail Price

LYNNE HN2329
Designer: M. Davies
Height: 7in., 17.8cm.
Issued: 1971-
Rec. Retail Price

LYNSEY HN3043
Designer: P. Parsons
Height: 4¾in., 12.0cm.
Issued: 1985-
Rec. Retail Price

LYRIC HN2757
Designer: E. Griffiths
Height: 6¼in., 16.0cm.
Issued: 1983-1986
Price: $64 £40

LYNNE HN2329

M

**MADONNA OF THE SQUARE
HN10**
Designer: P. Stabler
Height: 7in., 17.8cm.
Issued: 1913-1938
Price: $880 £550

**MADONNA OF THE SQUARE
HN10A**
Designer: P. Stabler
Height: 7in., 17.8cm.
Issued: 1913-1938
Colour variation
Price: $880 £550

**MADONNA OF THE SQUARE
HN11**
Designer: P. Stabler
Height: 7in., 17.8cm.
Issued: 1913-1938
Colour variation
Price: $880 £550

**MADONNA OF THE SQUARE
HN14**
Designer: P. Stabler
Height: 7in., 17.8cm.
Issued: 1913-1938
Colour variation
Price: $880 £550

**MADONNA OF THE SQUARE
HN27**
Designer: P. Stabler
Height: 7in., 17.8cm.
Issued: 1913-1938
Colour variation
Price: $880 £550

MADONNA OF THE SQUARE

193

MADONNA OF THE SQUARE
HN326
Designer: P. Stabler
Height: 7in., 17.8cm.
Issued: 1918-1938
          Colour variation
Price: $880 £550

MADONNA OF THE SQUARE
HN573
Designer: P. Stabler
Height: 7in., 17.8cm.
Issued: 1913-1938
          Colour variation
Price: $880 £550

MADONNA OF THE SQUARE
HN576
Designer: P. Stabler
Height: 7in., 17.8cm.
Issued: 1923-1938
          Colour variation
Price: $880 £550

MADONNA OF THE SQUARE
HN594
Designer: P. Stabler
Height: 7in., 17.8cm.
Issued: 1924-1938
          Colour variation
Price: $880 £550

MADONNA OF THE SQUARE
HN613
Designer: P. Stabler
Height: 7in., 17.8cm.
Issued: 1924-1938
          Colour variation
Price: $880 £550

MADONNA OF THE SQUARE
HN764
Designer: P. Stabler
Height: 7in., 17.8cm.
Issued: 1925-1938
          Colour variation
Price: $880 £550

MADONNA OF THE SQUARE
HN1968
Designer: P. Stabler
Height: 7in., 17.8cm.
Issued: 1941-1949
          Colour variation
Price: $800 £500

MADONNA OF THE SQUARE
HN1969
Designer: P. Stabler
Height: 7in., 17.8cm.
Issued: 1941-1949
          Colour variation
Price: $800 £500

MADONNA OF THE SQUARE
HN2034
Designer: P. Stabler
Height: 7in., 17.8cm.
Issued: 1949-1951
          Colour variation
Price: $800 £500

MAKE BELIEVE HN2225

MAGIC DRAGON HN2977

FIGURES

MAGIC DRAGON HN2977
Designer: A. Hughes
Height: 4¾in., 12.0cm.
Issued: 1983-1986
Price: $64 £40

MAGPIE RING HN2978
Designer: A. Hughes
Height: 8in., 20.0cm.
Issued: 1983-1986
Price: $64 £40

MAISIE HN1618
Designer: L. Harradine
Height: 6¼in., 15.9cm.
Issued: 1934-1949
Price: $200 £125

MAISIE HN1619
Designer: L. Harradine
Height: 6¼in., 15.9cm.
Issued: 1934-1949
Colour variation
Price: $200 £125

**MAJOR, 3rd NEW JERSEY
REGIMENT 1776 HN2752**
Designer: E. J. Griffiths
Height: 10in., 25.4cm.
Issued: 1975 in a limited
edition of 350
Price: $720 £450

MAKE BELIEVE HN2225
Designer: M. Nicoll
Height: 5¾in., 14.6cm.
Issued: 1962-1988
Price: $56 £35

**MAKE BELIEVE (white)
HN2224**
Designer: M. Nicoll
Height: 5¾in., 14.6cm.
Issued: 1984-1988
Colour variation
Price: $45 £28

MAM'SELLE HN658
Designer: L. Harradine
Height: 7in., 17.8cm.
Issued: 1924-1938
Price: $800 £500

MAM'SELLE HN659
Designer: L. Harradine
Height: 7in., 17.8cm.
Issued: 1924-1938
Colour variation
Price: $800 £500

MAM'SELLE HN724
Designer: L. Harradine
Height: 7in., 17.cm.
Issued: 1925-1938
Colour variation
Price: $800 £500

MAM'SELLE HN786
Designer: L. Harradine
Height: 7in., 17.8cm.
Issued: 1926-1938
Colour variation
Price: $800 £500

MAGPIE RING HN2978

MAJOR, 3rd NEW JERSEY REGIMENT 1776 HN2752

MAN IN TUDOR COSTUME
HN563
Designer: Unknown
Height: 3¾in., 9.5cm.
Issued: 1923-1938
Price: $1040 £650

MANDARIN (Style one) HN84
Designer: C. J. Noke
Height: 10¼in., 26.0cm.
Issued: 1918-1938
Price: $1760 £1100

MANDARIN (Style one) HN316
Designer: C. J. Noke
Height: 10¼in., 26.0cm.
Issued: 1918-1938
          Colour variation
Price: $1760 £1100

MANDARIN (Style one) HN318
Designer: C. J. Noke
Height: 10in., 25.4cm.
Issued: 1918-1938
          Colour variation
Price: $1760 £1100

MANDARIN (Style one) HN382
Designer: C. J. Noke
Height: 10in., 25.4cm.
Issued: 1920-1938
          Colour variation
Price: $1760 £1100

MANDARIN (Style one) HN611
Designer: C. J. Noke
Height: 10in., 25.4cm.
Issued: 1924-1938
          Colour variation
Price: $1600 £1000

MANDARIN (Style one) HN746
Designer: C. J. Noke
Height: 10in., 25.4cm.
Issued: 1925-1938
          Colour variation
Price: $1600 £1000

MANDARIN (Style one) HN787
Designer: C. J. Noke
Height: 10in., 25.4cm.
Issued: 1926-1938
          Colour variation
Price: $1600 £1000

MANDARIN (Style one) HN791
Designer: C.J. Noke
Height: 10in., 25.4cm.
Issued: 1926-1938
          Colour variation
Price: $1600 £1000

MANDARIN (Style two) HN366
Designer: C. J. Noke
Height: 10in., 25.4cm.
Issued: 1920-1938
Price: $1600 £1000

MANDARIN (Style two) HN455
Designer: C. J. Noke
Height: 10in., 25.4cm.
Issued: 1921-1938
Price: $1600 £1000

MANTILLA HN2712

MANDARIN (Style two) HN641
Designer: C. J. Noke
Height:　10in., 25.4cm.
Issued:　1924-1938
　　　　Colour variation
Price:　$1600　£1000

MANDARIN (Style three) HN450
Designer: C. J. Noke
Height:　Unknown
Issued:　1921-1938
Price:　$1600　£1000

MANDARIN (Style three) HN460
Designer: C. J. Noke
Height:　Unknown
Issued:　1921-1938
　　　　Colour variation
Price:　$1600　£1000

MANDARIN (Style three) HN461
Designer: C. J. Noke
Height:　Unknown
Issued:　1921-1938
　　　　Colour variation
Price:　$1600　£1000

MANDARIN (Style three) HN601
Designer: C. J. Noke
Height:　Unknown
Issued:　1924-1938
　　　　Colour variation
Price:　$1600　£1000

MANDY HN2476
Designer: P. Davies
Height:　4½in., 11.5cm.
Issued:　1982-
Rec. Retail Price

MANTILLA HN2712
Designer: E. J. Griffiths
Height:　11½in., 29.2cm.
Issued:　1974-1977
Price:　$232　£145

MARCH HN2707
Designer: P. Davies
Height:　7¾in., 19.7cm.
Issued:　1987
Price:　$96　£60

MARGARET HN1989
Designer: L. Harradine
Height:　7¼in., 18.4cm.
Issued:　1947-1959
Price:　$240　£150

MARGARET HN2397
Designer: P. Davies
Height:　7½in., 19.0cm.
Issued:　1982-
Rec. Retail Price

MARGARET OF ANJOU HN2012
Designer: M. Davies
Height:　9¼in., 23.5cm.
Issued:　1949-1953
Price:　$560　£350

MARGARET OF ANJOU HN2012

MARGARET HN2397

MARGERY HN1413
Designer: L. Harradine
Height: 11in., 27.9cm.
Issued: 1930-1949
Price: $280 £175

MARGOT HN1628
Designer: L. Harradine
Height: 5½in., 14.0cm.
Issued: 1934-1938
Price: $440 £275

MARGOT HN1636
Designer: L. Harradine
Height: 5¾in., 14.6cm.
Issued: 1934-1938
        Colour variation
Price: $440 £275

MARGOT HN1653
Designer: L. Harrradine
Height: 5¾in., 14.6cm.
Issued: 1934-1938
        Colour variation
Price: $440 £275

MARGUERITE HN1928
Designer: L. Harradine
Height: 8in., 20.3cm.
Issued: 1940-1959
Price: $240 £150

MARGUERITE HN1929
Designer: L. Harradine
Height: 8in., 20.3cm.
Issued: 1940-1949
        Colour variation
Price: $280 £175

MARGUERITE HN1930
Designer: L. Harradine
Height: 8in., 20.3cm.
Issued: 1940-1949
        Colour variation
Price: $280 £175

MARGUERITE HN1946
Designer: L. Harradine
Height: 8in., 20.3 cm.
Issued: 1940-1949
        Colour variation
Price: $240 £150

MARIANNE HN2074
Designer: L. Harradine
Height: 7¼in., 18.4cm.
Issued: 1951-1953
Price: $352 £220

MARIE (Style one) HN401
Designer: L. Harradine
Height: 7in., 17.7cm.
Issued: 1920-1938
Price: $1200 £750

MARIE (Style one) HN434
Designer: L. Harradine
Height: 7in., 17.7cm.
Issued: 1921-1938
        Colour variation
Price: $1200 £750

MARGERY HN1413

MARGUERITE HN1946

198

FIGURES

MARIE (Style one) HN502
Designer: L. Harradine
Height: 7in., 17.7cm.
Issued: 1921-1938
Colour variation
Price: $1200 £750

MARIE (Style one) HN504
Designer: L. Harradine
Height: 7in., 17.7cm.
Issued: 1921-1938
Colour variation
Price: $1200 £750

MARIE (Style one) HN505
Designer: L. Harradine
Height: 7in., 17.7cm.
Issued: 1921-1938
Colour variation
Price: $1200 £750

MARIE (Style one) HN506
Designer: L. Harradine
Height: 7in., 17.7cm.
Issued: 1921-1938
Colour variation
Price: $1200 £750

MARIE (Style two) HN1370
Designer: L. Harradine
Height: 4¾in., 12.0cm.
Issued: 1930-1988
Price: $48 £30

MARIE (Style two) HN1388
Designer: L. Harradine
Height: 4½in., 11.4cm.
Issued: 1930-1938
Colour variation
Price: $120 £75

MARIE (Style two) HN1417
Designer: L. Harradine
Height: 4¾in., 12.0cm.
Issued: 1930-1949
Colour variation
Price: $88 £55

MARIE (Style two) HN1489
Designer: L. Harradine
Height: 4½in., 11.4cm.
Issued: 1932-1949
Colour variation
Price: $88 £55

MARIE (Style two) HN1531
Designer: L. Harradine
Height: 4½in., 11.4cm.
Issued: 1932-1938
Colour variation
Price: $144 £90

MARIE (Style two) HN1635
Designer: L. Harradine
Height: 4¾in., 12.0cm.
Issued: 1934-1949
Colour variation
Price: $104 £65

MARIE (Style two) HN1655
Designer: L. Harradine
Height: 4½in., 11.4cm.
Issued: 1934-1938
Colour variation
Price: $144 £90

MARIE HN1370

MARIANNE HN2074

MARIETTA HN1341
Designer: L. Harradine
Height: 8in., 20.3cm.
Issued: 1929-1949
Price: $480 £300

MARIETTA HN1446
Designer: L. Harradine
Height: 8in., 20.3cm.
Issued: 1931-1949
Colour variation
Price: $480 £300

MARIETTA HN1699
Designer: L. Harradine
Height: 8in., 20.3cm.
Issued: 1935-1949
Price: $480 £300

MARIGOLD HN1447
Designer: L. Harradine
Height: 6in., 15.2cm.
Issued: 1931-1949
Price: $256 £160

MARIGOLD HN1451
Designer: L. Harradine
Height: 6in., 15.2cm.
Issued: 1931-1938
Price: $256 £160

MARIGOLD HN1555
Designer: L. Harradine
Height: 6in., 15.2cm.
Issued: 1933-1949
Colour variation
Price: $256 £160

MARILYN HN3002
Designer: P. Gee
Height: 7¼in., 18.5cm.
Issued: 1986
Rec. Retail Price

MARION HN1582
Designer: L. Harradine
Height: 6½in., 16.5cm.
Issued: 1933-1938
Price: $400 £250

MARION HN1583
Designer: L. Harradine
Height: 6½in., 16.5cm.
Issued: 1933-1938
Colour variation
Price: $400 £250

MARIQUITA HN1837
Designer: L. Harradine
Height: 8in., 20.3cm.
Issued: 1938-1949
Price: $800 £500

MARJORIE HN2788
Designer: M. Davies
Height: 5¼in., 13.3cm.
Issued: 1980-1984
Price: $109 £68

MARKET DAY HN1991
Designer: L. Harradine
Height: 7¼in., 18.4cm.
Issued: 1975-1981
Price: $192 £120
Also called Country Lass

MARIGOLD HN1447   **MARIETTA HN1341**

MARKET DAY HN1991   **MARJORIE HN2788**

MARRIAGE OF ART AND INDUSTRY HN2261
Designer: M. Davies
Height: 19in., 48.3cm.
Issued: 1958 in a limited edition of 12
Price: $4000 £2500

MARY HN2374
Designer: J. Bromley
Height: 7¾in., 19.5cm.
Issued: 1984-1986
Price: $56 £35

MARY HAD A LITTLE LAMB HN2048
Designer: M. Davies
Height: 3½in., 8.9cm.
Issued: 1949-1988
Price: $56 £35

MARY JANE HN1990
Designer: L. Harradine
Height: 7½in., 19.1cm.
Issued: 1947-1959
Price: $200 £125

MARY, MARY HN2044
Designer: L. Harradine
Height: 5in., 12.7cm.
Issued: 1949-1973
Price: $96 £60

MARY QUEEN OF SCOTS HN2931 (Ship's figurehead)
Designer: S. Keenan
Height: 9½in., 24.0cm.
Issued: 1983 in a limited edition of 950
Price: $240 £150

MARY QUEEN OF SCOTS HN3142
Designer: P. Parsons
Height: 9in., 22.5cm.
Issued: 1990 in a limited edition of 5000
Price: $240 £150

MASK HN656
Designer: L. Harradine
Height: 6¾in., 17.2cm.
Issued: 1924-1938
Price: $960 £600

MASK HN657
Designer: L. Harradine
Height: 6¾in., 17.2cm.
Issued: 1924-1938
Colour variation
Price: $960 £600

MASK HN729
Designer: L. Harradine
Height: 6¾in., 17.2cm.
Issued: 1925-1938
Colour variation
Price: $960 £600

MASK HN733
Designer: L. Harradine
Height: 6¾in., 17.2cm.
Issued: 1925-1938
Colour variation
Price: $960 £600

MARIQUITA HN1837

MARY JANE HN1990

MASK HN733

MARY QUEEN OF SCOTS

MASK HN785
Designer: L. Harradine
Height: 6¾in., 17.2cm.
Issued: 1926-1938
Colour variation
Price: $960 £600

MASK HN1271
Designer: L. Harradine
Height: 6¾in., 17.2cm.
Issued: 1928-1938
Colour variation
Price: $960 £600

MASK SELLER HN1361
Designer: L. Harradine
Height: 8½in., 21.6cm.
Issued: 1929-1938
Price: $560 £350

MASK SELLER HN2103
Designer: L. Harradine
Height: 8½in., 21.6cm.
Issued: 1953-
Colour variation
Rec. Retail Price

MASQUE HN2554
Designer: D. V. Tootle
Height: 8½in., 21.6cm.
Issued: 1973-1982
Price: $144 £90

MASQUE HN2554A
Designer: D. V. Tootle
Height: 8½in., 21.6cm.
Issued: 1973-1982
Colour variation
Price: $144 £90

MASQUERADE (Style one, man) HN599
Designer; L. Harradine
Height: 6¾in., 17.2cm.
Issued: 1924-1949
Price: $560 £350

MASQUERADE (Style one, man) HN636
Designer: L. Harradine
Height: 6¾in., 17.2cm.
Issued: 1924-1938
Colour variation
Price: $720 £450

MASQUERADE (Style one, man) HN683
Designer: L. Harradine
Height: 7¼in., 18.4cm.
Issued: 1924-1938
Colour variation
Price: $720 £450

MASQUERADE (Style one, woman) HN600
Designer: L. Harradine
Height: 6¾in., 17.2cm.
Issued: 1924-1949
Price: $560 £350

MASQUERADE (Style one, woman) HN600A
Designer: L. Harradine
Height: 6in., 15.2cm.
Issued: 1924-1949
Colour variation
Price: $560 £350

MASQUERADE (Style one, woman) HN600

MASK SELLER HN1361

MASK HN1271

MASK SELLER HN2103

MASQUERADE (Style one, woman) HN637
Designer: L. Harradine
Height: 6¾in., 17.2cm.
Issued: 1924-1938
Colour variation
Price: $720 £450

MASQUERADE (Style one, woman) HN674
Designer: L. Harradine
Height: 6¾in., 17.2cm.
Issued: 1924-1938
Colour variation
Price: $720 £450

MASQUERADE (Style two) HN2251
Designer: M. Davies
Height: 8½in., 21.6cm.
Issued: 1960-1965
Price: $288 £180

MASQUERADE (Style two) HN2259
Designer: M. Davies
Height: 8½in., 21.6cm.
Issued: 1960-1965
Colour variation
Price: $288 £180

MASTER HN2325
Designer: M. Davies
Height: 6¼in., 15.9cm.
Issued: 1967-
Rec. Retail Price

MASTER SWEEP HN2205
Designer: M. Nicoll
Height: 8½in., 21.6cm.
Issued: 1957-1962
Price: $352 £220

MATADOR AND BULL HN2324
Designer: M. Davies
Height: 16in., 40.6cm.
Issued: 1964-
Rec. Retail Price

MATILDA HN2011
Designer: M. Davies
Height: 9¼in., 23.5cm.
Issued: 1949-1953
Price: $560 £350

MAUREEN HN1770
Designer: L. Harradine
Height: 7½in., 19.1cm.
Issued: 1936-1959
Price: $256 £160

MAUREEN HN1771
Designer: L. Harradine
Height: 7½in., 19.1cm.
Issued: 1936-1949
Colour variation
Price: $280 £175

MAUREEN M84
Designer: L. Harradine
Height: 4in., 10.1cm.
Issued: 1939-1949
Price: $224 £140

MASTER SWEEP HN2205

MASQUE HN2554

MATILDA HN2011

MASTER HN2325

MAUREEN M85
Designer: L. Harradine
Height: 4in., 10.1cm.
Issued: 1939-1949
Colour variation
Price: $224 £140

MAUREEN HM2481
Designer: P. Davies
Height: 7½in., 19cm.
Issued: 1987
Rec. Retail Price

MAXINE HM3199
Designer: A. Hughes
Height: 9in., 23cm.
Issued: 1989
Rec. Retail Price

MAY HN2711
Designer: P. Davies
Height: 7¾in., 19.5cm.
Issued: 1987
Price: $96 £60

MAY HN2746
Designer: P. Tootle
Height: 8in., 20cm.
Issued: 1987
Rec. Retail Price

MAY HN3251
Designer: P. Tootle
Height: 8in., 20cm.
Issued: 1989 in a limited
edition of 2000
Rec. Retail Price

MAYOR HN2280
Designer: M. Nicholl
Height: 8¼in., 21.0cm.
Issued: 1963-1971
Price: $240 £150

MAYTIME HN2113
Designer: L. Harradine
Height: 7in., 17.8cm.
Issued: 1953-1967
Price: $152 £95

MEDITATION HN2330
Designer: M. Davies
Height: 5¾in., 14.6cm.
Issued: 1971-1983
Price: $128 £80

MEG HN2743
Designer: D. Tootle
Height: 8½in., 22cm.
Issued: 1988
Rec. Retail Price

MELANIE HN2271
Designer: M. Davies
Height: 7¾in., 19.7cm.
Issued: 1965-1980
Price: $109 £68

MELISSA HN2467
Designer: M. Davies
Height: 6¾in., 17.2cm.
Issued: 1981-
Rec. Retail Price

MELODY HN2202
Designer: M. Davies
Height: 6¼in., 15.9cm.
Issued: 1957-1962
Price: $192 £120

MELANIE HN2271   MEPHISTO HN723

MEDITATION HN2330

MEMORIES HN1855
Designer: L. Harradine
Height: 6in., 15.2cm.
Issued: 1938-1949
Price: $256 £160

MEMORIES HN1856
Designer: L. Harradine
Height: 6in., 15.2cm.
Issued: 1938-1949
Colour variation
Price: $256 £160

MEMORIES HN1857
Designer: L. Harradine
Height: 6in., 15.2cm.
Issued: 1938-1949
Colour variation
Price: $256 £160

MEMORIES HN2030
Designer: L. Harradine
Height: 6in., 15.2cm.
Issued: 1949-1959
Colour variation
Price: $256 £160

MENDICANT HN1355
Designer: L. Harradine
Height: 8¼in., 21.0cm.
Issued: 1929-1938
Price: $240 £150

MENDICANT HN1365
Designer: L. Harradine
Height: 8¼in., 21.0cm.
Issued: 1929-1969
Price: $136 £85

MEPHISTO HN722
Designer: L. Harradine
Height: 6½in., 16.5cm.
Issued: 1925-1938
Price: $1280 £800

MEPHISTO HN723
Designer: L. Harradine
Height: 6½in., 16.5cm.
Issued: 1925-1938
Colour variation
Price: $1280 £800

MEPHISTOPHELES AND MARGUERITE HN755
Designer: C. J. Noke
Height: 7¾in., 19.7cm.
Issued: 1925-1949
Price: $1200 £750

MEPHISTOPHELES AND MARGUERITE HN775
Designer: C. J. Noke
Height: 7¾in., 19.7cm.
Issued: 1925-1949
Colour variation
Price: $1200 £750

MERIEL HN1931
Designer: L. Harradine
Height: 7¼in., 18.4cm.
Issued: 1940-1949
Price: $640 £400

MERIEL HN1932
Designer: L. Harradine
Height: 7¼in., 18.4cm.
Issued: 1940-1949
Colour variation
Price: $640 £400

MAYTIME HN2113

MERIEL HN1932

MELISSA HN2467

MENDICANT HN1365

MERMAID HN97
Designer: H. Tittensor
Height: 7in., 17.8cm.
Issued: 1918-1936
Price: $640 £400

MERMAID HN300
Designer: H. Tittensor
Height: 7in., 17.8cm.
Issued: 1918-1936
Price: $640 £400

MERRY CHRISTMAS HN3096
Designer: P. Parsons
Height: 8½in., 22cm.
Issued: 1987
Rec. Retail Price

MERYLL HN1917
Designer: L. Harradine
Height: 6¾in., 17.2cm.
Issued: 1939-1940
Price: $960 £600
Also called Toinette

MEXICAN DANCER HN2866
Designer: M. Davies
Height: 8¼in., 21.0cm.
Issued: 1979 in a limited
edition of 750
Price: $520 £325

MICHELLE HN2234
Designer: M. Davies
Height: 7in., 17.8cm.
Issued: 1967-
Rec. Retail Price

MIDINETTE (Style one) HN1289
Designer: L. Harradine
Height: 9in., 22.9cm.
Issued: 1928-1938
Price: $1200 £750

MIDINETTE (Style one) HN1306
Designer: L. Harradine
Height: 9in., 22.9cm.
Issued: 1928-1938
Colour variation
Price: $1200 £750

MIDINETTE (Style two) HN2090
Designer: L. Harradine
Height: 7¼in., 18.4cm.
Issued: 1952-1965
Price: $272 £170

MIDSUMMER NOON HN1899
Designer: L. Harradine
Height: 4¾in., 12.0cm.
Issued: 1939-1949
Price: $560 £350

MIDSUMMER NOON HN1900
Designer: L. Harradine
Height: 4¾in., 12.0cm.
Issued: 1939-1949
Colour variation
Price: $560 £350

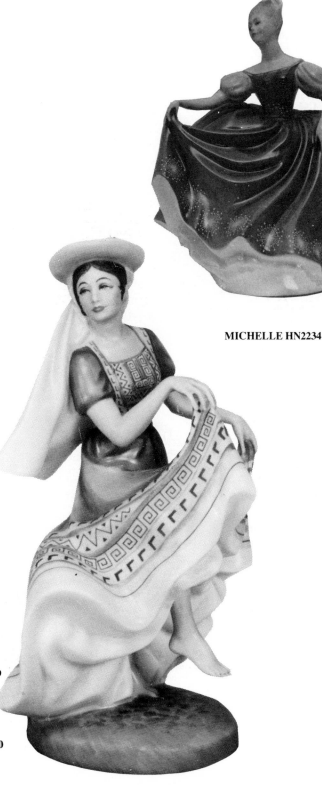

MICHELLE HN2234

MEXICAN DANCER HN2866

MIDSUMMER NOON HN2033
Designer: L. Harradine
Height: 4¾in., 12.0cm.
Issued: 1949-1955
　　　　Colour variation
Price: $560 £350

MILADY HN1970
Designer: L. Harradine
Height: 6½in., 16.5cm.
Issued: 1941-1949
Price: $480 £300

MILKING TIME HN3
Designer: P. Stabler
Height: Unknown
Issued: 1913-1938
Price: $2080 £1300

MILKING TIME HN306
Designer: P. Stabler
Height: Unknown
Issued: 1913-1938
　　　　Colour variation
Price: $2080 £1300

MILKMAID HN2057A
Designer: L. Harradine
Height: 6½in., 16.5cm.
Issued: 1975-1982
Price: $112 £70
Also called The Jersey Milkmaid

MILLICENT HN1714
Designer: L. Harradine
Height: 8in., 20.3cm.
Issued: 1935-1949
Price: $480 £300

MILLICENT HN1715
Designer: L. Harradine
Height: 8in., 20.3cm.
Issued: 1935-1949
　　　　Colour variation
Price: $480 £300

MILLICENT HN1860
Designer: L. Harradine
Height: 8in., 20.3cm.
Issued: 1938-1949
　　　　Colour variation
Price: $480 £300

MINUET HN2019
Designer: M. Davies
Height: 7¼in., 18.4cm.
Issued: 1949-1971
Price: $216 £135

MINUET HN2066
Designer: M. Davies
Height: 7¼in., 18.4cm.
Issued: 1950-1955
　　　　Colour variation
Price: $320 £200

MIRABEL HN1743
Designer: L. Harradine
Height: 7¾in., 19.7cm.
Issued: 1935-1949
Price: $400 £250

MIRABEL HN1744
Designer: L. Harradine
Height: 7¾in., 19.7cm.
Issued: 1935-1949
　　　　Colour variation
Price: $400 £250

MILKMAID HN2057

MINUET HN2019

MERMAID HN97

MIDINETTE (Style two)
HN2090

MIRABEL M68
Designer: L. Harradine
Height: 4in., 10.1cm.
Issued: 1936-1949
Price: $224 £140

MIRABEL M74
Designer: L. Harradine
Height: 4in., 10.1cm.
Issued: 1936-1949
Colour variation
Price: $224 £140

MIRANDA HN1818
Designer: L. Harradine
Height: 8½in., 21.6cm.
Issued: 1937-1949
Price: $560 £350

MIRANDA HN1819
Designer: L. Harradine
Height: 8½in., 21.6cm.
Issued: 1937-1949
Colour variation
Price: $560 £350

MIRANDA HN3037
Designer: A. Hughes
Height: 8¹/₂in., 21cm.
Issued: 1987
Rec. Retail Price

MIRROR HN1852
Designer: L. Harradine
Height: 7½in., 18.4cm.
Issued: 1938-1949
Price: $560 £350

MIRROR HN1853
Designer: L. Harradine
Height: 7½in., 18.4cm.
Issued: 1938-1949
Colour variation
Price: $560 £350

MISS DEMURE HN1402
Designer: L. Harradine
Height: 7½in., 19.1cm.
Issued: 1930-1975
Price: $152 £95

MISS DEMURE HN1440
Designer: L. Harradine
Height: 7in., 17.8cm.
Issued: 1930-1949
Colour variation
Price: $208 £130

MISS DEMURE HN1463
Designer: L. Harradine
Height: 7in., 17.8cm.
Issued: 1931-1949
Colour variation
Price: $208 £130

MISS DEMURE HN1499
Designer: L. Harradine
Height: 7in., 17.8cm.
Issued: 1932-1938
Colour variation
Price: $272 £170

MISS DEMURE HN1560
Designer: L. Harradine
Height: 7in., 17.7cm.
Issued: 1933-1949
Price: $144 £90

MISS DEMURE HN1463

MISS 1926 HN1205   MIRANDA HN1818

MISS FORTUNE HN1897
Designer: L. Harradine
Height: 6in., 15.2cm.
Issued: 1938-1949
Price: $320 £200

MISS FORTUNE HN1898
Designer: L. Harradine
Height: 5¾in., 14.6cm.
Issued: 1938-1949
        Colour variation
Price: $320 £200

MISS MUFFET HN1936
Designer: L. Harradine
Height: 5½in., 13.3cm.
Issued: 1940-1967
Price: $144 £90

MISS MUFFET HN1937
Designer: L. Harradine
Height: 5½in., 13.3cm.
Issued: 1940-1952
        Colour variation
Price: $160 £100

MISS 1926 HN1205
Designer: L. Harradine
Height: 7¼in., 18.4cm.
Issued: 1926-1938
Price: $1280 £800

MISS 1926 HN1207
Designer: L. Harradine
Height: 7¼in., 18.4cm.
Issued: 1926-1938
        Colour variation
Price: $1280 £800

MISS WINSOME HN1665
Designer: L. Harradine
Height: 6¾in., 17.2cm.
Issued: 1934-1949
Price: $208 £130

MISS WINSOME HN1666
Designer: L. Harradine
Height: 6¾in., 17.2cm.
Issued: 1934-1938
        Colour variation
Price: $272 £170

M'LADY'S MAID HN1795
Designer: L. Harradine
Height: 9in., 22.9cm.
Issued: 1936-1949
Price: $800 £500

M'LADY'S MAID HN1822
Designer: L. Harradine
Height: 9in., 22.9cm.
Issued: 1937-1949
        Colour variation
Price: $800 £500

MODENA HN1845
Designer: L. Harradine
Height: 7¼in., 18.4cm.
Issued: 1938-1949
Price: $560 £350

MODENA HN1846
Designer: L. Harradine
Height: 7¼in., 18.4cm.
Issued: 1938-1949
        Colour variation
Price: $560 £350

MISS DEMURE HN1402

209

MODERN PIPER HN756
Designer: L. Harradine
Height: 8½in., 21.6cm.
Issued: 1925-1938
Price: $1280 £800

MODESTY HN2744
Designer: D. Tootle
Height: 8¼in., 21cm.
Issued: 1988
Rec. Retail Price

MOIRA HN1347
Designer: L. Harradine
Height: 6½in., 16.5cm.
Issued: 1929-1938
Price: $1360 £850

MOLLY MALONE HN1455
Designer: L. Harradine
Height: 7in., 17.8cm.
Issued: 1931-1938
Price: $1360 £850

MONICA HN1458
Designer: L. Harradine
Height: 4in., 10.1cm.
Issued: 1931-1949
Price: $120 £75

MONICA HN1459
Designer: L. Harradine
Height: 4in., 10.1cm.
Issued: 1931-1949
Price: $120 £75

MONICA HN1467
Designer: L. Harradine
Height: 4in., 10.1cm.
Issued: 1931-
            Colour variation
Rec. Retail Price

MONICA M66
Designer: L. Harradine
Height: 3in., 7.6cm.
Issued: 1935-1949
Price: $192 £120

MONICA M72
Designer: L. Harradine
Height: 3in., 7.6cm.
Issued: 1936-1949
            Colour variation
Price: $192 £120

MONTE CARLO HN2332
Designer: P. Davies
Height: 8¼in., 20.9cm.
Issued: 1982 in a limited
            edition of 1500
Price: $288 £180

MOON DANCER HN3181
Designer: D. Tootle
Height: 11¾in., 30cm.
Issued: 1988
Rec. Retail Price

MOOR HN1308
Designer: C. J. Noke
Height: 16½in., 41.9cm.
Issued: 1929-1938
Price: $800 £500

MOOR HN1366
Designer: C. J. Noke
Height: 16½in., 41.9cm.
Issued: 1930-1949
            Colour variation
Price: $800 £500

MOIRA HN1347   MODERN PIPER HN756

MONTE CARLO HN2332   MOLLY MALONE HN1455

MOOR HN1425
Designer: C. J. Noke
Height: 16½in., 41.9cm.
Issued: 1930-1949
Colour variation
Price: $800 £500

MOOR HN1657
Designer: C. J. Noke
Height: 16½in., 41.9cm.
Issued: 1934-1949
Colour variation
Price: $800 £500

MOOR HN2082
Designer: C. J. Noke
Height: 16¼in., 41.2cm.
Issued: 1952-
Colour variation
Rec. Retail Price
Also called "An Arab"

MOORISH MINSTREL HN34
Designer: C. J. Noke
Height: 13½in., 34.3cm.
Issued: 1913-1938
Price: $1125 £750

MOORISH MINSTREL HN364
Designer: C. J. Noke
Height: 13½in., 34.3cm.
Issued: 1920-1938
Colour variation
Price: $1200 £750

MOORISH MINSTREL HN415
Designer: C. J. Noke
Height: 13½in., 34.3cm.
Issued: 1920-1938
Colour variation
Price: $1200 £750

MOORISH MINSTREL HN797
Designer: C. J. Noke
Height: 13½in., 34.3cm.
Issued: 1926-1949
Colour variation
Price: $1200 £750

**MOORISH PIPER
MINSTREL HN301**
Designer: C. J. Noke
Height: 13½in., 34.3cm.
Issued: 1918-1938
Price: $1200 £750

**MOORISH PIPER
MINSTREL HN328**
Designer: C. J. Noke
Height: 13½in., 34.3cm.
Issued: 1918-1938
Colour variation
Price: $1200 £750

**MOORISH PIPER
MINSTREL HN416**
Designer: C. J. Noke
Height: 13½in., 34.3cm.
Issued: 1920-1938
Colour variation
Price: $1200 £750

MORNING GLORY HN3093
Designer: P. Parsons
Height: 12¾in., 32cm.
Issued: 1987-1989
Price: $80 £50

MOORISH MINSTREL HN34

MOORISH PIPER MINSTREL HN301

MORNING MA'AM HN2895
Designer: W. K. Harper
Height: 9in., 23cm.
Issued: 1986-1989
Price: $96 £60

MOTHER AND DAUGHTER HN2843 (Black)
Designer: E. Griffiths
Height: 8½in., 21.5cm.
Issued: 1981
Rec. Retail Price

MOTHER AND DAUGHTER HN2841 (White)
Designer: E. Griffiths
Height: 8½in., 21.5cm.
Issued: 1981
Rec. Retail Price

MOTHER'S HELP HN2151
Designer: M. Davies
Height: 5in., 12.7cm.
Issued: 1962-1969
Price: $88 £55

MOTHERHOOD HN28
Designer: P. Stabler
Height: 8in., 20.3cm.
Issued: 1913-1938
Price: $1440 £900

MOTHERHOOD HN30
Designer: P. Stabler
Height: 8in., 20.3cm.
Issued: 1913-1938
Colour variation
Price: $1440 £900

MOTHERHOOD HN303
Designer: P. Stabler
Height: 8in., 20.3cm.
Issued: 1918-1938
Colour variation
Price: $1440 £900

MR. MICAWBER (Style one) HN532
Designer: L. Harradine
Height: 3½in., 8.9cm.
Issued: 1922-1932
Price: $56 £35

MR. MICAWBER (Style two) HN557
Designer: L. Harradine
Height: 7in., 17.8cm.
Issued: 1923-1939
Price: $288 £180

MR. MICAWBER (Style two) HN1895
Designer: L. Harradine
Height: 7in., 17.8cm.
Issued: 1938-1952
Colour variation
Price: $256 £160

MR MICAWBER (Style three) HN2097
Designer: L. Harradine
Height: 7½in., 19.1cm.
Issued: 1952-1967
Price: $192 £120

MR PICKWICK (Style two) HN556

MY LOVE HN2339

MUSICALE HN2756

MORNING MA'AM HN2895

MR MICAWBER M42
Designer: L. Harradine
Height: 4in., 10.1cm.
Issued: 1932-1982
Price: $48 £30

MR PICKWICK (Style one) HN529
Designer: L. Harradine
Height: 3¾in., 9.5cm.
Issued: 1922-1932
Price: $56 £35

MR PICKWICK (Style two) HN556
Designer: L. Harradine
Height: 7in., 17.8cm.
Issued: 1923-1939
Price: $288 £180

MR PICKWICK (Style two) HN1894
Designer: L. Harradine
Height: 7in., 17.8cm.
Issued: 1938-1952
           Colour variation
Price: $256 £160

MR PICKWICK (Style three) HN2099
Designer: L. Harradine
Height: 7½in., 19.1cm.
Issued: 1952-1967
Price: $192 £120

MR PICKWICK M41
Designer: L. Harradine
Height: 4in., 10.1cm.
Issued: 1932-1982
Price: $48 £30

MRS BARDELL M86
Designer: L. Harradine
Height: 4¼in., 10.1cm.
Issued: 1949-1982
Price: $48 £30

MRS FITZHERBERT HN2007
Designer: M. Davies
Height: 9¼in., 23.5cm.
Issued: 1948-1953
Price: $600 £375

MUSICALE HN2756
Designer: E. Griffiths
Height: 9in., 23cm.
Issued: 1983-1986
Price: $72 £45

MY LOVE HN2339
Designer: M. Davies
Height: 6¼in., 15.9cm.
Issued: 1969-
Rec. Retail Price

MY PET HN2238
Designer: M. Davies
Height: 2¾in., 7.0cm.
Issued: 1962-1975
Price: $109 £68

MR MICAWBER M42

MRS FITZHERBERT HN2007

MY PRETTY MAID HN2064
Designer: L. Harradine
Height: 5½in., 14.0cm.
Issued: 1950-1954
Price: $152 £95

MY TEDDY HN2177
Designer: M. Davies
Height: 3¼in., 8.3cm.
Issued: 1962-1967
Price: $176 £110

MYFANWY JONES HN39
Designer: E. W. Light
Height: 12in., 30.5cm.
Issued: 1914-1938
Price: $1600 £1000
See Welsh Girl

MYFANWY JONES HN92
Designer: E. W. Light
Height: 12in., 30.5cm.
Issued: 1918-1938
           Colour variation
Price: $1600 £1000
See Welsh Girl

MYFANWY JONES HN456
Designer: E. W. Light
Height: 12in., 30.5cm.
Issued: 1921-1938
           Colour variation
Price: $1600 £1000
See Welsh Girl

MYFANWY JONES HN514
Designer: E. W. Light;
Height: 12in., 30.5cm.
Issued: 1921-1938
           Colour variation
Price: $1600 £1000
See Welsh Girl

MYFANWY JONES HN516
Designer: E. W. Light
Height: 12in., 30.5cm.
Issued: 1921-1938
           Colour variation
Price: $1600 £1000
See Welsh Girl

MYFANWY JONES HN519
Designer: E. W. Light:
Height: 12in., 30.5cm.
Issued: 1921-1938
           Colour variation
Price: $1600 £1000
See Welsh Girl

MYFANWY JONES HN520
Designer: E. W. Light
Height: 12in., 30.5cm.
Issued: 1921-1938
           Colour variation
Price: $1600 £1000
See Welsh Girl

MYFANWY JONES HN660
Designer: E. W. Light
Height: 12in., 30.5cm.
Issued: 1924-1938
           Colour variation
Price: $1600 £1000
See Welsh Girl

MYFANWY JONES HN39

MYFANWY JONES HN668
Designer: E. W. Light
Height: 12in., 30.5cm.
Issued: 1924-1938
Colour variation
Price: $1600 £1000
See Welsh Girl

MYFANWY JONES HN669
Designer: E. W. Light
Height: 12in., 30.5cm.
Issued: 1924-1938
Colour variation
Price: $1600 £1000
See Welsh Girl

MYFANWY JONES HN701
Designer: E. W. Light
Height: 12in., 30.5cm.
Issued: 1925-1938
Colour variation
Price: $1600 £1000
See Welsh Girl

MYFANWY JONES HN792
Designer: E. W. Light
Height: 12in., 30.5cm.
Issued: 1926-1938
Colour variation
Price: $1600 £1000
See Welsh Girl

N

NADINE HN1885
Designer: L. Harradine
Height: 7¾in., 19.7cm.
Issued: 1938-1949
Price: $480 £300

NADINE HN1886
Designer: L. Harradine
Height: 7¾in., 19.7cm.
Issued: 1938-1949
Colour variation
Price: $480 £300

NANA HN1766
Designer: L. Harradine
Height: 4¾in., 12.0cm.
Issued: 1936-1949
Price: $160 £100

NANA HN1767
Designer: L. Harradine
Height: 4¾in., 12.0cm.
Issued: 1936-1949
Colour variation
Price: $160 £100

NANCY HN2955
Designer: P. Parsons
Height: 7½in., 19.0cm.
Issued: 1982-
Rec. Retail Price

NANNY HN2221
Designer: M. Davies
Height: 6in., 15.2cm.
Issued: 1958-
Rec. Retail Price

NANNY HN2221

NEGLIGEE HN1219

NATALIE HN3173
Designer: P. Davies
Height: 8in., 20cm.
Issued: 1988
Rec. Retail Price

NEGLIGEE HN1219
Designer: L. Harradine
Height: 5in., 12.7cm.
Issued: 1927-1938
Price: $720 £450

NEGLIGEE HN1228
Designer: L. Harradine
Height: 5in., 12.7cm.
Issued: 1927-1938
Colour variation
Price: $720 £450

NEGLIGEE HN1272
Designer: L. Harradine
Height: 5in., 12.7cm.
Issued: 1928-1938
Colour variation
Price: $720 £450

NEGLIGEE HN1273
Designer: L. Harradine
Height: 5in., 12.7cm.
Issued: 1928-1938
Colour variation
Price: $720 £450

NEGLIGEE HN1454
Designer: L. Harradine
Height: 5in., 12.7cm.
Issued: 1931-1938
Colour variation
Price: $720 £450

NELL HN3014
Designer: P. Parsons
Height: 4in., 10.0cm.
Issued: 1983-1989
Price: $48 £30

NELL GWYNN HN1882
Designer: L. Harradine
Height: 6¾in., 17.2cm.
Issued: 1938-1949
Price: $424 £265

NELL GWYNN HN1887
Designer: L. Harradine
Height: 6¾in., 17.2cm.
Issued: 1938-1949
Colour variation
Price: $424 £265

NELSON HN2928
(Ship's figurehead)
Designer: S. Keenan
Height: 8¾in., 22.2cm.
Issued: 1981 in a limited edition of 950
Price: $240 £150

NESTLING DOWN HN3531
Designer: A. Hughes
Height: 13in., 33cm.
Issued: 1986
Rec. Retail Price

NEW BONNET HN1728
Designer: L. Harradine
Height: 7in., 17.8cm.
Issued: 1935-1949
Price: $416 £260

NEWSVENDOR HN2891

NINETTE HN2379

NEW COMPANIONS HN2770

NICOLA HN2839

FIGURES

NEW BONNET HN1957
Designer: L. Harradine
Height: 7in., 17.8cm.
Issued: 1940-1949
Colour variation
Price: $416 £260

NEW COMPANIONS HN2770
Designer: W. K. Harper
Height: 7¾in., 19.5cm.
Issued: 1982-1986
Price: $109 £68

NEWHAVEN FISHWIFE HN1480
Designer: H. Fenton
Height: 7¾in., 19.7cm.
Issued: 1931-1938
Price: $1280 £800

NEWSBOY HN2244
Designer: M. Davies
Height: 8½in., 21.6cm.
Issued: 1959-1965
Price: $352 £220

NEWS VENDOR HN2891
Designer: W. Harper
Height: 7in., 17.8cm.
Issued: 1986 in a limited
edition of 2500
Price: $352 £220

NICOLA HN2839
Designer: M. Davies
Height: 7in., 17.8cm.
Issued: 1978-
Rec. Retail Price

NICOLA HN2804
Designer: P. Davies
Height: 7¹/₂in., 19.5cm.
Issued: 1987
Rec. Retail Price

NINA HN2347
Designer: M. Davies
Height: 7½in., 19.1cm.
Issued: 1969-1976
Price: $109 £68

NINETTE HN2379
Designer: M. Davies
Height: 7½in., 19.1cm.
Issued: 1971-
Rec. Retail Price

NINETTE HN3215
Designer: P. Davies
Height: 3¹/₂in., 9cm.
Issued: 1988
Rec. Retail Price

NOELLE HN2179
Designer: M. Davies
Height: 6¾in., 17.2cm.
Issued: 1957-1967
Price: $224 £140

NORMA M36
Designer: Unknown
Height: 4½in., 11.4cm.
Issued: 1933-1945
Price: $232 £145

NINA HN2347

NEWSBOY HN2244

NEW BONNET HN1728

NOELLE HN2179

217

NORMA M37
Designer: Unknown
Height: 4½in., 11.4cm.
Issued: 1933-1945
Colour variation
Price: $232 £145

**NORTH AMERICAN INDIAN
DANCER HN2809**
Designer: P. Davies
Height: 8½in., 21.5cm.
Issued: 1982 in a limited
edition of 750
Price: $520 £325

NOVEMBER HM2695
Designer: P. Davies
Height: 7¾in., 19.5cm.
Issued: 1987
Price: $96 £60

NUDE ON ROCK HN593
Designer: Unknown
Height: Unknown
Issued 1924-1938
Price: $640 £400

OCTOBER HN2693
Designer: P. Davies
Height: 7¾in., 19.5cm.
Issued: 1987
Price: $96 £60

ODDS AND ENDS HN1844
Designer: L. Harradine
Height: 7¾in., 19.6cm.
Issued: 1938-1949
Price: $560 £350

**OFFICER OF THE LINE
HN2733**
Designer: W. K. Harper
Height: 9in., 23.0cm.
Issued: 1983-1986
Price: $136 £85

**OLD BALLOON SELLER
HN1315**
Designer: L. Harradine
Height: 7½in., 19.1cm.
Issued: 1929-
Rec. Retail Price

**OLD BALLOON SELLER
HN2129**
Designer: L. Harradine
Height: 3¹/₂in., 9cm.
Issued: 1989
Rec. Retail Price

**OLD BALLOON SELLER
AND BULLDOG HN1791**
Designer: L. Harradine
Height: 7in., 17.8cm.
Issued: 1932-1938
Price: $592 £370

**OLD BALLOON SELLER
AND BULLDOG HN1912**
Designer: L. Harradine
Height: 7in., 17.8cm.
Issued: 1939-1949
Price: $560 £350

OLD MEG HN2494

OLD KING HN2134

OLGA HN2463

NORTH AMERICAN INDIAN
DANCER HN2809

OLD KING HN358
Designer: C. J. Noke
Height: 9¾in., 24.7cm.
Issued: 1919-1938
Price: $640 £400

OLD KING HN623
Designer: C. J. Noke
Height: 9¾in., 24.7cm.
Issued: 1924-1938
Colour variation
Price: $640 £400

OLD KING HN1801
Designer: C. J. Noke
Height: 9¾in., 24.7cm.
Issued: 1937-1954
Price: $480 £300

OLD KING HN2134
Designer: C. J. Noke
Height: 10¾in., 27.3cm.
Issued: 1954-
Colour variation
Rec. Retail Price

OLD KING COLE HN2217
Designer: M. Davies
Height: 6½in., 16.5cm.
Issued: 1963-1967
Price: $320 £200

OLD LAVENDER SELLER HN1492
Designer: L. Harradine
Height: 6in., 15.2cm.
Issued: 1932-1949
Price: $440 £275

OLD LAVENDER SELLER HN1571
Designer: L. Harradine
Height: 6½in., 16.5cm.
Issued: 1933-1949
Price: $440 £275

OLD MAN HN451
Designer: Unknown
Height: Unknown
Issued: 1921-1938
Price: $1360 £850

OLD MEG HN2494
Designer: M. Nicoll
Height: 8¼in., 21.0cm.
Issued: 1974-1976
Price: $144 £90

OLD MOTHER HUBBARD HN2314
Designer: M. Nicoll
Height: 8in., 20.3cm.
Issued: 1964-1975
Price: $208 £130

OLGA HN2463
Designer: J. Bromley
Height: 8¼in., 21.0cm
Issued: 1972-1975
Price: $128 £80

OLIVER TWIST M89
Designer: L. Harradine
Height: 4¼in., 10.8cm.
Issued: 1949-1982
Price: $48 £30

OFFICER OF THE LINE
HN2733

OLD MOTHER HUBBARD
HN2314

OLD LAVENDER SELLER HN1492

ODDS AND ENDS HN1844

OLIVIA HN1995
Designer: L. Harradine
Height: 7½in., 19.1cm.
Issued: 1947-1951
Price: $288 £180

OMAR KHAYYAM (Style one) HN408
Designer: C. J. Noke
Height: 6in., 15.2cm.
Issued: 1920-1938
Price: $2000 £1250

OMAR KHAYYAM (Style one) HN409
Designer: C. J. Noke
Height: 6in., 15.2cm.
Issued: 1920-1938
Colour variation
Price: $2000 £1250

OMAR KHAYYAM (Style two) HN2247
Designer: M. Nicoll
Height: 6¼in., 15.9cm.
Issued: 1965-1983
Price: $144 £90

OMAR KHAYYAM AND THE BELOVED HN407
Designer: C. J. Noke
Height: 10in., 25.4cm.
Issued: 1920-1938
Price: $2000 £1250

OMAR KHAYYAM AND THE BELOVED HN419
Designer: C. J. Noke
Height: 6in., 15.2cm.
Issued: 1920-1938
Price: $2000 £1250

OMAR KHAYYAM AND THE BELOVED HN459
Designer: C. J. Noke
Height: 10in., 25.4cm.
Issued: 1921-1938
Price: $2000 £1250

OMAR KHAYYAM AND THE BELOVED HN598
Designer: C. J. Noke
Height: 10in., 25.4cm.
Issued: 1924-1938
Price: $2000 £1250

ONCE UPON A TIME HN2047
Designer: L. Harradine
Height: 4¼in., 10.8cm.
Issued: 1949-1955
Price: $160 £100

ONE OF THE FORTY (Style one) HN417
Designer: H. Tittensor
Height: 8¼in., 21.0cm.
Issued: 1920-1938
Price: $768 £480

ONE OF THE FORTY (Style one) HN490
Designer: H. Tittensor
Height: 8¼in., 21.0cm.
Issued: 1921-1938
Colour variation
Price: $768 £480

ONCE UPON A TIME HN2047

OMAR KHAYYAM (Style two) HN2247

ONE OF THE FORTY
(Style one) HN495
Designer: H. Tittensor
Height: 8¼in., 21.0cm.
Issued: 1921-1938
Colour variation
Price: $768 £480

ONE OF THE FORTY
(Style one) HN501
Designer: H. Tittensor
Height: 8¼in., 21cm.
Issued: 1921-1938
Colour variation
Price: $768 £480

ONE OF THE FORTY
(Style one) HN648
Designer: H. Tittensor
Height: 8¼in., 21.0cm.
Issued: 1924-1938
Colour variation
Price: $768 £480

ONE OF THE FORTY
(Style one) HN528
Designer: H. Tittensor
Height: 8¼in., 21cm.
Issued: 1921-1938
Colour variation
Price: $768 £480

ONE OF THE FORTY
(Style one) HN677
Designer: H. Tittensor
Height: 8¼in., 21.0cm.
Issued: 1924-1938
Colour variation
Price: $768 £480

ONE OF THE FORTY
(Style one) HN1351
Designer: H. Tittensor
Height: 8¼in., 21.0cm
Issued: 1920-1949
Colour variation
Price: $768 £480

ONE OF THE FORTY
(Style one) HN1352
Designer: H. Tittensor
Height: 8¼in., 21.0cm.
Issued: 1929-1949
Colour variation
Price: $768 £480

ONE OF THE FORTY
(Style two) HN418
Designer: H. Tittensor
Height: 7¼in., 18.4cm.
Issued: 1920-1938
Price: $768 £480

ONE OF THE FORTY
(Style two) HN494
Designer: H. Tittensor
Height: 7¼in., 18.4cm.
Issued: 1921-1938
Colour variation
Price: $768 £480

ONE OF THE FORTY
(Style twelve) HN492

ONE OF THE FORTY
(Style thirteen) HN665

ONE OF THE FORTY
(Style one) HN677

ONE OF THE FORTY
(Style two) HN494

ONE OF THE FORTY
(Style two) HN498
Designer: H. Tittensor
Height: 7¼in., 18.4cm.
Issued: 1921-1938
Colour variation
Price: $768 £480

ONE OF THE FORTY
(Style two) HN647
Designer: H. Tittensor
Height: 7¼in., 18.4cm.
Issued: 1924-1938
Colour variation
Price: $768 £480

ONE OF THE FORTY
(Style two) HN666
Designer: H. Tittensor
Height: 7¼in., 18.4cm.
Issued: 1924-1938
Colour variation
Price: $768 £480

ONE OF THE FORTY
(Style two) HN704
Designer: H. Tittensor
Height: 7¼in., 18.4cm.
Issued: 1925-1938
Colour variation
Price: $768 £480

ONE OF THE FORTY
(Style two) HN1353
Designer: H. Tittensor
Height: 7¼in., 18.4cm.
Issued: 1929-1949
Colour variation
Price: $768 £480

ONE OF THE FORTY
(Style three) HN423
Designer: H. Tittensor
Height: 3in., 7.6cm.
Issued: 1921-1938
Price: $400 £250

ONE OF THE FORTY
(Style four) HN423A
Designer: H. Tittensor
Height: 3in., 7.6cm.
Issued: 1921-1938
Price: $400 £250

ONE OF THE FORTY
(Style five) HN423B
Designer: H. Tittensor
Height: 2¾in., 6.9cm.
Issued: 1921-1938
Price: $400 £250

ONE OF THE FORTY
(Style six) HN423C
Designer: H. Tittensor
Height: 2¾in., 6.9cm.
Issued: 1921-1938
Price: $400 £250

ONE OF THE FORTY
(Style seven) HN423D
Designer: H. Tittensor
Height: 2¾in., 6.9cm.
Issued: 1921-1938
Price: $400 £250

ONE OF THE FORTY
(Style ten) HN497

ONE OF THE FORTY
(Style three) HN423

ONE OF THE FORTY
(Style eight) HN423E
Designer: H. Tittensor
Height: 3in., 7.6cm.
Issued: 1921-1938
Price: $400 £250

ONE OF THE FORTY
(Style nine) HN427
Designer: H. Tittensor
Height: Unknown
Issued: 1921-1938
Price: $768 £480

ONE OF THE FORTY
(Style ten) HN480
Designer: H. Tittensor
Height: 7in., 17.8cm.
Issued: 1921-1938
Price: $768 £480

ONE OF THE FORTY
(Style ten) HN493
Designer: H. Tittensor
Height: 6¾in., 17.1cm.
Issued: 1921-1938
Price: $768 £480

ONE OF THE FORTY
(Style ten) HN497
Designer: H. Tittensor
Height: 6¾in., 17.1cm.
Issued: 1921-1938
Colour variation
Price: $768 £480

ONE OF THE FORTY
(Style ten) HN499
Designer: H. Tittensor
Height: 6¾in., 17.1cm.
Issued: 1921-1938
Colour variation
Price: $768 £480

ONE OF THE FORTY
(Style ten) HN664
Designer: H. Tittensor
Height: 7¾in., 19.7cm.
Issued: 1924-1938
Colour variation
Price: $768 £480

ONE OF THE FORTY
(Style ten) HN714
Designer: H. Tittensor
Height: 6¾in., 17.2cm.
Issued: 1925-1938
Colour variation
Price: $768 £480

ONE OF THE FORTY
(Style eleven) HN481
Designer: H. Tittensor
Height: Unknown
Issued: 1921-1938
Price: $768 £480

ONE OF THE FORTY
(Style eleven) HN483
Designer: H. Tittensor
Height: Unknown
Issued: 1921-1938
Colour variation
Price: $768 £480

FIGURES

ONE OF THE FORTY
(Style eleven) HN491
Designer: H. Tittensor
Height: Unknown
Issued: 1921-1938
        Colour variation
Price: $768 £480

ONE OF THE FORTY
(Style eleven) HN646
Designer: H. Tittensor
Height: Unknown
Issued: 1924-1938
        Colour variation
Price: $768 £480

ONE OF THE FORTY
(Style eleven) HN667
Designer: H. Tittensor
Height: Unknown
Issued: 1924-1938
        Colour variation
Price: $768 £480

ONE OF THE FORTY
(Style eleven) HN712
Designer: H. Tittensor
Height: Unknown
Issued: 1925-1938
        Colour variation
Price: $768 £480

ONE OF THE FORTY
(Style eleven) HN1336
Designer: H. Tittensor
Height: Unknown
Issued: 1929-1938
        Colour variation
Price: $768 £480

ONE OF THE FORTY
(Style eleven) HN1350
Designer: H. Tittensor
Height: Unknown
Issued: 1929-1949
        Colour variation
Price: $768 £480

ONE OF THE FORTY
(Style twelve) HN482
Designer: H. Tittensor
Height: 6in., 15.2cm.
Issued: 1921-1938
Price: $768 £480

ONE OF THE FORTY
(Style twelve) HN484
Designer: H. Tittensor
Height: 6in., 15.2cm.
Issued: 1921-1938
        Colour variation
Price: $768 £480

ONE OF THE FORTY
(Style twelve) HN492
Designer: H. Tittensor
Height: 6in., 15.2cm.
Issued: 1921-1938
        Colour variation
Price: $768 £480

ONE OF THE FORTY
(Style eleven) HN483

ONE THAT GOT AWAY
HN2153

ONE OF THE FORTY
(Style twelve) HN645
Designer: H. Tittensor
Height: 6in., 15.2cm.
Issued: 1924-1938
        Colour variation
Price: $768 £480

ONE OF THE FORTY
(Style twelve) HN663
Designer: H. Tittensor
Height: 6in., 15.2cm.
Issued: 1924-1938
        Colour variation
Price: $768 £480

ONE OF THE FORTY
(Style twelve) HN 713
Designer: H. Tittensor
Height: 6in., 15.2cm.
Issued: 1925-1938
        Colour variation
Price: $768 £480

ONE OF THE FORTY
(Style thirteen) HN496
Designer: H. Tittensor
Height: 7¾in., 19.6cn.
Issued: 1921-1938
Price: $768 £480

ONE OF THE FORTY
(Style thirteen) HN500
Designer: H. Tittensor
Height: 7¾in., 19.7cm.
Issued: 1921-1938
        Colour variation
Price: $768 £480

ONE OF THE FORTY
(Style thirteen) HN649
Designer: H. Tittensor
Height: 7¾in., 19.7cm.
Issued: 1924-1938
        Colour variation
Price: $768 £480

ONE OF THE FORTY
(Style thirteen) HN665
Designer: H. Tittensor
Height: 7¾in., 19.7cm.
Issued: 1924-1938
        Colour variation
Price: $768 £480

ONE OF THE FORTY
(Style thirteen) HN1354
Designer: H. Tittensor
Height: 7¾in., 19.7cm.
Issued: 1929-1949
        Colour variation
Price: $768 £480

ONE THAT GOT AWAY
HN2153
Designer: M. Davies
Height: 6¼in., 15.9cm.
Issued: 1955-1959
Price: $128 £80

FIGURES

ORANGE LADY HN1759
Designer: L. Harradine
Height: 8¾in., 22.2cm.
Issued: 1936-1975
Price: $144 £90

ORANGE LADY HN1953
Designer: L. Harradine
Height: 8½in., 21.6cm.
Issued: 1940-1975
　　　　Colour variation
Price: $152 £95

ORANGE SELLER HN1325
Designer: L. Harradine
Height: 7in., 17.8cm.
Issued: 1929-1949
Price: $480 £300

ORANGE VENDOR HN72
Designer: C. J. Noke
Height: 6¼in., 15.9cm.
Issued: 1917-1938
Price: $720 £450

ORANGE VENDOR HN508
Designer: C. J. Noke
Height: 6¼in., 15.8cm.
Issued: 1921-1938
Price: $720 £450

ORANGE VENDOR HN521
Designer: C. J. Noke
Height: 6¼in., 15.8cm.
Issued: 1921-1938
　　　　Colour variation
Price: $720 £450

ORANGE VENDOR HN1966
Designer: C. J. Noke
Height: 6¼in., 15.9cm.
Issued: 1941-1949
　　　　Colour variation
Price: $600 £375

ORGAN GRINDER HN2173
Designer: M. Nicoll
Height: 8¾in., 22.2cm.
Issued: 1956-1965
Price: $440 £275

OUT FOR A WALK HN86
Designer: H. Tittensor
Height: Unknown
Issued: 1918-1936
Price: $1360 £850

OUT FOR A WALK HN443
Designer: H. Tittensor
Height: Unknown
Issued: 1921-1936
Price: $1360 £850

OUT FOR A WALK HN748
Designer: H. Tittensor
Height: 10in., 25.4cm.
Issued: 1925-1936
Price: $1360 £850

OVER THE THRESHOLD HN3274
Designer: R. Tabbenor
Height: 12in., 30.5cm.
Issued: 1989
Rec. Retail Price

ORANGE VENDOR HN508

ORANGE SELLER HN1325

ORGAN GRINDER HN2173

OWD WILLUM HN2042
Designer: L. Harradine
Height: 6¾in., 17.2cm.
Issued: 1949-1973
Price: $224 £140

P

PAINTING HN3012
Designer: P. Parsons
Height: 6in., 15cm.,
Issued: 1988 in a limited
edition of 750
Price: $640 £400

PAISLEY SHAWL (Style one)
HN1392
Designer: L. Harradine
Height: 8¼in., 21.0cm.
Issued: 1930-1949
Price: $264 £165

PAISLEY SHAWL (Style one)
HN1460
Designer: L. Harradine
Height: 8¼in., 21.0cm.
Issued: 1931-1949
Colour variation
Price: $224 £140

PAISLEY SHAWL (Style one)
HN1707
Designer: L. Harradine
Height: 8¼in., 21.0cm.
Issued: 1935-1949
Colour variation
Price: $240 £150

PAISLEY SHAWL (Style one)
HN1739
Designer: L. Harradine
Height: 8¼in., 21.0cm.
Issued: 1935-1949
Colour variation
Price: $240 £150

PAISLEY SHAWL (Style one)
HN1987
Designer: L. Harradine
Height: 8¼in., 21.0cm.
Issued: 1946-1949
Colour variation
Price: $224 £140

PAISLEY SHAWL (Style two)
HN1914
Designer: L. Harradine
Height: 6½in., 16.5cm.
Issued: 1939-1949
Price: $144 £90

PAISLEY SHAWL (Style two)
HN1988
Designer: L. Harradine
Height: 6¼in., 15.9cm.
Issued: 1946-1975
Colour variation
Price: $144 £90

PAISLEY SHAWL M3
Designer: L. Harradine
Height: 4in., 10.1cm.
Issued: 1932-1938
Price: $192 £120

ORANGE LADY HN1953   OWD WILLIAM HN2042

PAINTING HN3012

225

PAISLEY SHAWL M4
Designer: L. Harradine
Height: 4in., 10.1cm.
Issued: 1932-1945
Colour variation
Price: $160 £100

PAISLEY SHAWL M26
Designer: L. Harradine
Height: 3¾in., 9.5cm.
Issued: 1932-1945
Colour variation
Price: $160 £100

PALIO HN2428
Designer: M. Davies
Height: 17½in., 44.5cm.
Issued: 1971 in a limited
edition of 500
Price: $3520 £2200

PAMELA HN1468
Designer: L. Harradine
Height: 7½in., 19.1cm.
Issued: 1931-1938
Price: $400 £250

PAMELA HN1469
Designer: L. Harradine
Height: 7½in., 19.1cm.
Issued: 1931-1938
Colour variation
Price: $400 £250

PAMELA HN1564
Designer: L. Harradine
Height: 8in., 20.3cm.
Issued: 1933-1938
Colour variation
Price: $400 £250

PAMELA HN3223
Designer: P. Davies
Height: 7in., 18cm.
Issued: 1989
Rec. Retail Price

PAMELA HN2479
Designer: P. Davies
Height: 7in., 17.5cm.
Issued: 1986
Rec. Retail Price

PAN ON ROCK HN621
Designer: Unknown
Height: 5³/₄in., 13.3cm.
Issued: 1924-1938
Price: $800 £500

PAN ON ROCK HN622
Designer: Unknown
Height: 5³/₄in., 13.3cm.
Issued: 1924-1938
Price: $800 £500

PANORAMA HN3028
Designer: R. Jefferson
Height: 12¼in., 31cm.
Issued: 1987-1989
Price: $72 £45

PANTALETTES HN1362
Designer: L. Harradine
Height: 7¾in., 19.7cm.
Issued: 1929-1938
Price: $288 £180

PAISLEY SHAWL HN1988

PARISIAN HN2445   PAMELA HN1469

PANTALETTES HN1412
Designer: L. Harradine
Height: 7¾in., 19.7cm.
Issued: 1930-1949
          Colour variation
Price: $232 £145

PANTALETTES HN1507
Designer: L. Harradine
Height: 7¾in., 19.7cm.
Issued: 1932-1949
          Colour variation
Price: $232 £145

PANTALETTES HN1709
Designer: L. Harradine
Height: 8in., 20.3cm.
Issued: 1935-1938
          Colour variation
Price: $232 £145

PANTALETTES M15
Designer: L. Harradine
Height: 3¾in., 9.5cm.
Issued: 1932-1945
Price: $208 £130

PANTALETTES M16
Designer: L. Harradine
Height: 3¾in., 9.5cm.
Issued: 1932-1945
          Colour variation
Price: $208 £130

PANTALETTES M31
Designer: L. Harradine
Height: 4in., 10.1cm.
Issued: 1932-1945
          Colour variation
Price: $208 £130

PARADISE HN3074
Designer: A. Hughes
Height: 13½in., 34.5cm.
Issued: 1985
Rec. Retail Price

PARISIAN HN2445
Designer: M. Nicoll
Height: 8in., 20.3cm.
Issued: 1972-1975
Price: $144 £90

PARK PARADE HN3116
Designer: A. Maslankowski
Height: 11¾in., 30cm.
Issued: 1987
Rec. Retail Price

**PARSON'S DAUGHTER
HN337**
Designer: H. Tittensor
Height: 10in., 25.4cm.
Issued: 1919-1938
Price: $400 £250

**PARSON'S DAUGHTER
HN338**
Designer: H. Tittensor
Height: 10in., 25.4cm.
Issued: 1919-1938
          Colour variation
Price: $400 £250

**PARSON'S DAUGHTER
HN441**
Designer: H. Tittensor
Height: 10in., 25.4cm.
Issued: 1921-1938
          Colour variation
Price: $400 £250

PANTALETTES HN1362

227

PARSON'S DAUGHTER
HN564
Designer: H. Tittensor
Height: 9½in., 24.1cm.
Issued: 1923-1949
Colour variation
Price: $208 £130

PARSON'S DAUGHTER
HN790
Designer: H. Tittensor
Height: 10in., 25.4cm.
Issued: 1926-1938
Colour variation
Price: $240 £150

PARSON'S DAUGHTER
HN1242
Designer: H. Tittensor
Height: 10in., 25.4cm.
Issued: 1927-1938
Colour variation
Price: $240 £150

PARSON'S DAUGHTER
HN1356
Designer: H. Tittensor
Height: 9¼in., 23.5cm.
Issued: 1929-1938
Colour variation
Price: $192 £120

PARSON'S DAUGHTER
HN2018
Designer: H. Tittensor
Height: 9¾in., 24.7cm.
Issued: 1949-1953
Colour variation
Price: $176 £110

PAST GLORY HN2484
Designer: M. Nicoll
Height: 7½in., 19.1cm.
Issued: 1973-1978
Price: $192 £120

PATCHWORK QUILT
HN1984
Designer: L. Harradine
Height: 6in., 15.2cm.
Issued: 1945-1959
Price: $200 £125

PATRICIA HN1414
Designer: L. Harradine
Height: 8½in., 21.6cm.
Issued: 1930-1949
Price: $264 £165

PATRICIA HN1431
Designer: L. Harradine
Height: 8½in., 21.6cm.
Issued: 1930-1949
Colour variation
Price: $264 £165

PATRICIA HN1462
Designer: L. Harradine
Height: 8in., 20.3cm.
Issued: 1931-1938
Colour variation
Price: $264 £165

PATRICIA HN1567
Designer: L. Harradine
Height: 8½in., 21.6cm.
Issued: 1933-1949
Colour variation
Price: $288 £180

PAST GLORY HN2484

PARSON'S DAUGHTER HN564

PATRICIA M7
Designer: L. Harradine
Height: 4in., 10.1cm.
Issued: 1932-1945
Price: $160 £100

PATRICIA M8
Designer: L. Harradine
Height: 4in., 10.1cm.
Issued: 1932-1938
Colour variation
Price: $192 £120

PATRICIA M28
Designer: L. Harradine
Height: 4in., 10.1cm.
Issued: 1932-1945
Colour variation
Price: $160 £100

PATRICIA HN2715
Designer: E. Griffiths
Height: 7½in., 19.0cm.
Issued: 1982-1985
Price: $112 £70

PAULA HN2906
Designer: P. Parsons
Height: 7in., 17.8cm.
Issued: 1980-1986
Price: $96 £60

PAULINE HN1444
Designer: L. Harradine
Height: 6in., 15.2cm.
Issued: 1931-1938
Price: $192 £120

PAULINE HN2441
Designer: P. Davies
Height: 5in., 12.5cm.
Issued: 1984-1989
Price: $112 £70

PAVLOVA HN487
Designer: C. J. Noke
Height: 4¼in., 11.4cm.
Issued: 1921-1938
Price: $1360 £850

PAVLOVA HN676
Designer: Unknown
Height: 4¼in., 10.8cm.
Issued: 1924-1938
Colour variation
Price: $1360 £850

PEACE HN2433 (Black)
Designer: P. Davies
Height: 8in., 20.3cm.
Issued: 1981
Rec. Retail Price

PEACE HN2470 (White)
Designer: P. Davies
Height: 8in., 20.3cm.
Issued: 1981
Rec. Retail Price

PEARLY BOY (Style one) HN1482
Designer: W.K. Harper
Height: 8in., 20.3cm.
Issued: 1931-1949
Price: $256 £160

PAULA HN2906

PATRICIA HN1567

PEARLY BOY (Style one)
HN1547
Designer: W.K. Harper
Height: 8in., 20.3cm.
Issued: 1933-1949
         Colour variation
Price: $256 £160

PEARLY BOY (Style two)
HN2035
Designer: W.K. Harper
Height: 8in., 20.3cm.
Issued: 1949-1959
Price: $176 £110

PEARLY BOY HN2767
Designer: W. K. Harper
Height: 8in., 20.3cm.
Issued: 1989
Rec. Retail Price

PEARLY GIRL (Style one)
HN1483
Designer: W.K. Harper
Height: 7³/₄in., 19.7cm.
Issued: 1931-1949
Price: $256 £160

PEARLY GIRL (Style one)
HN1548
Designer: W.K. Harper
Height: 7³/₄in., 19.7cm.
Issued: 1933-1949
         Colour variation
Price: $256 £160

PEARLY GIRL (Style one)
HN1483

PEARLY GIRL (Style two)
HN2036
Designer: W.K. Harper
Height: 7³/₄in., 19.7cm.
Issued: 1949-1959
Price: $176 £110

PEARLY GIRL HN2769
Designer: W. K. Harper
Height: 8in., 20.3cm.
Issued: 1989
Rec. Retail Price

PECKSNIFF (Style one) HN535
Designer: L. Harradine
Height: 3¾in., 9.5cm.
Issued: 1922-1932
Price: $48 £30

PECKSNIFF (Style two) HN553
Designer: L. Harradine
Height: 7in., 17.8cm.
Issued: 1923-1939
Price: $288 £180

PECKSNIFF (Style two)
HN1891
Designer: L. Harradine
Height: 7in., 17.8cm.
Issued: 1938-1952
Price: $256 £160

PECKSNIFF (Style three)
HN2098
Designer: L. Harradine
Height: 7¼in., 18.4cm.
Issued: 1952-1967
Price: $192 £120

PEARLY BOY (Style two)
HN2035

PHILIPPA OF HAINAULT HN2008

FIGURES

PECKSNIFF, MR M43
Designer: L. Harradine
Height: 4¼in., 10.8cm.
Issued: 1932-1982
Price: $48 £30

PEDLAR WOLF HN7
Designer: C. J. Noke
Height: 5½in., 14.0cm.
Issued: 1913-1938
Price: $1600 £1000

PEGGY HN1941
Designer: L. Harradine
Height: 5in., 12.7cm.
Issued: 1940-1949
Price: $88 £55

PEGGY HN2038
Designer: L. Harradine
Height: 5in., 12.7cm.
Issued: 1949-1978
Price: $72 £45

PENELOPE HN1901
Designer: L. Harradine
Height: 7in., 17.8cm.
Issued: 1939-1975
Price: $192 £120

PENELOPE HN1902
Designer: L. Harradine
Height: 7in., 17.8cm.
Issued: 1939-1949
          Colour variation
Price: $280 £175

PENNY HN2338
Designer: M. Davies
Height: 4¾in., 12.0cm.
Issued: 1968-
Rec. Retail Price

PENNY HN2424
Designer: P. Davies
Height: 4¾in., 12.0cm.
Issued: 1983-
Rec. Retail Price

PENSIVE HN3109
Designer: R. Jefferson
Height: 13in., 33cm.
Issued: 1987-1989
Price: $80 £50

PENSIVE MOMENTS HN2704
Designer: M. Davies
Height: 5in., 12.7cm.
Issued: 1975-1982
Price: $104 £65

PERFECT PAIR HN581
Designer: L. Harradine
Height: 6¾in., 17.2cm.
Issued: 1923-1938
Price: $720 £450

PHILIPPA OF HAINAULT
HN2008
Designer: M. Davies
Height: 9¾in., 24.7cm.
Issued: 1948-1953
Price: $560 £350

PERFECT PAIR HN581

PENSIVE MOMENTS HN2704

231

PHILIPPINE DANCER
HN2439
Designer: M. Davies
Height: 9½in., 24.1cm.
Issued: 1978 in a limited
edition of 750
Price: $520 £325

PHYLLIS HN1420
Designer: L. Harradine
Height: 9in., 22.9cm.
Issued: 1930-1949
Price: $320 £200

PHYLLIS HN1430
Designer: L. Harradine
Height: 9in., 22.9cm.
Issued: 1930-1938
Colour variation
Price: $320 £200

PHYLLIS HN1486
Designer: L. Harradine
Height: 9in., 22.9cm.
Issued: 1931-1949
Colour variation
Price: $400 £250

PHYLLIS HN1698
Designer: L. Harradine
Height: 9in., 22.9cm.
Issued: 1935-1949
Colour variation
Price: $400 £250

PHYLLIS HN3180
Designer: D. Tootle
Height: 7¼in., 18.5cm.
Issued: 1988
Rec. Retail Price

PICARDY PEASANT (man)
HN13
Designer: P. Stabler
Height: 9in., 22.9cm.
Issued: 1913-1938
Price: $800 £500

PICARDY PEASANT (man)
HN17
Designer: P. Stabler
Height: 9½in., 24.0cm.
Issued: 1913-1938
Colour variation
Price: $800 £500

PICARDY PEASANT (man)
HN19
Designer: P. Stabler
Height: 9½in., 24.0cm.
Issued: 1913-1938
Colour variation
Price: $800 £500

PICARDY PEASANT (woman)
HN4
Designer: P. Stabler
Height: 9¼in., 23.5cm.
Issued: 1913-1938
Price: $800 £500

PICARDY PEASANT (woman)
HN5
Designer: P. Stabler
Height: 9¼in., 23.5cm.
Issued: 1913-1938
Colour variation
Price: $800 £500

PICNIC HN2308

PHILIPPINE DANCER HN2439

FIGURES

PICARDY PEASANT (woman)
HN17A
Designer: P. Stabler
Height: 9½in., 24.0cm.
Issued: 1913-1938
Colour variation
Price: $800 £500

PICARDY PEASANT (woman)
HN351
Designer: P. Stabler
Height: 9½in., 24.0cm.
Issued: 1919-1938
Colour variation
Price: $800 £500

PICARDY PEASANT (woman)
HN513
Designer: P. Stabler
Height: 9½in., 24.0cm.
Issued: 1921-1938
Colour variation
Price: $800 £500

PICNIC HN2308
Designer: M. Davies
Height: 3¾in., 9.5cm.
Issued: 1965-1988
Price: $64 £40

PIERETTE HN644   PIERETTE HN643

PIED PIPER HN1215
Designer: L. Harradine
Height: 8¼in., 21.0cm.
Issued: 1926-1938
Price: $640 £400

PIED PIPER HN2102
Designer: L. Harradine
Height: 8½in., 21.6cm.
Issued: 1953-1976
Colour variation
Price: $192 £120

PIERETTE (Style one) HN642
Designer: L. Harradine
Height: 7¼in., 18.4cm.
Issued: 1924-1938
Price: $560 £350

PIERETTE (Style one) HN643
Designer: L. Harradine
Height: 7¼in., 18.4cm.
Issued: 1924-1938
Colour variation
Price: $560 £350

PIERETTE (Style one) HN644
Designer: L. Harradine
Height: 7¼in., 18.4cm.
Issued: 1924-1938
Colour variation
Price: $480 £300

PIERETTE (Style one) HN691
Designer: L. Harradine
Height: 7¼in., 18.4cm.
Issued: 1925-1938
Colour variation
Price: $720 £450

PIED PIPER HN1215   PHYLLIS HN1420

233

PIERETTE (Style one) HN721
Designer: L. Harradine
Height: 7¼in., 18.4cm.
Issued: 1925-1938
         Colour variation
Price: $560 £350

PIERETTE (Style one) HN731
Designer: L. Harradine
Height: 7¼in., 18.4cm.
Issued: 1925-1938
         Colour variation
Price: $480 £300

PIERETTE (Style one) HN732
Designer: L. Harradine
Height: 7¼in., 18.4cm.
Issued: 1925-1938
         Colour variation
Price: $480 £300

PIERETTE (Style one) HN784
Designer: L. Harradine
Height: 7¼in., 18.4cm.
Issued: 1926-1938
         Colour variation
Price: $480 £300

PIERETTE (Style two) HN795
Designer: L. Harradine
Height: 3½in., 8.9cm.
Issued: 1926-1938
Price: $480 £300

PIERETTE (Style two) HN796
Designer: L. Harradine
Height: 3½in., 8.9cm.
Issued: 1926-1938
Price: $480 £300

PIERETTE (Style three) HN1391
Designer: L. Harradine
Height: 8½in., 21.6cm.
Issued: 1930-1938
Price: $560 £350

PIERETTE (Style three) HN1749
Designer: L. Harradine
Height: 8½in., 21.6cm.
Issued: 1936-1949
         Colour variation
Price: $560 £350

PILLOW FIGHT HN2270
Designer: M. Davies
Height: 5in., 12.7cm.
Issued: 1965-1969
Price: $200 £125

PINKIE HN1552
Designer: L. Harradine
Height: 5in., 12.7cm.
Issued: 1933-1938
Price: $136 £85

PINKIE HN1553
Designer: L. Harradine
Height: 5in., 12.7cm.
Issued: 1933-1938
         Colour variation
Price: $136 £85

PIROUETTE HN2216

PIERETTE (Style three) HN1749

PIERETTE HN1391

POACHER HN2043

PIPER HN2907
Designer: M. Abberley
Height: 8in., 20.3cm.
Issued: 1980-
Rec. Retail Price

PIRATE KING HN2901
Designer: W. K. Harper
Height: 10in., 25.4cm.
Issued: 1981-1986
Price: $176 £110

PIROUETTE HN2216
Designer: M. Davies
Height: 5¾in., 14.6cm.
Issued: 1959-1967
Price: $144 £90

PLAYMATES HN3127
Designer: P. Parsons
Height: 8½in., 22cm.
Issued: 1988
Rec. Retail Price

PLEASE KEEP STILL HN2967
Designer: P. Parsons
Height: 4½in., 11.5cm.
Issued: 1982-1985
Price: $64 £40

POACHER HN2043
Designer: L. Harradine
Height: 6in., 15.2cm.
Issued: 1949-1959
Price: $224 £140

POCAHONTAS HN2930
(Ship's figurehead)
Designer: S. Keenan
Height: 8in., 20.3cm.
Issued: 1982 in a limited
          edition of 950
Price: $256 £160

POKE BONNET HN362
Designer: C, J. Noke
Height: 8¾in., 22.2cm.
Issued: 1919-1938
Price: $640 £400

POKE BONNET HN612
Designer: C. J. Noke
Height: 9½in., 24.1cm.
Issued: 1924-1938
         Colour variation
Price: $640 £400

POKE BONNET HN765
Designer: C. J. Noke
Height: 8¾in., 22.2cm.
Issued: 1925-1938
         Colour variation
Price: $640 £400
Also called 'Grandma's Days'
and Lilac Shawl

PIRATE KING HN2901

PIPER HN2907

POLISH DANCER HN2836
Designer: M. Davies
Height: 9½in., 24.1cm.
Issued: 1980 in a limited
edition of 750
Price: $520 £325

POLKA HN2156
Designer: M. Davies
Height: 7½in., 19.1cm.
Issued: 1955-1969
Price: $192 £120

POLLY HN3178
Designer: D. Tootle
Height: 8¼in., 21cm.
Issued: 1988
Rec. Retail Price

POLLY PEACHUM M23
Designer: L. Harradine
Height: 2¼in., 5.7cm.
Issued: 1932-1938
Colour variation
Price: $192 £120

POLLY PEACHUM (Style one)
HN463
Designer: L. Harradine
Height: 6¼in., 15.9cm.
Issued: 1921-1949
Price: $240 £150

POLLY PEACHUM (Style one)
HN465
Designer: L. Harradine
Height: 6½in., 16.5cm.
Issued: 1921-1949
Colour variation
Price: $240 £150

POLLY PEACHUM (Style one)
HN550
Designer: L. Harradine
Height: 6½in., 16.5cm.
Issued: 1922-1949
Colour variation
Price: $256 £160

POLLY PEACHUM (Style one)
HN589
Designer: L. Harradine
Height: 6½in., 16.5cm.
Issued: 1924-1949
Colour variation
Price: $240 £150

POLLY PEACHUM (Style one)
HN614
Designer: L. Harradine
Height: 6½in., 16.5cm.
Issued: 1924-1949
Colour variation
Price: $240 £150

POLLY PEACHUM (Style one)
HN680
Designer: L. Harradine
Height: 6½in., 16.5cm.
Issued: 1924-1949
Colour variation
Price: $240 £150

POLISH DANCER HN2836

POLLY PEACHUM (Style one)
HN693
Designer: L. Harradine
Height: 6½in., 16.5cm.
Issued: 1925-1949
Colour variation
Price: $240 £150

POLLY PEACHUM (Style two)
HN489
Designer: L. Harradine
Height: 4¼in., 10.8cm.
Issued: 1921-1938
Price: $256 £160

POLLY PEACHUM (Style two)
HN549
Designer: L. Harradine
Height: 4¼in., 10.8cm.
Issued: 1922-1949
Colour variation
Price: $256 £160

POLLY PEACHUM (Style two)
HN620
Designer: L. Harradine
Height: 4¼in., 10.8cm.
Issued: 1924-1938
Colour variation
Price: $240 £150

POLLY PEACHUM (Style two)
HN694
Designer: L. Harradine
Height: 4¼in., 10.8cm.
Issued: 1925-1949
Colour variation
Price: $240 £150

POLLY PEACHUM (Style two)
HN734
Designer: L. Harradine
Height: 4¼in., 10.8cm.
Issued: 1925-1949
Colour variation
Price: $240 £150

POLLY PEACHUM
(Style three) HN698
Designer: L. Harradine
Height: 2¼in., 5.7cm.
Issued: 1925-1949
Price: $240 £150

POLLY PEACHUM
(Style three) HN699
Designer: L. Harradine
Height: 2¼in., 5.7cm.
Issued: 1925-1949
Colour variation
Price: $240 £150

POLLY PEACHUM
(Style three) HN757
Designer: L. Harradine
Height: 2¼in., 5.7cm.
Issued: 1925-1949
Colour variation
Price: $160 £100

POLLY PEACHUM   HN550

POLLYANNA HN2965

237

POLLY PEACHUM
(Style three) HN758
Designer: L. Harradine
Height: 2¼in., 5.7cm.
Issued: 1925-1949
Colour variation
Price: $160 £100

POLLY PEACHUM
(Style three) HN759
Designer: L. Harradine
Height: 2¼in., 5.7cm.
Issued: 1925-1949
Colour variation
Price: $160 £100

POLLY PEACHUM
(Style three) HN760
Designer: L Harradine
Height: 2¼in., 5.7cm.
Issued: 1925-1949
Colour variation
Price: $160 £100

POLLY PEACHUM
(Style three) HN761
Designer: L. Harradine
Height: 2¼in., 5.7cm.
Issued: 1925-1949
Colour variation
Price: $160 £100

POLLY PEACHUM
(Style three) HN762
Designer: L. Harradine
Height: 2¼in., 5.7cm.
Issued: 1925-1949
Colour variation
Price: $160 £100

POLLY PEACHUM M21
Designer: L. Harradine
Height: 2¼in., 5.7cm.
Issued: 1932-1945
Price: $160 £100

POLLY PEACHUM M22
Designer: L. Harradine
Height: 2¼in., 5.7cm.
Issued: 1932-1938
Colour variation
Price: $192 £120

**POLLY PUT THE KETTLE
ON HN3021**
Designer: P. Parsons
Height: 8in., 20.0cm.
Issued: 1984-1987
Price: $64 £40

POLLYANNA HN2965
Designer: P. Parsons
Height: 6¾in., 17.0cm.
Issued: 1982-1985
Price: $61 £38

POPE JOHN PAUL II HN2888
Designer: E. Griffiths
Height: 10in., 25.4cm.
Issued: 1982
Rec. Retail Price

POTTER HN1493
Designer: C. J. Noke
Height: 7in., 17.8cm.
Issued: 1932-
Rec. Retail Price

POLLYANNA HN2965

POPE JOHN PAUL II HN2888

POLLY PEACHUM HN549

FIGURES

POTTER HN1518
Designer: C. J. Noke
Height: 6¾in., 17.2cm.
Issued: 1932-1949
　　　　Colour variation
Price: $240 £150

POTTER HN1522
Designer: C. J. Noke
Height: 6¾in., 17.2cm.
Issued: 1932-1949
　　　　Colour variation
Price: $240 £150

PREMIERE HN2343
Designer: M. Davies
Height: 7½in., 19.1cm.
Issued: 1969-1978
Price: $109 £68

PRETTY LADY HN69
Designer: H. Tittensor
Height: 9½in., 24.1cm.
Issued: 1916-1938
Price: $720 £450

PRETTY LADY HN70
Designer: H. Tittensor
Height: 9½in., 24.1cm.
Issued: 1916-1938
　　　　Colour variation
Price: $720 £450

PRETTY LADY HN302
Designer: H. Tittensor
Height: 9½in., 24.1cm.
Issued: 1918-1938
　　　　Colour variation
Price: $720 £450

PRETTY LADY HN330
Designer: H. Tittensor
Height: 9½in., 24.1cm.
Issued: 1918-1938
　　　　Colour variation
Price: $720 £450

PRETTY LADY HN361
Designer: H. Tittensor
Height: 9½in., 24.1cm.
Issued: 1919-1938
　　　　Colour variation
Price: $720 £450

PRETTY LADY HN384
Designer: H. Tittensor
Height: 9½in., 24.1cm.
Issued: 1920-1938
　　　　Colour variation
Price: $720 £450

PRETTY LADY HN565
Designer: H. Tittensor
Height: 10in., 25.4cm.
Issued: 1923-1938
　　　　Colour variation
Price: $720 £450

PRETTY LADY HN700
Designer: H. Tittensor
Height: 9½in., 24.1cm.
Issued: 1925-1938
　　　　Colour variation
Price: $720 £450

PREMIERE HN2343

POTTER HN1493

239

PRETTY LADY HN763
Designer: H. Tittensor
Height: 9½in., 24.1cm.
Issued: 1925-1938
Colour variation
Price: $720 £450

PRETTY LADY HN783
Designer: H. Tittensor
Height: 9½in., 24.1cm.
Issued: 1926-1938
Colour variation
Price: $720 £450

PRETTY POLLY HN2768
Designer: W. K. Harper
Height: 6in., 15.0cm.
Issued: 1984-1988
Price: $109 £68

PRIDE AND JOY HN2945
Designer: R. Tabbenor
Height: 7in., 17.8cm.
Issued: 1984
Price: $256 £160

PRIMROSES HN1617
Designer: L. Harradine
Height: 6½in., 16.5cm.
Issued: 1934-1949
Price: $320 £200

PRINCE OF WALES HN1217
Designer: L. Harradine
Height: 7½in., 19.1cm.
Issued: 1926-1938
Price: $1280 £800

PRINCE OF WALES HN2883
Designer: E. Griffiths
Height: 8in., 20.3cm.
Issued: 1981 in a limited
edition of 1500
Price: $800 £500

PRINCE OF WALES HN2884
Designer: E. Griffiths
Height: 8in., 20.3cm.
Issued: 1981 in a limited
edition of 1500
Price: $720 £450

PRINCESS HN391
Designer: Unknown
Height: 9¼in., 23.5cm.
Issued: 1920-1938
Price: $2000 £1250

PRINCESS HN392
Designer: Unknown
Height: 9¼in., 23.5cm.
Issued: 1920-1938
Colour variation
Price: $2000 £1250

PRINCESS HN420
Designer: Unknown
Height: 9¼in., 23.5cm.
Issued: 1920-1938
Colour variation
Price: $2000 £1250

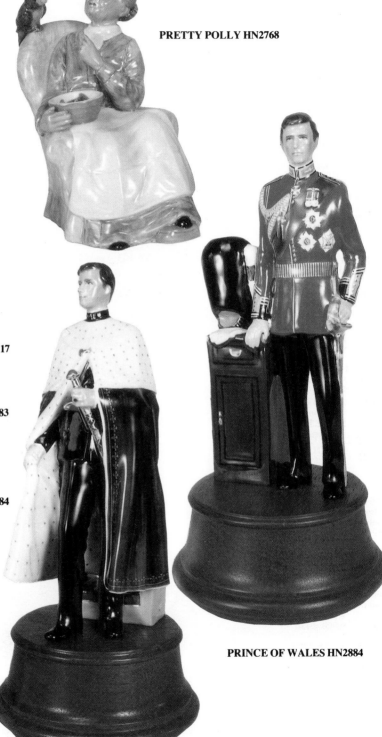

PRETTY POLLY HN2768

PRINCE OF WALES HN2884

PRINCE OF WALES HN2883

FIGURES

PRINCESS HN430
Designer: Unknown
Height: 9¼in., 23.5cm.
Issued: 1921-1938
Colour variation
Price: $2000 £1250

PRINCESS HN431
Designer: Unknown
Height: 9¼in., 23.5cm.
Issued: 1921-1938
Colour variation
Price: $2000 £1250

PRINCESS HN633
Designer: Unknown
Height: 9¼in., 23.5cm.
Issued: 1924-1938
Colour variation
Price: $2000 £1250

PRINCESS BADOURA HN2081
Designer: H. Tittensor, H. E. Stanton and F. Van Allen Phillips
Height: 20in., 50.8cm.
Issued: 1952-
Rec. Retail Price

PRINCESS OF WALES HN2887
Designer: E. Griffiths
Height: 7¾in., 19.6cm.
Issued: 1982 in a limited edition of 1500
Price: $432 £270

PRINTEMPS HN3066
Designer: R. Jefferson
Height: 11½in., 29cm.
Issued: 1987 in a limited edition of 300
Price: $800 £500

PRISCILLA HN1337
Designer: L. Harradine
Height: 8in., 20.3cm.
Issued: 1929-1938
Price: $288 £180

PRISCILLA HN1340
Designer: L. Harradine
Height: 8in., 20.3cm.
Issued: 1929-1949
Colour variation
Price: $216 £135

PRISCILLA HN1495
Designer: L. Harradine
Height: 8in., 20.3cm.
Issued: 1932-1949
Colour variation
Price: $232 £145

PRISCILLA HN1501
Designer: L. Harradine
Height: 8in., 20.3cm.
Issued: 1932-1938
Colour variation
Price: $288 £180

PRISCILLA HN1559
Designer: L. Harradine
Height: 8in., 20.3cm.
Issued: 1933-1949
Colour variation
Price: $216 £135

PRISCILLA HN1340

PRINCESS OF WALES HN2887

PRISCILLA M13
Designer: L. Harradine
Height: 4in., 10.1cm.
Issued: 1932-1938
Price: $160 £100

PRISCILLA M14
Designer: L. Harradine
Height: 3¾in., 9.5cm.
Issued: 1932-1945
Colour variation
Price: $160 £100

PRISCILLA M24
Designer: L. Harradine
Height: 3¾in., 9.5cm.
Issued: 1932-1945
Colour variation
Price: $160 £100

PRIVATE, CONNECTICUT REGIMENT 1777 HN2845
Designer: E. J. Griffiths
Height: 11¼in., 28.5cm.
Issued: 1978 in a limited
edition of 350
Price: $608 £380

PRIVATE, DELAWARE REGIMENT 1776 HN2761
Designer: E. J. Griffiths
Height: 12in., 30.5cm.
Issued: 1977 in a limited
edition of 350
Price: $608 £380

PRIVATE, 1ST GEORGIA REGIMENT 1777 HN2779
Designer: E. J. Griffiths
Height: 11in., 27.9cm.
Issued: 1975 in a limited
edition of 350
Price: $608 £380

PRIVATE, MASSACHUSETTS REGIMENT 1778 HN2760
Designer: E. J. Griffiths
Height: 12½in., 31.7cm.
Issued: 1977 in a limited
edition of 350
Price: $608 £380

PRIVATE, PENNSYLVANIA RIFLE BATTALION 1776 HN2846
Designer: E. J. Griffiths
Height: 11¼in., 28.5cm.
Issued: 1978 in a limited
edition of 350
Price: $608 £380

PRIVATE, RHODE ISLAND REGIMENT 1781 HN2759
Designer: E. J. Griffiths
Height: 11¾in., 29.8cm.
Issued: 1977 in a limited
edition of 350
Price: $608 £380

PRIZED POSSESSIONS HN2942

PROFESSOR HN2281

242

FIGURES

**PRIVATE, 2ND SOUTH
CAROLINA REGIMENT
1781 HN2717**
Designer: E. J. Griffiths
Height: 11½in., 29.2cm.
Issued: 1975 in a limited
         edition of 350
Price: $608 £380

**PRIVATE, 3RD NORTH
CAROLINA REGIMENT 1778
HN2754**
Designer: E. J. Griffiths
Height: 11in., 27.9cm.
Issued: 1976 in a limited
         edition of 350
Price: $560 £350

**PRIZED POSSESSIONS
HN2942**
Designer: R. Tabbenor
Height: 7in., 17.8cm.
Issued: 1982
Price: $256 £160

PROFESSOR HN2281
Designer: M. Nicoll
Height: 7¼in., 18.4cm.
Issued: 1965-1980
Price: $136 £85

PROMENADE HN2076
Designer: M. Davies
Height: 8in., 20.3cm.
Issued: 1951-1953
Price: $1280 £800

PROMENADE HN3072
Designer: A. Hughes
Height: 13in., 33cm.
Issued: 1987
Rec. Retail Price

PROPOSAL (Man) HN725
Designer: Unknown
Height: 5½in., 14.0cm.
Issued: 1925-1938
Price: $720 £450

PROPOSAL (Man) HN1209
Designer: Unknown
Height: 5½in., 14.0cm.
Issued: 1926-1938
         Colour variation
Price: $720 £450

PROPOSAL (Woman) HN715
Designer: Unknown
Height: 5¾in., 14.6cm.
Issued: 1925-1938
Price: $720 £450

PROPOSAL (Woman) HN716
Designer: Unknown
Height: 5¾in., 14.6cm.
Issued: 1925-1938
         Colour variation
Price: $720 £450

PROPOSAL (Woman) HN788
Designer: Unknown
Height: 5¾in., 14.6cm.
Issued: 1926-1938
         Colour variation
Price: $720 £450

PROMENADE HN2076

PROPOSAL (Woman) HN716

243

PRUDENCE HN1883
Designer: L. Harradine
Height: 6¾in., 17.2cm.
Issued: 1938-1949
Price: $320 £200

PRUDENCE HN1884
Designer: L. Harradine
Height: 6¾in., 17.2cm.
Issued: 1938-1949
       Colour variation
Price: $320 £200

PRUE HN1996
Designer: L. Harradine
Height: 6¾in., 17.2cm.
Issued: 1947-1955
Price: $192 £120

PUFF AND POWDER HN397
Designer: L. Harradine
Height: 6½in., 16.4cm.
Issued: 1920-1938
Price: $1440 £900

PUFF AND POWDER HN398
Designer: L. Harradine
Height: 6½in., 16.4cm.
Issued: 1920-1938
       Colour variation
Price: $1440 £900

PUFF AND POWDER HN400
Designer: L. Harradine
Height: 6½in., 16.4cm.
Issued: 1920-1938
       Colour variation
Price: $1440 £900

PUFF AND POWDER HN432
Designer: L. Harradine
Height: 6½in., 16.4cm.
Issued: 1921-1938
       Colour variation
Price: $1440 £900

PUFF AND POWDER HN433
Designer: L. Harradine
Height: 6½in., 16.4cm.
Issued: 1921-1938
       Colour variation
Price: $1440 £900

PUNCH AND JUDY MAN
HN2765
Designer: W. K. Harper
Height: 9in., 22.9cm.
Issued: 1981-
Rec. Retail Price

PUPPETMAKER HN2253
Designer: M. Nicoll
Height: 8in., 20.3cm.
Issued: 1962-1973
Price: $296 £185

PUSSY HN18
Designer: F. C. Stone
Height: 7¾in., 19.7cm.
Issued: 1913-1938
Price: $1600 £1000

PUNCH AND JUDY MAN
HN2765

PRUDENCE HN1883

QUEEN MOTHER AS THE
DUCHESS OF YORK HN3230

FIGURES

PUSSY HN325
Designer: F. C. Stone
Height: 7½in., 19.1cm.
Issued: 1918-1938
           Colour variation
Price: $1600 £1000

PUSSY HN507
Designer: F. C. Stone
Height: 7½in., 19.0cm.
Issued: 1921-1938
           Colour variation
Price: $1600 £1000

PYJAMAS HN1942
Designer: L. Harradine
Height: 5¼in., 13.3cm.
Issued: 1940-1949
Price: $160 £100

Q

QUALITY STREET HN1211
Designer: Unknown
Height: 7¼in., 18.4cm.
Issued: 1926-1938
Price: $640 £400

QUALITY STREET HN1211A
Designer: Unknown
Height: 7¼in., 18.4cm.
Issued: 1926-1938
           Colour variation
Price: $640 £400

QUEEN ANNE HN3141
Designer: P. Parsons
Height: 9½in., 24cm.
Issued: 1989 in a limited
           edition of 5000
Price: $240 £150

QUEEN ELIZABETH I HN3099
Designer: P. Parsons
Height: 9in., 22.5cm.
Issued: 1987 in a limited
           edition of 5000
Price: $240 £150

**QUEEN ELIZABETH II
HN2502**
Designer: M. Davies
Height: 7¾in., 19.7cm.
Issued: 1973 in a limited
           edition of 750
Price: $1200 £750

QUEEN MOTHER HN2882
Designer: E. Griffiths
Height: 8in., 20.3cm.
Issued: 1980 in a limited
           edition of 1500
Price: $560 £350

**QUEEN MOTHER AS THE
DUCHESS OF YORK HN3230**
Designer: P. Parsons
Height: 9in., 22.5cm.
Issued: 1989 in a limited
           edition of 9500
Price: $360 £225

QUEEN MOTHER HN2882

QUEEN ELIZABETH II
HN2502

QUEEN ANNE HN3141

QUEEN OF SHEBA HN2328
Designer: P. Davies
Height: 9in., 22.8cm.
Issued: 1982 in a limited
edition of 750
Price: $1360 £850

**QUEEN OF THE DAWN
HN2437**
Designer: P. Davies
Height: 8½in., 21.5cm.
Issued: 1983-1986
Price: $72 £45

QUEEN OF THE ICE HN2435
Designer: P. Davies
Height: 8in., 20.0cm.
Issued: 1983-1986
Price: $72 £45

QUEEN VICTORIA HN3125
Designer: P. Parsons
Height: 8in., 20cm.
Issued: 1988 in a limited
edition of 5000
Price: $240 £150

R

RACHEL HN2919
Designer: P. Gee
Height: 7½in., 19.1cm.
Issued: 1980-1984
Price: $120 £75

RACHEL HN2936
Designer: P. Gee
Height: 7¾in., 19.5cm.
Issued: 1985-
Colour variation
Rec. Retail Price

RAG DOLL HN2142
Designer: M. Davies
Height: 4¾in., 12.0cm.
Issued: 1954-1986
Price: $61 £38

RAG DOLL SELLER HN2944
Designer: R. Tabbenor
Height: 7in., 17.5cm.
Issued: 1984-
Rec. Retail Price

REBECCA HN2805
Designer: M. Davies
Height: 7¼in., 18.4cm.
Issued: 1980-
Rec. Retail Price

REFLECTION HN3039
Designer: A. Hughes
Height: 8in., 22cm.
Issued: 1988-1989
Price: $72 £45

REFLECTIONS HN1820
Designer: L. Harradine
Height: 5in., 12.7cm.
Issued: 1937-1938
Price: $560 £350

QUEEN OF THE ICE HN2435

RACHEL HN2919

QUEEN VICTORIA HN3125

FIGURES

REFLECTIONS HN1821
Designer: L. Harradine
Height: 5in., 12.7cm.
Issued: 1937-1938
Colour variation
Price: $560 £350

REFLECTIONS HN1847
Designer: L. Harradine
Height: 4½in., 11.4cm.
Issued: 1938-1949
Colour variation
Price: $560 £350

REFLECTIONS HN1848
Designer: L. Harradine
Height: 5in., 12.7cm.
Issued: 1938-1949
Colour variation
Price: $560 £350

REGAL LADY HN2709
Designer: M. Davies
Height: 7½in., 19.1cm.
Issued: 1975-1984
Price: $120 £75

REGENCY HN1752
Designer: L. Harradine
Height: 8in., 20.3cm.
Issued: 1936-1949
Price: $320 £200

REGENCY BEAU HN1972
Designer: H. Fenton
Height: 8in., 20.3cm.
Issued: 1941-1949
Price: $720 £450

RENDEZVOUS HN2212
Designer: M. Davies
Height: 7¼in., 18.4cm.
Issued: 1962-1971
Price: $192 £120

REPOSE HN2272
Designer: M. Davies
Height: 5¼in., 13.3cm.
Issued: 1972-1978
Price: $136 £85

REST AWHILE HN2728
Designer: W. K. Harper
Height: 8in., 20.3cm.
Issued: 1981-1984
Price: $109 £68

RETURN OF PERSEPHONE HN31
Designer: C. Vyse
Height: 16in., 40.6cm.
Issued: 1913-1938
Price: $2400 £1500

REVERIE HN2306
Designer: M. Davies
Height: 6½in., 16.5cm.
Issued: 1964-1982
Price: $128 £80

RHAPSODY HN2267
Designer: M. Davies
Height: 6¾in., 17.2cm.
Issued: 1961-1973
Price: $152 £95

REVERIE HN2306

REST AWHILE HN2728

QUEEN OF SHEBA HN2328

247

RHODA HN1573
Designer: L. Harradine
Height: 10¼in., 26.7cm.
Issued: 1933-1949
Price: $280 £175

RHODA HN1574
Designer: L. Harradine
Height: 10¼in., 26.7cm.
Issued: 1933-1938
          Colour variation
Price: $280 £175

RHODA HN1688
Designer: L. Harradine
Height: 10¼in., 26.7cm.
Issued: 1935-1949
          Colour variation
Price: $280 £175

RHYTHM HN1903
Designer: L. Harradine
Height: 6¾in., 17.2cm.
Issued: 1939-1949
Price: $480 £300

RHYTHM HN1904
Designer: L. Harradine
Height: 6¾in., 17.2cm.
Issued: 1939-1949
          Colour variation
Price: $480 £300

RITA HN1448
Designer: L. Harradine
Height: 7in., 17.8cm.
Issued: 1931-1938
Price: $480 £300

RITA HN1450
Designer: L. Harradine
Height: 7in., 17.8cm.
Issued: 1931-1938
          Colour variation
Price: $480 £300

RIVER BOY HN2128
Designer: M. Davies
Height: 4in., 10.1cm.
Issued: 1962-1975
Price: $104 £65

RITZ BELL BOY HN2772
Designer: W. Harper
Height: 8in., 20cm.
Issued: 1989
Rec. Retail Price

ROBERT BURNS HN42
Designer: E. W. Light
Height: 18in., 45.7cm.
Issued: 1914-1938
Price: $2400 £1500

ROBIN M38
Designer: Unknown
Height: 2½in., 6.4cm.
Issued: 1933-1945
Price: $224 £140

RHYTHM HN1904

RHYTHM HN1903

ROBIN M39
Designer: Unknown
Height: 2½in., 6.4cm.
Issued: 1933-1945
Colour variation
Price: $224 £140

ROBIN HOOD HN2773
Designer: W. K. Harper
Height: 8in., 20.0cm.
Issued: 1985-
Rec. Retail Price

ROCKING HORSE HN2072
Designer: L. Harradine
Height: 7in., 17.8cm.
Issued: 1951-1953
Price: $1280 £800

ROMANCE HN2430
Designer: M. Davies
Height: 5¼in., 13.3cm.
Issued: 1972-1980
Price: $109 £68

ROMANY SUE HN1757
Designer: L. Harradine
Height: 9¼in., 23.5cm.
Issued: 1936-1949
Price: $608 £380

ROMANY SUE HN1758
Designer: L. Harradine
Height: 9½in., 24.1cm.
Issued: 1936-1949
Colour variation
Price: $608 £380

ROSABELL HN1620
Designer: L. Harradine
Height: 6¾in., 17.1cm.
Issued: 1934-1938
Price: $480 £300

ROSALIND HN2393
Designer: M. Davies
Height: 5½in., 14.0cm.
Issued: 1970-1975
Price: $112 £70

ROSAMUND (Style one)
HN1320
Designer: L. Harradine
Height: 7¼in., 18.4cm.
Issued: 1929-1938
Price: $1280 £800

ROSAMUND (Style two)
HN1497
Designer: L. Harradine
Height: 8½in., 21.6cm.
Issued: 1932-1938
Price: $640 £400

ROSAMUND (Style two)
HN1551
Designer: L. Harradine
Height: 8½in., 21.6cm.
Issued: 1933-1938
Colour variation
Price: $464 £290

ROMANY SUE HN1758

ROMANCE HN2430

249

ROSAMUND M32
Designer: L. Harradine
Height: 4¼in., 10.8cm.
Issued: 1932-1945
Price: $208 £130

ROSAMUND M33
Designer: L. Harradine
Height: 4in., 10.1cm.
Issued: 1932-1945
        Colour variation
Price: $208 £130

ROSE HN1368
Designer: L. Harradine
Height: 4½in., 11.4cm.
Issued: 1930-
Rec. Retail Price

ROSE HN1387
Designer: L. Harradine
Height: 4½in., 11.4cm.
Issued: 1930-1938
        Colour variation
Price: $120 £75

ROSE HN1416
Designer: L. Harradine
Height: 4½in., 11.4cm.
Issued: 1930-1949
        Colour variation
Price: $96 £60

ROSE HN1506
Designer: L. Harradine
Height: 4½in., 11.4cm.
Issued: 1932-1938
        Colour variation
Price: $120 £75

ROSE HN1654
Designer: L. Harradine
Height: 4½in., 11.4cm.
Issued: 1934-1938
        Colour variation
Price: $120 £75

ROSE HN2123
Designer: L. Harradine
Height: 4½in., 11.4cm.
Issued: 1983-
Rec. Retail Price

ROSE ARBOUR HN3145
Designer: D. Brindley
Height: 12in., 30.5cm.
Issued: 1987
Rec. Retail Price

ROSEANNA HN1921
Designer: L. Harradine
Height: 8in., 20.3cm.
Issued: 1940-1949
Price: $288 £180

ROSEANNA HN1926
Designer: L. Harradine
Height: 8in., 20.3cm.
Issued: 1940-1959
        Colour variation
Price: $216 £135

ROSEBUD (Style one) HN1580
Designer: L. Harradine
Height: 3in., 7.6cm.
Issued: 1933-1938
Price: $352 £220

ROSEANNA HN1926

ROSEBUD (Style one) HN1581
Designer: L. Harradine
Height: 3in., 7.6cm.
Issued: 1933-1938
Colour variation
Price: $352 £220

ROSEBUD (Style two) HN1983
Designer: L. Harradine
Height: 7½in., 19.1cm.
Issued: 1945-1952
Price: $224 £140

ROSEMARY HN2091
Designer: L. Harradine
Height: 7in., 17.8cm.
Issued: 1952-1959
Price: $224 £140

ROSEMARY HN3143
Designer: P. Parsons
Height: 7¹/₂in., 19cm.
Issued: 1988
Rec. Retail Price

ROSINA HN1358
Designer: L. Harradine
Height: 5¾in., 14.6cm.
Issued: 1929-1938
Price: $330 £220

ROSINA HN1364
Designer: L. Harradine
Height: 5¼in., 13.3cm.
Issued: 1929-1938
Colour variation
Price: $330 £220

ROSINA HN1556
Designer: L. Harradine
Height: 5¾in., 14.6cm.
Issued: 1933-1938
Colour variation
Price: $330 £220

ROWENA HN2077
Designer: L. Harradine
Height: 7¼in., 18.4cm.
Issued: 1951-1955
Price: $272 £170

ROYAL CANADIAN MOUNTED POLICE 1873 (BUST.) HN2555
Designer: D. Tootle
Height: 8¼in., 21.0cm.
Issued: 1973 in a limited edition of 1500
Price: $320 £200

ROYAL CANADIAN MOUNTED POLICE 1973 HN2547
Designer: D. Tootle
Height: 8in., 20.3cm.
Issued: 1973 in a limited edition of 1500
Price: $320 £200

ROYAL GOVERNOR'S COOK HN2233
Designer: M. Davies
Height: 6in., 15.2cm.
Issued: 1960-1984
Price: $144 £90

ROSE HN1368

ROYAL GOVERNOR'S COOK HN2233

RUBY HN1724
Designer: L. Harradine
Height: 5¼in., 13.3cm.
Issued: 1935-1949
Price: $152 £95

RUBY HN1725
Designer: L. Harradine
Height: 5¼in., 13.3cm.
Issued: 1935-1949
Colour variation
Price: $152 £95

RUMPELSTILTSKIN HN3025
Designer: R. Jefferson
Height: 8in., 20.0cm.
Issued: 1983-1986
Price: $72 £45

RUSTIC SWAIN HN1745
Designer: L. Harradine
Height: 5¼in., 13.3cm.
Issued: 1935-1949
Price: $1200 £750

RUSTIC SWAIN HN1746
Designer: L. Harradine
Height: 5¼in., 13.3cm.
Issued: 1935-1949
Colour variation
Price: $1200 £750

RUTH HN2799
Designer: M. Davies
Height: 6in., 15.2cm.
Issued: 1976-1982
Price: $61 £38

RUTH THE PIRATE MAID
HN2900
Designer: W. K. Harper
Height: 11¾in., 29.8cm.
Issued: 1981-1986
Price: $192 £120

RUMPELSTILTSKIN HN3025

RUTH THE PIRATE MAID HN2900

S

SABBATH MORN HN1982
Designer: L. Harradine
Height: 7¼in., 18.4cm.
Issued: 1945-1959
Price: $280 £175

SAILOR'S HOLIDAY HN2442
Designer: M. Nicoll
Height: 6¼in., 15.9cm.
Issued: 1972-1978
Price: $120 £75

SAIREY GAMP M46
Designer: L. Harradine
Height: 4in., 10.1cm.
Issued: 1932-1982
Price: $48 £30

SAIREY GAMP (Style one)
HN533
Designer: L. Harradine
Height: 4in., 10.1cm.
Issued: 1922-1932
Price: $48 £30

RUSTIC SWAIN HN1745

FIGURES

SAIREY GAMP (Style two) HN558
Designer: L. Harradine
Height: 7in., 17.8cm.
Issued: 1923-1939
Price: $288 £180

SAIREY GAMP (Style two) HN1896
Designer: L. Harradine
Height: 7in., 17.8cm.
Issued: 1938-1952
Colour variation
Price: $208 £130

SAIREY GAMP (Style three) HN2100
Designer: L. Harradine
Height: 7¼in., 18.4cm.
Issued: 1952-1967
Price: $176 £110

SALOME HN1775
Designer: R. Garbe
Height: 8in., 24.4cm.
Issued: 1933 in a limited edition of 100
Price: $2400 £1500

SALOME HN1828
Designer: R. Garbe
Height: 8in., 24.4cm.
Issued: 1937-1949
Colour variation
Price: $2400 £1500

SALOME HN3267
Designer: P. Davies
Height: 9½in., 24.1cm.
Issued: 1990 in a limited edition of 1000
Rec. Retail Price

SALLY HN2741
Designer: P. Tootle
Height: 5½in., 13.5cm.
Issued: 1988
Rec. Retail Price

SAM WELLER HN531
Designer: L. Harradine
Height: 4in., 10.1cm.
Issued: 1922-1932
Price: $48 £30

SAM WELLER M48
Designer: L. Harradine
Height: 4in., 10.1cm.
Issued: 1932-1982
Price: $48 £30

SAMANTHA HN2954
Designer: P. Parsons
Height: 7in., 17.5cm.
Issued: 1982-1984
Price: $96 £60

SAMWISE HN2925
Designer: D. Lyttleton
Height: 4½in., 11.5cm.
Issued: 1982-1984
Price: $56 £35

SANDRA HN2275
Designer: M. Davies
Height: 7¾in., 19.7cm.
Issued: 1969-
Rec. Retail Price

SANDRA HN2401
Designer: P. Davies
Height: 8in., 20.0cm.
Issued: 1983-
Rec. Retail Price

SANDRA HN2275

SAIREY GAMP HN558

SAMWISE HN2925

SAILOR'S HOLIDAY HN2442

253

SANTA CLAUS HN2725
Designer: W. K. Harper
Height: 9½in., 24.0cm.
Issued: 1982-
Rec. Retail Price

SARA HN2265
Designer: M. Davies
Height: 7½in., 19.1cm.
Issued: 1981-
Rec. Retail Price

SARA HN3219
Designer: P. Davies
Height: 3¹/₄in., 9.5cm.
Issued: 1988
Rec. Retail Price

SAUCY NYMPH HN1539
Designer: Unknown
Height: 4½in., 11.4cm.
Issued: 1933-1949
Price: $200 £125

SAVE SOME FOR ME HN2959
Designer: P. Parsons
Height: 7¼in., 18.0cm.
Issued: 1982-1985
Price: $72 £45

SCHOOLMARM HN2223
Designer: M. Davies
Height: 6¾in., 17.2cm.
Issued: 1958-1980
Price: $120 £75

SCOTCH GIRL HN1269
Designer: L. Harradine
Height: 7½in., 19.1cm.
Issued: 1928-1938
Price: $1248 £780

SCOTTIES HN1281
Designer: L. Harradine
Height: 5½in., 14.0cm.
Issued: 1928-1938
Price: $800 £500

SCOTTIES HN1349
Designer: L. Harradine
Height: 5¼in., 13.3cm.
Issued: 1929-1949
          Colour variation
Price: $640 £400

**SCOTTISH HIGHLAND
DANCER HN2436**
Designer: M. Davies
Height: 9½in., 24.1cm.
Issued: 1978 in a limited
           edition of 750
Price: $520 £325

SCRIBE HN305
Designer: C. J. Noke
Height: 6in., 15.2cm.
Issued: 1918-1936
Price: $800 £500

SCRIBE HN324
Designer: C. J. Noke
Height: 6in., 15.2cm.
Issued: 1918-1938
           Colour variation
Price: $800 £500

SAUCY NYMPH HN1539   **SANTA CLAUS HN2725**

SEAFARER HN2455   **SAVE SOME FOR ME HN2959**

SCRIBE HN1235
Designer: C. J. Noke
Height: 6in., 15.2cm.
Issued: 1927-1938
          Colour variation
Price: $800 £500

SCROOGE M87
Designer: L. Harradine
Height: 4in., 10.1cm.
Issued: 1949-1982
Price: $48 £30

SEA HARVEST HN2257
Designer: M. Nicoll
Height: 7½in., 19.1cm.
Issued: 1969-1976
Price: $120 £75

SEA SHORE HN2263
Designer: M. Davies
Height: 3½in., 8.9cm.
Issued: 1961-1965
Price: $160 £100

**SEA SPRITE (Style one)
HN1261**
Designer: L. Harradine
Height: 5in., 12.7cm.
Issued: 1927-1938
Price: $264 £165

**SEA SPRITE (Style two)
HN2191**
Designer: M. Davies
Height: 7in., 17.8cm.
Issued: 1958-1962
Price: $256 £160

SEAFARER HN2455
Designer: M. Nicoll
Height: 8½in., 21.6cm.
Issued: 1972-1976
Price: $136 £85

SECRET MOMENT HN3106
Designer: R. Jefferson
Height: 12¼in., 31cm.
Issued: 1987-1989
Price: $72 £45

SECRET THOUGHTS HN2382
Designer: M. Davies
Height: 6¼in., 15.9cm.
Issued: 1971-1988
Price: $112 £70

**SENTIMENTAL PIERROT
HN36**
Designer: C. J. Noke
Height: 5½in., 14.0cm.
Issued: 1914-1938
Price: $1280 £800

**SENTIMENTAL PIERROT
HN307**
Designer: C. J. Noke
Height: 5½in., 14.0cm.
Issued: 1918-1938
Price: $1280 £800

SENTINEL HN523
Designer: Unknown
Height: 17½in., 44.4cm.
Issued: 1921-1938
Price: $2880 £1800

SCHOOLMARM HN2223

SCOTTISH HIGHLAND
DANCER HN2436

SECRET THOUGHTS HN2382

SEPTEMBER HN3166
Designer: P. Davies
Height: 7¾in., 19.7cm.
Issued: 1987
Rec. Retail Price

SERENA HN1868
Designer: L. Harradine
Height: 11in., 27.9cm.
Issued: 1938-1949
Price: $440 £275

SERENADE HN2753
Designer: E. Griffiths
Height: 9in., 23.0cm.
Issued: 1983-1986
Price: $64 £40

**SERGEANT, 6TH
MARYLAND REGIMENT
1777 HN2815**
Designer: E. J. Griffiths
Height: 13¾in., 34.9cm.
Issued: 1976 in a limited
edition of 350
Price: $608 £380

**SERGEANT, VIRGINIA 1ST
REGIMENT CONTINENTAL
LIGHT DRAGOONS, 1777
HN2844**
Designer: E. J. Griffiths
Height: 14¼in., 36.1cm.
Issued: 1978 in a limited
edition of 350
Price: $608 £380

SHARON HN3047
Designer: P. Parsons
Height: 5½in., 14.0cm.
Issued: 1984-
Rec. Retail Price

SHE LOVES ME NOT HN2045
Designer: L. Harradine
Height: 5½in., 14.0cm.
Issued: 1949-1962
Price: $112 £70

SHEIKH HN3083
Designer: E.J. Griffiths
Height: 9³/₄in., 25cm.
Issued: 1988-1989
Price: $88 £55

SHEILA HN2742
Designer: D. Tootle
Height: 8¼in., 21.0cm.
Issued: 1984-
Rec. Retail Price

SHEPHERD (Style one) HN81
Designer: C. J. Noke
Height: 13¼in., 33.6cm.
Issued: 1918-1938
Price: $1760 £1100

SHEPHERD (Style one) HN617
Designer: C. J. Noke
Height: 13¼in., 33.6cm.
Issued: 1924-1938
Colour variation
Price: $1760 £1100

SHEPHERD (Style one) HN632
Designer: C. J. Noke
Height: 13¼in., 33.6cm.
Issued: 1924-1938
Colour variation
Price: $1760 £1100

SHEILA HN2742

FIGURES

SHEPHERD (Style two) HN709
Designer: Unknown
Height: 3½in., 8.8cm.
Issued: 1925-1938
Price: $480 £300

SHEPHERD (Style three) HN751
Designer: Unknown
Height: 7½in., 19.1cm.
Issued: 1925-1938
Price: $480 £300

SHEPHERD (Style four) HN1975
Designer: H. Fenton
Height: 8½in., 21.6cm.
Issued: 1945-1975
Price: $112 £75

SHEPHERD HN3160
Designer: A. Hughes
Height: 8¹/₂in., 22cm.
Issued: 1988-1989
Price: $96 £60

SHEPHERD M17
Designer: Unknown
Height: 3¾in., 9.5cm.
Issued: 1932-1938
Price: $480 £300

SHEPHERD M19
Designer: Unknown
Height: 3¾in., 9.5cm.
Issued: 1932-1938
Colour variation
Price: $480 £300

SHEPHERDESS (Style one) HN708
Designer: Unknown
Height: 3½in., 8.8cm.
Issued: 1925-1948
Price: $480 £300

SHEPHERDESS (Style two) HN735
Designer: Unknown
Height: 7in., 17.8cm.
Issued: 1925-1938
Price: $720 £450

SHEPHERDESS (Style two) HN750
Designer: Unknown
Height: 7in., 17.8cm.
Issued: 1925-1938
Colour variation
Price: $720 £450

SHEPHERDESS HN2990
Designer: R. Tabbenor
Height: 8in., 20.3cm.
Issued: 1988-1989
Price: $96 £60

SHEPHERDESS M18
Designer: Unknown
Height: 3½in., 8.9cm.
Issued: 1932-1938
Price: $480 £300

SHEPHERD HN1975

SERENADE HN2753

SHEPHERDESS M20
Designer: Unknown
Height: 3¾in., 9.5cm.
Issued: 1932-1938
Colour variation
Price: $480 £300

SHIRLEY HN2702
Designer: P. Davies
Height: 7¼in., 18.0cm.
Issued: 1985-
Rec. Retail Price

SHORE LEAVE HN2254
Designer: M. Nicholl
Height: 7½in., 19.1cm.
Issued: 1965-1978
Price: $136 £85

SHY ANNE HN60
Designer: L. Perugini
Height: 7¾in., 19.7cm.
Issued: 1916-1938
Price: $1280 £800

SHY ANNE HN64
Designer: L. Perugini
Height: 7¾in., 19.7cm.
Issued: 1916-1938
Colour variation
Price: $1280 £800

SILVERSMITH OF
WILLIAMSBURG HN2208

SILKS AND RIBBONS HN2017

SHY ANNE HN65
Designer: L. Perugini
Height: 7¾in., 19.7cm.
Issued: 1916-1938
Colour variation
Price: $1280 £800

SHY ANNE HN568
Designer: L. Perugini
Height: 7½in., 19.1cm.
Issued: 1923-1938
Colour variation
Price: $1280 £800

SHYLOCK HN79
Designer: C. J. Noke
Height: Unknown
Issued: 1917-1938
Price: $1440 £900

SHYLOCK HN317
Designer: C. J. Noke
Height: Unknown
Issued: 1918-1938
Colour variation
Price: $1440 £900

SIBELL HN1668
Designer: L. Harradine
Height: 6½in., 16.5cm.
Issued: 1934-1949
Price: $440 £275

SIBELL HN1695
Designer: L. Harradine
Height: 6½in., 16.5cm.
Issued: 1935-1949
Colour variation
Price: $440 £275

SIMONE HN2378

SHORE LEAVE HN2254

FIGURES

SIBELL HN1735
Designer: L. Harradine
Height: 6½in., 16.5cm.
Issued: 1935-1949
Colour variation
Price: $440 £275

SIESTA HN1305
Designer: L. Harradine
Height: 4¾in., 12.0cm.
Issued: 1928-1938
Price: $1360 £850

SILKS AND RIBBONS HN2017
Designer: L. Harradine
Height: 6in., 15.2cm.
Issued: 1949-
Rec. Retail Price

SILVERSMITH OF WILLIAMSBURG HN2208
Designer: M. Davies
Height: 6¼in., 15.9cm.
Issued: 1960-1983
Price: $128 £80

SIMONE HN2378
Designer: M. Davies
Height: 7¼in., 18.4cm.
Issued: 1971-1982
Price: $112 £70

SIR EDWARD HN2370
Designer: J. Bromley
Height: 11in., 27.9cm.
Issued: 1979 in a limited edition of 500
Price: $304 £190

SIR RALPH HN2371
Designer: J. Bromley
Height: 7½in., 19.1cm.
Issued: 1979 in a limited edition of 500
Price: $304 £190

SIR THOMAS HN2372
Designer: J. Bromley
Height: 11in., 27.9cm.
Issued: 1979 in a limited edition of 500
Price: $304 £190

SIR THOMAS LOVELL HN356
Designer: C. J. Noke
Height: 7¾in., 19.7cm.
Issued: 1919-1938
Price: $1120 £700

SIR WALTER RALEIGH HN1742
Designer: L. Harradine
Height: 10½in., 26.7cm.
Issued: 1935-1949
Price: $480 £300

SIR WALTER RALEIGH HN1751
Designer: L. Harradine
Height: 11½in., 29.2cm.
Issued: 1936-1949
Colour variation
Price: $480 £300

SIR THOMAS HN2372　　　SIBELL HN1668

SIR EDWARD HN2370　　　SIR RALPH HN2371

SIR WALTER RALEIGH
HN2015
Designer: L. Harradine
Height: 11½in., 29.2cm.
Issued: 1948-1955
       Colour variation
Price: $416 £260

SIR WINSTON CHURCHILL
HN3057
Designer: A. Hughes
Height: 10½in., 26.5cm.
Issued: 1985-
Rec. Retail Price

SISTERLY LOVE HN3130
Designer: P. Parsons
Height: 8½in., 21.5cm.
Issued: 1987
Rec. Retail Price

SISTERS HN3018
Designer: P. Parsons
Height: 8½in., 21.5cm.
Issued: 1983-
Rec. Retail Price

SISTERS HN3019
Designer: P. Parsons
Height: 8½in., 21.5cm.
Issued: 1983-
       Colour variation
Rec. Retail Price

SKATER HN2117
Designer: M. Davies
Height: 7¼in., 18.4cm.
Issued: 1953-1971
Price: $240 £150

SKETCH GIRL Model 444
Designer: L. Harradine
Height: 7in., 17.7cm.
Issued: 1924-1938
Price: $528 £330

SLEEP HN24
Designer: P. Stabler
Height: 8¼in., 21.0cm.
Issued: 1913-1938
Price: $1360 £850

SLEEP HN24A
Designer: P. Stabler
Height: 8¼in., 21.0cm.
Issued: 1913-1938
       Colour variation
Price: $1360 £850

SLEEP HN25
Designer: P. Stabler
Height: 8¼in., 21.0cm.
Issued: 1913-1938
       Colour variation
Price: $1360 £850

SLEEP HN25A
Designer: P. Stabler
Height: 8¼in., 21.0cm.
Issued: 1913-1938
       Colour variation
Price: $1360 £850

SLEEP HN424
Designer: P. Stabler
Height: 6in., 15.2cm.
Issued: 1921-1938
       Colour variation
Price: $1360 £850

SIR WINSTON CHURCHILL
HN3057

SIR WALTER RALEIGH HN2015

SKATER HN2117

SLEEP HN692
Designer: P. Stabler
Height: 8¼in., 21.0cm.
Issued: 1925-1938
Colour variation
Price: $1360 £850

SLEEP HN710
Designer: P. Stabler
Height: 8¼in., 21.0cm.
Issued: 1925-1938
Colour variation
Price: $1360 £850

SLEEPING BEAUTY HN3079
Designer: A. Hughes
Height: 4½in. x 8in.,
11cm. x 22cm.
Issued: 1987-1989
Price: $104 £65

SLEEPY DARLING HN2953
Designer: P. Parsons
Height: 7¼in., 18.4cm.
Issued: Only available in
1981
Price: $120 £75
(Collectors Club Issue)

SLEEPY SCHOLAR HN15
Designer: W. White
Height: 6¾in., 17.2cm.
Issued: 1913-1938
Price: $1280 £800

SLEEPY SCHOLAR HN16
Designer: W. White
Height: 6¾in., 17.2cm.
Issued: 1913-1938
Colour variation
Price: $1280 £800

SLEEPY SCHOLAR HN29
Designer: W. White
Height: 6¾in., 17.2cm.
Issued: 1913-1938
Colour variation
Price: $1280 £800

SLEEPYHEAD HN2114
Designer: M. Davies
Height: 5in., 12.7cm.
Issued: 1953-1955
Price: $720 £450

SMILING BUDDHA HN454
Designer: C. J. Noke
Height: 6¼in., 15.9cm.
Issued: 1921-1938
Price: $960 £600

SNAKE CHARMER HN1317
Designer: Unknown
Height: 4in., 10.1cm.
Issued: 1929-1938
Price: $960 £600

SOIRÉE HN2312
Designer: M. Davies
Height: 7½in., 19.1cm.
Issued: 1967-1984
Price: $88 £55

SOLITUDE HN2810
Designer: M. Davies
Height: 5½in., 14.0cm.
Issued: 1977-1983
Price: $104 £65

STEPHANIE HN2807

SLEEPY DARLING HN2953

SOLITUDE HN2810

SONATA HN2438
Designer: P. Davies
Height: 6½in., 16.5cm.
Issued: 1983-1986
Price: $64 £40

SONG OF THE SEA HN2729
Designer: W. K. Harper
Height: 7¼in., 18.0cm.
Issued: 1983-
Rec. Retail Price

SONIA HN1692
Designer: L. Harradine
Height: 6¼in., 15.9cm.
Issued: 1935-1949
Price: $440 £275

SONIA HN1738
Designer: L. Harradine
Height: 6½in., 16.5cm.
Issued: 1935-1949
           Colour variation
Price: $440 £275

SONNY HN1313
Designer: L. Harradine
Height: 3½in., 8.9cm.
Issued: 1929-1938
Price: $512 £320

SONNY HN1314
Designer: L. Harradine
Height: 3½in., 8.9cm.
Issued: 1929-1938
           Colour variation
Price: $512 £320

SOPHIE HN2833
Designer: M. Davies
Height: 6in., 15.2cm.
Issued: 1977-1987
Price: $64 £40

SOPHISTICATION HN3059
Designer: A. Hughes
Height: 11½in., 29cm.
Issued: 1988
Rec. Retail Price

SOUTHERN BELLE HN2229
Designer: M. Davies
Height: 7½in., 19.1cm.
Issued: 1958-
Rec. Retail Price

SOUTHERN BELLE HN2425
Designer: P. Davies
Height: 7½in., 19.0cm.
Issued: 1983-
           Colour variation
Rec. Retail Price

SOUTHERN BELLE HN3174
Designer: P. Davies
Height: 4in., 10cm.
Issued: 1988
Rec. Retail Price

**SPANISH FLAMENCO
DANCER HN2831**
Designer: M. Davies
Height: 7¼in., 18.4cm.
Issued: 1977 in a limited
           edition of 750
Price: $560 £350

SONATA HN2438

**SPANISH FLAMENCO
DANCER HN2831**

SPANISH LADY HN1262
Designer: L. Harradine
Height: 8½in., 21.6cm.
Issued: 1927-1938
Price: $560 £350

SPANISH LADY HN1290
Designer: L. Harradine
Height: 8¼in., 21.0cm.
Issued: 1928-1938
        Colour variation
Price: $560 £350

SPANISH LADY HN1293
Designer: L. Harradine
Height: 8¼in., 21.0cm.
Issued: 1928-1938
        Colour variation
Price: $560 £350

SPANISH LADY HN1294
Designer: L. Harradine
Height: 8¼in., 21.0cm.
Issued: 1928-1938
        Colour variation
Price: $560 £350

SPANISH LADY HN1309
Designer: L. Harradine
Height: 8¼in., 21.0cm.
Issued: 1929-1938
        Colour variation
Price: $560 £350

SPINNING HN2390
Designer: P. Davies
Height: 7½in., 19cm.
Issued: 1984 in a limited
        edition of 750
Price: $680 £425

SPIRIT OF THE WIND HN1777
Designer: R. Garbe
Height: Unknown
Issued: 1933 in a limited
        edition of 50
Price: $2400 £1500

SPIRIT OF THE WIND HN1825
Designer: R. Garbe
Height: Unknown
Issued: 1937-1949
        Colour variation
Price: $2080 £1300

SPOOK HN50
Designer: H. Tittensor
Height: 7in., 17.8cm.
Issued: 1916-1938
Price: $960 £600

SPOOK HN51
Designer: H. Tittensor
Height: 7in., 17.8cm.
Issued: 1916-1938
        Colour variation
Price: $960 £600

SPOOK HN51A
Designer: H. Tittensor
Height: 7in., 17.8cm.
Issued: 1916-1938
        Colour variation
Price: $960 £600

SOUTHERN BELLE HN2229   SONG OF THE SEA HN2729

SPINNING HN2390

263

SPOOK HN51B
Designer: H. Tittensor
Height: 7in., 17.8cm.
Issued: 1916-1938
Colour variation
Price: $960 £600

SPOOK HN58
Designer: H. Tittensor
Height: 7in., 17.8cm.
Issued: 1916-1938
Colour unknown
Price: $960 £600

SPOOK HN512
Designer: H. Tittensor
Height: 7in., 17.8cm.
Issued: 1921-1938
Colour variation
Price: $960 £600

SPOOK HN625
Designer: H. Tittensor
Height: 7in., 17.8cm.
Issued: 1924-1938
Colour variation
Price: $960 £600

SPOOK HN1218
Designer: H. Tittensor
Height: 7in., 17.8cm.
Issued: 1926-1938
Colour variation
Price: $960 £600

SPOOKS HN88
Designer: C. J. Noke
Height: 7¼in., 18.4cm.
Issued: 1918-1936
Price: $960 £600

SPOOKS HN89
Designer: C. J. Noke
Height: 7¼in., 18.4cm.
Issued: 1918-1936
Colour variation
Price: $960 £600

SPOOKS HN372
Designer: C. J. Noke
Height: 7¼in., 18.4cm.
Issued: 1920-1936
Colour variation
Price: $960 £600

SPRING (Style one) HN312
Designer: Unknown
Height: 7½in., 19.1cm.
Issued: 1918-1938
Price: $1440 £900

SPRING (Style one) HN472
Designer: Unknown
Height: 7½in., 19.1cm.
Issued: 1921-1938
Colour variation
Price: $1440 £900

SPRING (Style two) HN1774
Designer: R. Garbe
Height: 21in., 53.3cm.
Issued: 1933 in a limited
edition of 100
Price: $2000 £1250

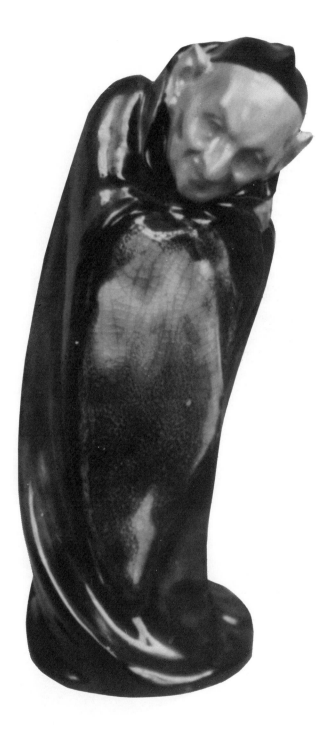

SPOOK HN51

SPRING (Style two) HN1827
Designer: R. Garbe
Height: 21in., 53.3cm.
Issued: 1937-1949
Colour variation
Price: $2000 £1250

SPRING (Style three) HN2085
Designer: M. Davies
Height: 7¾in., 19.6cm.
Issued: 1952-1959
Price: $296 £185

SPRING FLOWERS HN1807
Designer: L. Harradine
Height: 7¼in., 18.4cm.
Issued: 1937-1959
Price: $272 £170

SPRING FLOWERS HN1945
Designer: L. Harradine
Height: 7¼in., 18.4cm.
Issued: 1940-1949
Colour variation
Price: $320 £200

SPRING MORNING HN1922
Designer: L. Harradine
Height: 7½in., 19.1cm.
Issued: 1940-1973
Price: $160 £100

SPRING MORNING HN1923
Designer: L. Harradine
Height: 7½in., 19.1cm.
Issued: 1940-1949
Colour variation
Price: $208 £130

SPRINGTIME HN1971
Designer: L. Harradine
Height: 6in., 15.2cm.
Issued: 1941-1949
Price: $640 £400

SPRINGTIME HN3033
Designer: A. Hughes
Height: 8in., 22cm.
Issued: 1983
Price: $128 £80

SQUIRE HN1814
Designer: Unknown
Height: 9¾in., 24.7cm.
Issued: 1937-1949
Price: $1600 £1000
Also called "Hunting Squire'

ST. GEORGE (Style one)
HN385
Designer: S. Thorogood
Height: 16in., 40.6cm.
Issued: 1920-1938
Price: $1600 £1000

ST. GEORGE (Style one)
HN386
Designer: S. Thorogood
Height: 16in., 40.6cm.
Issued: 1920-1938
Colour variation
Price: $1600 £1000

ST. GEORGE (Style one)
HN1800
Designer: S. Thorogood
Height: 16in., 40.6cm.
Issued: 1934-1950
Colour variation
Price: $1280 £800

SPRING FLOWERS HN1945

SPRINGTIME HN3033

SPRING FLOWERS HN1807

265

ST. GEORGE (Style one)
HN2067
Designer: S. Thorogood
Height: 15¾in., 40.0cm.
Issued: 1950-1976
Colour variation
Price: $1200 £750

ST. GEORGE (Style two)
HN2051
Designer: M. Davies
Height: 7½in., 19.1cm.
Issued: 1950-1986
Price: $288 £180

ST. GEORGE AND THE
DRAGON (Style three) HN2856
Designer: W. K. Harper
Height: 16in., 40.6cm.
Issued: 1978-
Rec. Retail Price

STAR GAZER HN3182
Designer: D. V. Tootle
Height: 10½in., 26.5cm.
Issued: 1988-
Rec. Retail Price

STATESMAN HN2859
Designer: W. Harper
Height: 9¼in., 23.5cm.
Issued: 1988
Rec. Retail Price

STAYED AT HOME HN2207
Designer: M. Davies
Height: 5in., 12.7cm.
Issued: 1958-1969
Price: $120 £75

STEPHANIE HN2807
Designer: M. Davies
Height: 7¼in., 18.4cm.
Issued: 1977-1982
Price: $96 £60

STEPHANIE HN2811
Designer: P. Davies
Height: 7½in., 19.0cm.
Issued: 1983-
Rec. Retail Price

STICK 'EM UP HN2981
Designer: A. Hughes
Height: 7in., 17.5cm.
Issued: 1984-1985
Price: $72 £45

STIGGINS HN536
Designer: L. Harradine
Height: 3¾in., 9.5cm.
Issued: 1922-1932
Price: $48 £30

STIGGINS M50
Designer: L. Harradine
Height: 4in., 10.1cm.
Issued: 1932-1982
Price: $48 £30

STITCH IN TIME HN2352
Designer: M. Nicoll
Height: 6¼in., 15.9cm.
Issued: 1966-1980
Price: $109 £68

STOP PRESS HN2683
Designer: M. Nicoll
Height: 7½in., 19.1cm.
Issued: 1977-1980
Price: $120 £75

SUMMERTIME HN3137

ST. GEORGE HN2051

STORYTIME HN3126
Designer: P. Parsons
Height: 6in., 15.2cm.
Issued: 1987
Rec. Retail Price

STROLLING HN3073
Designer: A. Hughes
Height: 13½in., 34.5cm.
Issued: 1985
Rec. Retail Price

SUITOR HN2132
Designer: M. Davies
Height: 7¼in., 18.4cm.
Issued: 1962-1971
Price: $192 £120

SUMMER (Style one) HN313
Designer: Unknown
Height: 7½in., 19.1cm.
Issued: 1918-1938
Price: $1280 £800

SUMMER (Style one) HN473
Designer: Unknown
Height: 7½in., 19.1cm.
Issued: 1921-1938
Price: $1280 £800

SUMMER (Style two) HN2086
Designer: M. Davies
Height: 7¼in., 18.4cm.
Issued: 1952-1959
Price: $288 £180

SUMMER ROSE HN3085
Designer: E. Griffiths
Height: 8½in., 21.5cm.
Issued: 1987
Rec. Retail Price

SUMMER'S DARLING HN3091
Designer: P. Parsons
Height: 11¼in., 28cm.
Issued: 1986
Rec. Retail Price

SUMMER'S DAY HN2181
Designer: M. Davies
Height: 5¾in., 14.6cm.
Issued: 1957-1962
Price: $224 £140

SUMMERTIME HN3137
Designer: P. Parsons
Height: 8in., 20.0cm.
Issued: 1987
Price: $128 £80

SUNDAY BEST HN3218
Designer: P. Davies
Height: 3¾in., 9.5cm.
Issued: 1988
Rec. Retail Price

SUNDAY BEST HN2206
Designer: M. Davies
Height: 7½in., 19.1cm.
Issued: 1979-1984
Price: $104 £65

SUNDAY BEST HN2698
Designer: P. Davies
Height: 7½in., 19.1cm.
Issued: 1985-
Rec. Retail Price

SUNDAY MORNING HN2184
Designer: M. Davies
Height: 7½in., 19.1cm.
Issued: 1963-1969
Price: $208 £130

SUNDAY BEST HN2206

STITCH IN TIME HN2352

STOP PRESS HN2683

SUMMER (Style two) HN2086

267

FIGURES

SUNSHINE GIRL HN1344
Designer: L. Harradine
Height: 5in., 12.7cm.
Issued: 1929-1938
Price: $1360 £850

SUNSHINE GIRL HN1348
Designer: L. Harradine
Height: 5in., 12.7cm.
Issued: 1929-1938
           Colour variation
Price: $1360 £850

SUSAN HN2056
Designer: L. Harradine
Height: 7in., 17.8cm.
Issued: 1950-1959
Price: $192 £120

SUSAN HN2952
Designer: P. Parsons
Height: 8½in., 21.5cm.
Issued: 1982-
Rec. Retail Price

SUSAN (Red) HN3050
Designer: P. Parsons
Height: 8½in., 21.5cm.
Issued: 1986
Rec. Retail Price

SUSANNA HN1233
Designer: L. Harradine
Height: 6in., 15.2cm.
Issued: 1927-1938
Price: $448 £280

SUSANNA HN1288
Designer: L. Harradine
Height: 6in., 15.2cm.
Issued: 1928-1938
Price: $448 £280

SUSANNA HN1299
Designer: L. Harradine
Height: 6in., 15.2cm.
Issued: 1928-1938
           Colour variation
Price: $448 £280

SUZETTE HN1487
Designer: L. Harradine
Height: 7½in., 19.1cm.
Issued: 1931-1950
Price: $192 £120

SUZETTE HN1577
Designer: L. Harradine
Height: 7½in., 19.1cm.
Issued: 1933-1949
           Colour variation
Price: $192 £120

SUZETTE HN1585
Designer: L. Harradine
Height: 7½in., 19.1cm.
Issued: 1933-1938
           Colour variation
Price: $256 £160

SUZETTE HN1696
Designer: L. Harradine
Height: 7½in., 19.1cm.
Issued: 1935-1949
           Colour variation
Price: $192 £120

SUZETTE HN1487

SUNSHINE GIRL HN1344

SUZETTE HN2026
Designer: L. Harradine
Height: 7¼in., 18.4cm.
Issued: 1949-1959
Colour variation
Price: $192 £120

SWEET AND FAIR HN1864
Designer: L. Harradine
Height: 7½in., 19.1cm.
Issued: 1938-1949
Price: $360 £225

SWEET AND FAIR HN1865
Designer: L. Harradine
Height: 7¼in., 18.4cm.
Issued: 1938-1949
Colour variation
Price: $360 £225

SWEET AND TWENTY
(Style one) HN1298
Designer: L. Harradine
Height: 5¾in., 14.6cm.
Issued: 1928-1969
Price: $192 £120

SWEET AND TWENTY
(Style one) HN1360
Designer: L. Harradine
Height: 6in., 15.2cm.
Issued: 1929-1938
Colour variation
Price: $288 £180

SWEET AND TWENTY
(Style one) HN1437
Designer: L. Harradine
Height: 6in., 15.2cm.
Issued: 1930-1938
Colour variation
Price: $288 £180

SWEET AND TWENTY
(Style one) HN1438
Designer: L. Harradine
Height: 6in., 15.2cm.
Issued: 1930-1938
Colour variation
Price: $288 £180

SWEET AND TWENTY
(Style one) HN1549
Designer: L. Harradine
Height: 6in., 15.2cm.
Issued: 1933-1949
Colour variation
Price: $144 £90

SWEET AND TWENTY
(Style one) HN1563
Designer: L. Harradine
Height: 6in., 15.2cm.
Issued: 1933-1938
Colour variation
Price: $288 £180

SWEET AND TWENTY
(Style one) HN1649
Designer: L. Harradine
Height: 6in., 15.2cm.
Issued: 1934-1949
Colour variation
Price: $288 £180

SUSAN HN2952

SWEET AND TWENTY HN1298

269

SWEET AND TWENTY
(Style two) HN1589
Designer: L. Harradine
Height: 3½in., 8.9cm.
Issued: 1933-1949
Price: $160 £100

SWEET AND TWENTY
(Style two) HN1610
Designer: L. Harradine
Height: 3½in., 8.9cm.
Issued: 1933-1938
Colour variation
Price: $208 £130

SWEET ANNE HN1318
Designer: L. Harradine
Height: 7½in., 19.1cm.
Issued: 1929-1949
Price: $136 £85

SWEET ANNE HN1330
Designer: L. Harradine
Height: 7¼in., 18.4cm.
Issued: 1929-1949
Colour variation
Price: $160 £100

SWEET ANNE HN1331
Designer: L. Harradine
Height: 7¼in., 18.4cm.
Issued: 1929-1949
Colour variation
Price: $160 £100

SWEET ANNE HN1453
Designer: L. Harradine
Height: 7in., 17.8cm.
Issued: 1931-1949
Colour variation
Price: $160 £100

SWEET ANNE HN1496
Designer: L. Harradine
Height: 7in., 17.8cm.
Issued: 1932-1967
Colour variation
Price: $152 £95

SWEET ANNE HN1631
Designer: L. Harradine
Height: 7in., 17.8cm.
Issued: 1934-1938
Colour variation
Price: $256 £160

SWEET ANNE HN1701
Designer: L. Harradine
Height: 7in., 17.8cm.
Issued: 1935-1938
Colour variation
Price: $240 £160

SWEET ANNE M5
Designer: L. Harradine
Height: 4in., 10.1cm.
Issued: 1932-1945
Price: $150 £100

SWEET ANNE M6
Designer: L. Harradine
Height: 4in., 10.1cm.
Issued: 1932-1945
Colour variation
Price: $150 £100

SWEET DREAMS HN2380

SWEET SEVENTEEN HN2734

270

SWEET ANNE M27
Designer: L. Harradine
Height: 4in., 10.1cm.
Issued: 1932-1945
           Colour variation
Price: $150 £100

SWEET APRIL HN2215
Designer: M. Davies
Height: 7¼in., 18.4cm.
Issued: 1965-1967
Price: $208 £130

SWEET DREAMS HN2380
Designer: M. Davies
Height: 5in., 12.7cm.
Issued: 1971-
Rec. Retail Price

SWEET LAVENDER HN1373
Designer: L. Harradine
Height: 9in., 22.8cm.
Issued: 1930-1949
Price: $400 £250

SWEET MAID (Style one)
HN1504
Designer: L. Harradine
Height: 8in., 20.3cm.
Issued: 1932-1938
Price: $320 £200

SWEET MAID (Style one)
HN1505
Designer: L. Harradine
Height: 8in., 20.3cm.
Issued: 1932-1938
           Colour variation
Price: $320 £200

SWEET MAID (Style two)
HN2092
Designer: L. Harradine
Height: 7in., 17.8cm.
Issued: 1952-1955
Price: $160 £100

SWEET PERFUME HN3094
Designer: P. Parsons
Height: 13in., 33cm.
Issued: 1986
Rec. Retail Price

SWEET SEVENTEEN HN2734
Designer: D. V. Tootle
Height: 7½in., 19.1cm.
Issued: 1975-
Rec. Retail Price

SWEET SIXTEEN HN2231
Designer: M. Davies
Height: 7¼in., 18.4cm.
Issued: 1958-1965
Price: $208 £130

SWEET SUZY HN1918
Designer: L. Harradine
Height: 6½in., 16.5cm.
Issued: 1939-1949
Price: $288 £180

SWEET VIOLETS HN3175
Designer: D. Tootle
Height: 10¼in., 26.0cm.
Issued: 1988-89
Price: $72 £45

SWEETING HN1935
Designer: L. Harradine
Height: 6in., 15.2cm.
Issued: 1940-1973
Price: $88 £55

SWEET ANNE HN1453

SWEET LAVENDER HN1373

SWEET MAID HN1505

271

FIGURES

SWEETING HN1938
Designer: L. Harradine
Height: 6in., 15.2cm.
Issued: 1940-1949
Colour variation
Price: $88 £55

SWIMMER HN1270
Designer: L. Harradine
Height: 7¼in., 18.4cm.
Issued: 1928-1938
Price: $960 £600

SWIMMER HN1326
Designer: L. Harradine
Height: 7½in., 19.1cm.
Issued: 1929-1938
Colour variation
Price: $1040 £650

SWIMMER HN1329
Designer: L. Harradine
Height: 7½in., 19.1cm.
Issued: 1929-1938
Colour variation
Price: $1040 £650

SYLVIA HN1478
Designer: L. Harradine
Height: 10½in., 26.7cm.
Issued: 1931-1938
Price: $288 £180

SYMPATHY HN2838 (Black)
Designer: P. Davies
Height: 11¾in., 29.8cm.
Issued: 1981-1986
Price: $48 £30

SYMPATHY HN2876 (White)
Designer: P. Davies
Height: 11¾in., 29.8cm.
Issued: 1981-1986
Price: $48 £30

SYMPHONY HN2287
Designer: D. B. Lovegrove
Height: 5¼in., 13.3cm.
Issued: 1961-1965
Price: $192 £120

T

TAILOR HN2174
Designer: M. Nicholl
Height: 5in., 12.7cm.
Issued: 1956-1959
Price: $480 £300

TAKING THINGS EASY HN2677
Designer: M. Nicoll
Height: 6¾in., 17.2cm.
Issued: 1975-1987
Price: $104 £65

TAKING THINGS EASY HN2680
Designer: M. Nicoll
Height: 7½in., 19.5cm.
Issued: 1987
Rec. Retail Price

SWIMMER HN1270

TAPESTRY WEAVING ⁋ HN3048

272

TALL STORY HN2248
Designer: M. Nicoll
Height: 6½in., 16.5cm.
Issued: 1968-1975
Price: $144 £90

TANGO HN3075
Designer: A. Hughes
Height: 13in., 33cm.
Issued: 1985
Rec. Retail Price

TAPESTRY WEAVING HN3048
Designer: P. Parsons
Height: 7½in., 19.0cm.
Issued: 1985 in a limited edition of 750
Price: $680 £425

TEATIME HN2255
Designer: M. Nicoll
Height: 7¼in., 18.4cm.
Issued: 1972-
Rec. Retail Price

TEENAGER HN2203
Designer: M. Davies
Height: 7¼in., 18.4cm.
Issued: 1957-1962
Price: $288 £180

TENDERNESS HN2713
Designer: E. Griffiths
Height: 11¾in., 29.5cm.
Issued: 1982-
Colour variation White
Rec. Retail Price

TENDERNESS HN2714
Designer: E. Griffiths
Height: 11¾in., 29.5cm.
Issued: 1982-
Colour variation Black
Rec. Retail Price

TERESA HN1682
Designer: L. Harradine
Height: 5¾in., 14.6cm.
Issued: 1935-1949
Price: $560 £350

TERESA HN1683
Designer: L. Harradine
Height: 5¾in., 14.6cm.
Issued: 1935-1938
Colour variation
Price: $640 £400

TERESA HN3206
Designer: A. Hughes
Height: 7¹/₄in., 19.6cm.
Issued: 1989
Rec. Retail Price

TESS HN2865
Designer: M. Davies
Height: 5¾in., 14.6cm.
Issued: 1978-1983
Price: $56 £35

TÊTE-À-TÊTE (Style one) HN798
Designer: L. Harradine
Height: 5¾in., 14.6cm.
Issued: 1926-1938
Price: $640 £400

TÊTE-À-TÊTE (Style one)
HN799

TEATIME HN2255

TAKING THINGS EASY

TÊTE-À-TÊTE (Style one)
HN799
Designer: L. Harradine
Height: 5¾in., 14.6cm.
Issued: 1926-1938
          Colour variation
Price: $640 £400

TÊTE-À-TÊTE (Style two)
HN1236
Designer: C. J. Noke
Height: 3in., 7.6cm.
Issued: 1927-1938
Price: $520 £325

TÊTE-À-TÊTE HN1237
Designer: C. J. Noke
Height: 3in., 7.6cm.
Issued: 1927-1938
          Colour variation
Price: $520 £325

THANK YOU HN2732
Designer: W. K. Harper
Height: 8¼in., 21.0cm.
Issued: 1983-1986
Price: $96 £60

THANKFUL (White) HN3129
Designer: P. Parsons
Height: 8½in., 21.5cm.
Issued: 1987
Rec. Retail Price

THANKFUL (Black) HN3135
Designer: P. Parsons
Height: 8½in., 21.5cm.
Issued: 1987
Rec. Retail Price

THANKS DOC HN2731
Designer: W. K. Harper
Height: 8¾in., 22.2cm.
Issued: 1975-
Rec. Retail Price

THANKSGIVING HN2446
Designer: M. Nicoll
Height: 8in., 20.3cm.
Issued: 1972-1976
Price: $112 £70

THIS LITTLE PIG HN1793
Designer: L. Harradine
Height: 4in., 10.1cm.
Issued: 1936-
Rec. Retail Price

THIS LITTLE PIG HN1794
Designer: L. Harradine
Height: 4in., 10.1cm.
Issued: 1936-1949
          Colour variation
Price: $136 £85

THIS LITTLE PIG HN2125
Designer: L. Harradine
Height: 4in., 10.0cm.
Issued: 1984-
          Colour variation
Rec. Retail Price

TOM BROWN HN2941

THANKS DOC HN2731

THANK YOU HN2732

THIS LITTLE PIG HN1793

FIGURES

TILDY HN1576
Designer: L. Harradine
Height: 5in., 12.7cm.
Issued: 1933-1938
Price: $400 £250

TILDY HN1859
Designer: L. Harradine
Height: 5½in., 14.0cm.
Issued: 1938-1949
       Colour variation
Price: $320 £200

TINKLE BELL HN1677
Designer: L. Harradine
Height: 4¾in., 12.0cm.
Issued: 1935-1988
Price: $56 £35

TINSMITH HN2146
Designer: M. Nicoll
Height: 6½in., 16.5cm.
Issued: 1962-1967
Price: $296 £185

TINY TIM HN539
Designer: L. Harradine
Height: 3½in., 8.9cm.
Issued: 1922-1932
Price: $48 £30

TINY TIM M56
Designer: L. Harradine
Height: 3¾in., 9.5cm.
Issued: 1932-1983
Price: $48 £30

TO BED HN1805
Designer: L. Harradine
Height: 6in., 15.2cm.
Issued: 1937-1959
Price: $160 £100

TO BED HN1806
Designer: L. Harradine
Height: 6in., 15.2cm.
Issued: 1937-1949
       Colour variation
Price: $160 £100

TOINETTE HN1940
Designer: L. Harradine
Height: 6¾in., 17.1cm.
Issued: 1940-1949
Price: $960 £600
Also called "Meryll"

TOM HN2864
Designer: M. Davies
Height: 5¾in., 14.6cm.
Issued: 1978-1982
Price: $56 £35

TOM BOMBADIL HN2924
Designer: D. Lyttleton
Height: 5¾in., 14.6cm.
Issued: 1982-1984
Price: $56 £35

TOM BROWN HN2941
Designer: R. Tabbenor
Height: 6¾in., 17.0cm.
Issued: 1983-1985
Price: $56 £35

TILDY HN1859

TINSMITH HN2146

THANKSGIVING HN2446

TOM BOMBADIL HN2924

TOM SAWYER HN2926
Designer: D. Lyttleton
Height: 5¼in., 13.0cm.
Issued: 1982-1985
Price: $56 £35

TOM, TOM THE PIPERS SON HN3032
Designer: A. Hughes
Height: 7in., 17.5cm.
Issued: 1984-1987
Price: $64 £40

TOMORROWS DREAMS HN3128
Designer: P. Parsons
Height: 6½in., 16.5cm.
Issued: 1988
Rec. Retail Price

TONY WELLER (Style one) HN346
Designer: C. J. Noke
Height: 10½in., 26.7cm.
Issued: 1919-1938
Price: $1216 £760

TONY WELLER (Style one) HN368
Designer: C. J. Noke
Height: 10½in., 26.7cm.
Issued: 1920-1938
Colour variation
Price: $1216 £760

TONY WELLER (Style one) HN684
Designer: C. J. Noke
Height: 10¼in., 26.0cm.
Issued: 1924-1938
Colour variation
Price: $1216 £760

TONY WELLER (Style two) HN544
Designer: L. Harradine
Height: 3½in., 8.9cm.
Issued: 1922-1932
Price: $48 £30

TONY WELLER (Style two) M47
Designer: L. Harradine
Height: 4in., 10.1cm.
Issued: 1932-1982
Price: $48 £30

TOOTLES HN1680
Designer: L. Harradine
Height: 4¾in., 12.0cm.
Issued: 1935-1975
Price: $64 £40

TOP O'THE HILL HN1833
Designer: L. Harradine
Height: 7in., 17.8cm.
Issued: 1937-1971
Price: $152 £95

TOP O'THE HILL HN1834
Designer: L. Harradine
Height: 7in., 17.8cm.
Issued: 1937-
Colour variation
Rec. Retail Price

TOM SAWYER HN2926

TOP O' THE HILL HN2126

TOP O'THE HILL HN1849
Designer: L. Harradine
Height: 7¼in., 18.4cm.
Issued: 1938-1975
Colour variation
Price: $136 £85

TOP O' THE HILL HN2126
Designer: P. Gee
Height: 4in., 10cm.
Issued: 1988
Price: $64 £40

TOWN CRIER HN3261
Designer: P. Davies
Height: 4½in., 11.5cm.
Issued: 1989
Rec. Retail Price

TOWN CRIER HN2119
Designer: M. Davies
Height: 8½in., 21.6cm.
Issued: 1953-1976
Price: $176 £110

TOYMAKER HN2250
Designer: M. Nicoll
Height: 6in., 15.2cm.
Issued: 1959-1973
Price: $320 £200

TOYS HN1316
Designer: L. Harradine
Height: Unknown
Issued: 1929-1938
Price: $1280 £800

TRACY HN2736
Designer: D. Tootle
Height: 7½in., 19.0cm.
Issued: 1983-
Rec. Retail Price

TRANQUILITY HN2426
(Black)
Designer: P. Davies
Height: 12in., 30.5cm.
Issued: 1981-1986
Price: $64 £40

TRANQUILITY HN2469
(White)
Designer: P. Davies
Height: 12in., 30.5cm.
Issued: 1981-1986
Price: $64 £40

TRAVELLERS TALES
HN3185
Designer: E.J. Griffiths
Height: 9½in., 23.5cm.
Issued: 1988-1989
Price: $72 £45

TREASURE ISLAND HN2243
Designer: M. Davies
Height: 4¾in., 12.0cm.
Issued: 1962-1975
Price: $112 £70

TROTTY VECK M91
Designer: L. Harradine
Height: 4¼in., 10.8cm.
Issued: 1949-1982
Price: $48 £30

TOP O'THE HILL HN1834

TOP O'THE HILL HN1833

TOP O'THE HILL HN1849

TULIPS HN466
Designer: Unknown
Height: 9½in., 24.1cm.
Issued: 1921-1938
Price: $800 £500

TULIPS HN488
Designer: Unknown
Height: 9½in., 24.1cm.
Issued: 1921-1938
Colour variation
Price: $800 £500

TULIPS HN672
Designer: Unknown
Height: 9½in., 24.1cm.
Issued: 1924-1938
Colour variation
Price: $800 £500

TULIPS HN747
Designer: Unknown
Height: 9½in., 24.1cm.
Issued: 1925-1938
Colour variation
Price: $800 £500

TULIPS HN1334
Designer: Unknown
Height: 9½in., 24.1cm.
Issued: 1929-1938
Colour variation
Price: $800 £500

TUMBLER HN3181
Designer: D. Tootle
Height: 9in., 23cm.
Issued: 1989
Rec. Retail Price

TUPPENCE A BAG HN2320
Designer: M. Nicoll
Height: 5½in., 14.0cm.
Issued: 1968-
Rec. Retail Price

TWILIGHT HN2256
Designer: M. Nicoll
Height: 5in., 12.7cm.
Issued: 1971-1976
Price: $109 £68

TWO-A-PENNY HN1359
Designer: L. Harradine
Height: 8¼in., 21.0cm.
Issued: 1929-1938
Price: $800 £500

**TZ'U HSI, THE EMPRESS
DOWAGER HN2391**
Designer: P. Davies
Height: 8in., 20.0cm.
Issued: 1983 in a limited
edition of 750
Price: $640 £400

U

UNCLE NED HN2094
Designer: H. Fenton
Height: 6¾in., 17.2cm.
Issued: 1952-1965
Price: $256 £160

TUPPENCE A BAG HN2320

TZ'U HSI, THE EMPRESS DOWAGER HN2391

278

FIGURES

**UNDER THE GOOSEBERRY
BUSH HN49**
Designer: C. J. Noke
Height: 3½in., 8.9cm.
Issued: 1916-1938
Price: $800 £500

**"UPON HER CHEEKS SHE
WEPT" HN59**
Designer: L. Perugini
Height: 9in., 22.8cm.
Issued: 1916-1938
Price: $1280 £800

**"UPON HER CHEEKS SHE
WEPT" HN511**
Designer: L. Perugini
Height: 9in., 22.8cm.
Issued: 1921-1938
  Colour variation
Price: $1280 £800

**"UPON HER CHEEKS SHE
WEPT" HN522**
Designer: L. Perugini
Height: 9in., 22.8cm.
Issued: 1921-1938
Price: $1280 £800

**URIAH HEEP (Style one)
HN545**
Designer: L. Harradine
Height: 4in., 10.1cm.
Issued: 1922-1932
Price: $48 £30

**URIAH HEEP (Style one)
M45**
Designer: L. Harradine
Height: 4in., 10.1cm.
Issued: 1932-1982
Price: $48 £30

**URIAH HEEP (Style two)
HN554**
Designer: L. Harradine
Height: 7¼in., 18.4cm.
Issued: 1923-1939
Price: $288 £180

**URIAH HEEP (Style two)
HN1892**
Designer: L. Harradine
Height: 7in., 17.8cm.
Issued: 1938-1952
Price: $224 £140

**URIAH HEEP (Style three)
HN2101**
Designer: L. Harradine
Height: 7½in., 19.1cm.
Issued: 1952-1967
Price: $192 £120

V

VALERIE HN2107
Designer: M. Davies
Height: 4¾in., 12.0cm.
Issued: 1953-
Rec. Retail Price

UNCLE NED HN2094

TWILIGHT HN2256

VALERIE HN2107

VANESSA HN1836
Designer: L. Harradine
Height: 7½in., 19.1cm.
Issued: 1938-1949
Price: $288 £180

VANESSA HN1838
Designer: L. Harradine
Height: 7½in., 19.1cm.
Issued: 1938-1949
          Colour variation
Price: $288 £180

VANESSA HN3198
Designer: A. Hughes
Height: 8½in., 21.5cm.
Issued: 1989
Rec. Retail Price

VANITY HN2475
Designer: M. Davies
Height: 5¼in., 13.3cm.
Issued: 1973-
Rec. Retail Price

VENETA HN2722
Designer: W. K. Harper
Height: 8in., 20.3cm.
Issued: 1974-1980
Price: $109 £68

VERA HN1729
Designer: L. Harradine
Height: 4¼in., 10.8cm.
Issued: 1935-1938
Price: $480 £300

VERA HN1730
Designer: L. Harradine
Height: 4¼in., 10.8cm.
Issued: 1935-1938
          Colour variation
Price: $480 £300

VERENA HN1835
Designer: L. Harradine
Height: 8¼in., 21.0cm.
Issued: 1938-1949
Price: $400 £250

VERENA HN1854
Designer: L. Harradine
Height: 8¼in., 21.0cm.
Issued: 1938-1949
          Colour variation
Price: $400 £250

**VERONICA (Style one)
HN1517**
Designer: L. Harradine
Height: 8in., 20.3cm.
Issued: 1932-1951
Price: $176 £110

**VERONICA (Style one)·
HN1519**
Designer: L. Harradine
Height: 8in., 20.3cm.
Issued: 1932-1938
          Colour variation
Price: $216 £135

VERENA HN1835   **VICTORIAN LADY HN726**

VICTORIAN LADY HN728   **VANITY HN2475**

VERONICA (Style one)
HN1650
Designer: L. Harradine
Height: 8in., 20.3cm.
Issued: 1934-1949
Colour variation
Price: $216 £135

VERONICA (Style one)
HN1943
Designer: L. Harradine
Height: 8in., 20.3cm.
Issued: 1940-1949
Colour variation
Price: $176 £110

VERONICA (Style two)
HN1915
Designer: L. Harradine
Height: 5¾in., 14.6cm.
Issued: 1939-1949
Price: $240 £150

VERONICA HN3205
Designer: A. Hughes
Height: 8in., 20.3cm.
Issued: 1989
Rec. Retail Price

VERONICA M64
Designer: L. Harradine
Height: 4½in., 10.8cm.
Issued: 1934-1949
Price: $192 £120

VERONICA M70
Designer: L. Harradine
Height: 4¼in., 10.8cm.
Issued: 1936-1949
Colour variation
Price: $192 £120

VICTORIA HN2471
Designer: M. Davies
Height: 6½in., 16.5cm.
Issued: 1973-
Rec. Retail Price

VICTORIAN LADY HN726
Designer: L. Harradine
Height: 7½in., 19.1cm.
Issued: 1925-1938
Price: $240 £150

VICTORIAN LADY HN727
Designer: L. Harradine
Height: 7½in., 19.1cm.
Issued: 1925-1938
Colour variation
Price: $240 £150

VICTORIAN LADY HN728
Designer: L. Harradine
Height: 7¾in., 19.7cm.
Issued: 1925-1952
Colour variation
Price: $160 £100

VICTORIAN LADY HN736
Designer: L. Harradine
Height: 7¾in., 19.7cm.
Issued: 1925-1938
Colour variation
Price: $240 £150

VENETA HN2722

VERONICA (Style one)
HN1517

VICTORIA HN2471

VICTORIAN LADY HN739
Designer: L. Harradine
Height: 7¾in., 19.7cm.
Issued: 1925-1938
Colour variation
Price: $240 £150

VICTORIAN LADY HN740
Designer: L. Harradine
Height: 7¾in., 19.7cm.
Issued: 1925-1938
Colour variation
Price: $240 £150

VICTORIAN LADY HN742
Designer: L. Harradine
Height: 7¾in., 19.7cm.
Issued: 1925-1938
Colour variation
Price: $240 £150

VICTORIAN LADY HN745
Designer: L. Harradine
Height: 7¾in., 19.7cm.
Issued: 1925-1938
Colour variation
Price: $240 £150

VICTORIAN LADY HN1208
Designer: L. Harradine
Height: 7¾in., 19.7cm.
Issued: 1926-1938
Colour variation
Price: $240 £150

VICTORIAN LADY HN1258
Designer: L. Harradine
Height: 7¾in., 19.7cm.
Issued: 1927-1938
Colour variation
Price: $240 £150

VICTORIAN LADY HN1276
Designer: L. Harradine
Height: 7½in., 19.1cm.
Issued: 1928-1938
Colour variation
Price: $240 £150

VICTORIAN LADY HN1277
Designer: L. Harradine
Height: 7¾in., 19.7cm.
Issued: 1928-1938
Colour variation
Price: $240 £150

VICTORIAN LADY HN1345
Designer: L. Harradine
Height: 7¾in., 19.7cm.
Issued: 1929-1949
Colour variation
Price: $176 £110

VICTORIAN LADY HN1452
Designer: L. Harradine
Height: 7¾in., 19.7cm.
Issued: 1931-1949
Colour variation
Price: $160 £100

VICTORIAN LADY HN1529
Designer: L. Harradine
Height: 7¾in., 19.7cm.
Issued: 1932-1938
Colour variation
Price: $240 £150

VIRGINALS HN2427

VIOLA D'AMORE HN2797

VICTORIAN LADY M1
Designer: L. Harradine
Height: 3¾in., 9.5cm.
Issued: 1932-1945
Price: $160 £100

VICTORIAN LADY M2
Designer: L. Harradine
Height: 3¾in., 9.5cm.
Issued: 1932-1945
Colour variation
Price: $160 £100

VICTORIAN LADY M25
Designer: L. Harradine
Height: 3¾in., 9.5cm.
Issued: 1932-1945
Colour variation
Price: $160 £100

VIKING HN2375
Designer: J. Bromley
Height: 8¾in., 22.2cm.
Issued: 1973-1976
Price: $176 £110

VIOLA D'AMORE HN2797
Designer: M. Davies
Height: 6in., 15.2cm.
Issued: 1976 in a limited
edition of 750
Price: $512 £320

VIOLIN HN2432
Designer: M. Davies
Height: 6¼in., 15.9cm.
Issued: 1972 in a limited
edition of 750
Price: $512 £320

VIRGINALS HN2427
Designer: M. Davies
Height: 6¼in., 15.9cm.
Issued: 1971 in a limited
edition of 750
Price: $512 £320

VIRGINIA HN1693
Designer: L. Harradine
Height: 7½in., 19.1cm.
Issued: 1935-1949
Price: $424 £265

VIRGINIA HN1694
Designer: L. Harradine
Height: 7½in., 19.1cm.
Issued: 1935-1949
Colour variation
Price: $424 £265

VIVIENNE HN2073
Designer: L. Harradine
Height: 7¾in., 19.7cm.
Issued: 1951-1967
Price: $216 £135

VOTES FOR WOMEN HN2816
Designer: W. K. Harper
Height: 9¾in., 24.7cm.
Issued: 1978-1981
Price: $112 £70

VIVIENNE HN2073   VIKING HN2375

VIOLIN HN2432   VOTES FOR WOMEN HN2816

W

WANDERING MINSTREL
HN1224
Designer: L. Harradine
Height: 7in., 17.8cm.
Issued: 1927-1938
Price: $1280 £800

WARDROBE MISTRESS
HN2145
Designer: M. Davies
Height: 5¾in., 14.6cm.
Issued: 1954-1967
Price: $224 £140

WATER MAIDEN HN3155
Designer: A. Hughes
Height: 12in., 30.5cm.
Issued: 1988
Rec. Retail Price

WAYFARER HN2362
Designer: M. Nicoll
Height: 5½in., 14.0cm.
Issued: 1970-1976
Price: $112 £70

WEDDING DAY HN2748
Designer: D. Tootle
Height: 12½in., 31.5cm.
Issued: 1987
Rec. Retail Price

WEDDING MORN HN1866
Designer: L. Harradine
Height: 10½in., 26.7cm.
Issued: 1938-1949
Price: $800 £500

WEDDING MORN HN1867
Designer: L. Harradine
Height: 10½in., 26.7cm.
Issued: 1938-1949
        Colour variation
Price: $800 £500

WEDDING VOWS HN2750
Designer: D. Tootle
Height: 8in., 20cm.
Issued: 1988
Rec. Retail Price

WEE WILLIE WINKIE
HN2050
Designer: M. Davies
Height: 5¼in., 13.3cm.
Issued: 1949-1953
Price: $208 £130

WEE WILLIE WINKIE
HN3031
Designer: A. Hughes
Height: 7¾in., 19.5cm.
Issued: 1984-1987
Price: $64 £40

WELSH GIRL HN39
Designer: E. W. Light
Height: 12in., 30.5cm.
Issued: 1914-1938
Price: $1600 £1000

WANDERING MINSTREL HN1224

WIGMAKER OF WILLIAMSBURG HN2239

WARDROBE MISTRESS HN2145

FIGURES

WELSH GIRL HN92
Designer: E. W. Light
Height: 12in., 30.5cm.
Issued: 1918-1938
Colour variation
Price: $1600 £1000

WELSH GIRL HN456
Designer: E. W. Light
Height: 12in., 30.5cm.
Issued: 1921-1938
Colour variation
Price: $1600 £1000

WELSH GIRL HN514
Designer: E. W. Light
Height: 12in., 30.5cm.
Issued: 1921-1938
Colour variation
Price: $1600 £1000

WELSH GIRL HN516
Designer: E. W. Light
Height: 12in., 30.5cm.
Issued: 1921-1938
Colour variation
Price: $1600 £1000

WELSH GIRL HN519
Designer: E. W. Light
Height: 12in., 30.5cm.
Issued: 1921-1938
Colour variation
Price: $1600 £1000

WELSH GIRL HN520
Designer: E. W. Light
Height: 12in., 30.5cm.
Issued: 1921-1938
Colour variation
Price: $1600 £1000

WELSH GIRL HN660
Designer: E. W. Light
Height: 12in., 30.5cm.
Issued: 1924-1938
Colour variation
Price: $1600 £1000

WELSH GIRL HN668
Designer: E. W. Light
Height: 12in., 30.5cm.
Issued: 1924-1938
Colour variation
Price: $1600 £1000

WELSH GIRL HN669
Designer: E. W. Light
Height: 12in., 30.5cm.
Issued: 1924-1938
Colour variation
Price: $1600 £1000

WELSH GIRL HN701
Designer: E. W. Light
Height: 12in., 30.5cm.
Issued: 1925-1938
Colour variation
Price: $1600 £1000

WEE WILLIE WINKIE HN2050

WEST INDIAN DANCER HN2384

WELSH GIRL HN792
Designer: E. W. Light
Height: 12in., 30.5cm.
Issued: 1926-1938
Colour variation
Price: $1600 £1000

WENDY HN2109
Designer: L. Harradine
Height: 5in., 12.7cm.
Issued: 1953-
Rec. Retail Price

WEST INDIAN DANCER HN2384
Designer: P. Davies
Height: 8¾in., 22.2cm.
Issued: 1981 in a limited
edition of 750
Price: $520 £325

WEST WIND HN1776
Designer: R. Garbe
Height: 14½in., 36.8cm.
Issued: 1933 in a limited
edition of 25
Price: $3872 £1900

WEST WIND HN1826
Designer: R. Garbe
Height: 14½in., 36.8cm.
Issued: 1937-1949
Price: $3872 £1900|

**WIGMAKER OF
WILLIAMSBURG HN2239**
Designer: M. Davies
Height: 7½in., 19.1cm.
Issued: 1960-1983
Price: $136 £85

WILLY-WON'T-HE HN1561
Designer: L. Harradine
Height: 6in., 15.2cm.
Issued: 1933-1949
Price: $224 £140

WILLY-WON'T-HE HN1584
Designer: L. Harradine
Height: 6in., 15.2cm.
Issued: 1933-1949
Colour variation
Price: $224 £140

WILLY-WON'T-HE HN2150
Designer: L. Harradine
Height: 5½in., 14.0cm.
Issued: 1955-1959
Colour variation
Price: $200 £125

**WINDFLOWER (Style one)
HN1763**
Designer: L. Harradine
Height: 7¼in., 18.4cm.
Issued: 1936-1949
Price: $288 £180

**WINDFLOWER (Style one)
HN1764**
Designer: L. Harradine
Height: 7¼in., 18.4cm.
Issued: 1936-1949
Colour variation
Price: $288 £180

WINDFLOWER (Style one)
HN2029
Designer: L. Harradine
Height: 7¾in., 12.0cm.
Issued: 1949-1952
Colour variation
Price: $288 £180

WINDFLOWER (Style two)
HN1920
Designer: L. Harradine
Height: 11in., 27.9cm.
Issued: 1939-1949
Price: $288 £180

WINDFLOWER (Style two)
HN1939
Designer: L. Harradine
Height: 11in., 27.9cm.
Issued: 1940-1949
Colour variation
Price: $288 £180

WINDFLOWER M78
Designer: L. Harradine
Height: 4in., 10.1cm.
Issued: 1939-1949
Price: $200 £125

WINDFLOWER M79
Designer: L. Harradine
Height: 4in., 10.1cm.
Issued: 1939-1949
Colour variation
Price: $200 £125

WINDFLOWER HN3077
Designer: A. Hughes
Height: 12¼in., 31cm.
Issued: 1987
Rec. Retail Price

WINDMILL LADY HN1400
Designer: L. Harradine
Height: 8½in., 21.6cm.
Issued: 1930-1938
Price: $960 £600

WINDSWEPT HN3027
Designer: R. Jefferson
Height: 12in., 30.5cm.
Issued: 1985
Rec. Retail Price

WINNER HN1407
Designer: Unknown
Height: 6¾in., 17.2cm.
Issued: 1930-1938
Price: $2400 £1500

WINSOME HN2220
Designer: M. Davies
Height: 8in., 20.3cm.
Issued: 1960-1985
Price: $112 £70

WINTER (Style one) HN315
Designer: Unknown
Height: 7½in., 19.1cm.
Issued: 1918-1938
Price: $1200 £750

WINTER (Style one) HN475
Designer: Unknown
Height: 7½in., 19.1cm.
Issued: 1921-1938
Colour variation
Price: $1200 £750

WISTFUL HN2396

WINDFLOWER HN2029

WOOD NYMPH HN2192

WINTER (Style two) HN2088
Designer: M. Davies
Height: 6¼in., 15.9cm.
Issued: 1952-1959
Price: $288 £180

WINTER'S WALK HN3052
Designer: A. Hughes
Height: 12¼in., 31cm.
Issued: 1987
Rec. Retail Price

WINTERTIME HN3060
Designer: A. Hughes
Height: 8¾in., 22.2cm.
Issued: 1985
Price: $112 £70

WISTFUL HN2396
Designer: M. Davies
Height: 6½in., 16.5cm.
Issued: 1979-
Rec. Retail Price

WISTFUL HN2472
Designer: T. Davies
Height: 6½in., 16.5cm.
Issued: 1985-1986
Price: $112 £70

WIZARD HN2877
Designer: A. Maslankowski
Height: 9¾in., 24.8cm.
Issued: 1979-
Rec. Retail Price

WOMAN HOLDING CHILD HN462
Designer: Unknown
Height: 9¼in., 23.5cm.
Issued: 1921-1938
Price: $1360 £850

WOMAN HOLDING CHILD HN570
Designer: Unknown
Height: 9¼in., 23.5cm.
Issued: 1923-1938
          Colour variation
Price: $1360 £850

WOMAN HOLDING CHILD HN703
Designer: Unknown
Height: 9¼in., 23.5cm.
Issued: 1925-1938
          Colour variation
Price: $1360 £850

WOMAN HOLDING CHILD HN743
Designer: Unknown
Height: 9¼in., 23.5cm.
Issued: 1925-1938
          Colour variation
Price: $1360 £850

WOMAN OF THE TIME OF HENRY VI HN43
Designer: E. W. Light
Height: 9¼in., 23.4cm.
Issued: 1914-1938
Price: $1600 £1000

WOOD NYMPH HN2192
Designer: M. Davies
Height: 7¼in., 18.4cm.
Issued: 1958-1962
Price: $256 £160

WINTERTIME HN3060

WIZARD HN2877

WINTER HN2088

WRITING HN3049
Designer: P. Parsons
Height: 7¾in., 19.5cm.
Issued: 1986 in a limited
edition of 750
Price: $680 £425

Y

YEARNING HN2920 (White)
Designer: P. Gee
Height: 11¾in., 29.8cm.
Issued: 1982-1986
Price: $64 £40

YEARNING HN2921 (Black)
Designer: P. Gee
Height: 11¾in., 29.8cm.
Issued: 1982-1986
Price: $64 £40

**YEOMAN OF THE GUARD
HN688**
Designer: L. Harradine
Height: 5¾in., 14.6cm.
Issued: 1924-1938
Price: $800 £500

**YEOMAN OF THE GUARD
HN2122**
Designer: L. Harradine
Height: 5¾in., 14.6cm.
Issued: 1954-1959
Price: $640 £400

YOUNG DREAMS HN3176
Designer: D. Tootle
Height: 6¼in., 16cm.
Issued: 1988
Rec. Retail Price

YOUNG KNIGHT HN94
Designer: C. J. Noke
Height: 9½in., 24.1cm.
Issued: 1918-1936
Price: $1920 £1200

YOUNG LOVE HN2735
Designer: D. V. Tootle
Height: 10in., 25.4cm.
Issued: 1975-
Rec. Retail Price

YOUNG MASTER HN2872
Designer: M. Davies
Height: 7in., 17.8cm.
Issued: 1980-1989
Price: $104 £65

**YOUNG MISS
NIGHTINGALE HN2010**
Designer: M. Davies
Height: 9¼in., 23.5cm.
Issued: 1948-1953
Price: $560 £350

YOUNG WIDOW HN1399
Designer: L. Harradine
Height: 8in., 20.3cm.
Issued: 1930-1938
Price: $1040 £650
Also called "Little Mother"
(Style two)

YUM-YUM (Style one) HN1268
Designer: L. Harradine
Height: 5in., 12.7cm.
Issued: 1928-1938
Price: $384 £240

YUM-YUM (Style one) HN1287
Designer: L. Harradine
Height: 5in., 12.7cm.
Issued: 1928-1939
Colour variation
Price: $384 £240

YUM-YUM (Style two) HN2899
Designer: W. K. Harper
Height: 10¾in., 27.3cm.
Issued: 1980-1986
Price: $224 £140

YVONNE HN3038
Designer: A. Hughes
Height: 9in., 23cm.
Issued: 1987
Rec. Retail Price

YUM-YUM HN2899

YOUNG
MASTER HN2872

YOUNG
MISS NIGHTINGALE HN2010

KINGSWARE

Sailor's Story, a Royal Doulton Kingsware flask, circa 1910, 6½in. high.　　　$320　£200

Pied Piper, a Royal Doulton Kingsware teapot, with silver mounts, circa 1905. $240　£150

Gillie and Fisherman, a Royal Doulton Kingsware flask made for Bulloch & Lade, circa 1919, 8½in. high.　　　$336　£210

The Watchman, a Royal Doulton Kinsware flask made for Dewar's Whisky, 10½in. high, circa 1902.　　$208　£130

Royal Doulton Holbein Kingsware wall plaque decorated with a portrait of a gentleman in relief, 15¾in. diam. $416　£260

George The Guard, a Kingsware pear shaped ewer made for Dewar's, 8¼in. high, issued 1908.　　　$192　£120

Beefeater, a Royal Doulton Kingsware flask made for Dewar's Whisky, by Noke, 7¼in. high, circa 1908.　　　　$384　£240

Royal Doulton Kingsware tobacco jar decorated in relief with a gentleman smoking, 8¼in. high.　　　$120　£75

'Nelson', a Royal Doulton Kingsware flask, 7½in. high, circa 1909.　　　$384　£240

The Macnab, a Kingsware flask, made for Dewar's, 9in. high, circa 1915. $208 £130

Weller, Senior, a miniature Royal Doulton Kingsware vase, with silver hallmarked rim, circa 1909, 2¹/₄in. high.
$42 £28

Fagin, a Kingsware water jug, 8¹/₄in. high, circa 1908.
$336 £210

'For Thy Sake Tobacco I Would Do Anything But Die', a Royal Doulton Kingsware water jug, hallmarked silver rim, 8³/₄in. high, circa 1908. $304 £190

The Leather Bottle, a Royal Doulton Kingsware flask, circa 1918, 6¹/₄in. high, 6in. long.
$480 £300

Monks in the Cellar, a Royal Doulton Kingsware two-handled vase, 10¹/₄in. high, circa 1912.
$272 £170

Mr. Pickwick and Sam Weller on the reverse, a Royal Doulton Kingsware flask, circa 1930, 9¹/₂in. high. $400 £250

Uncle Sam, a Kingsware flask made for Dewar's, yellow glaze, 7¹/₂in. high, circa 1908.
$432 £270

The Connoisseur, a Kingsware pear shaped flask made for Dewar's, 8³/₄in. high.
$432 £270

Stiggins, a Royal Doulton Kingsware whisky flask, issued 1936, 8in. high. $320 £200

Bardolph, a Royal Doulton Kingsware mustard pot with silver hallmarked rim, circa 1904, 3in. high. $88 £55

Artful Dodger and Oliver Twist, a Royal Doulton Kingsware whisky flask, circa 1912, 8in. high. $448 £280

A Hunting Scene (low relief) a Royal Doulton Kingsware water jug, circa 1909, 11in. high. $256 £160

A Royal Doulton Kingsware jardiniere decorated with seagulls, circa 1910, 5$\frac{1}{2}$in. high, 9in. wide. $224 £140

Pied Piper, a Royal Doulton Kingsware two-handled vase, signed Noke, circa 1910, 11$\frac{3}{4}$in. high. $272 £170

George The Guard, a Royal Doulton Kingsware whisky flask, Dewar's Scotch Whisky, circa 1908, 8$\frac{1}{4}$in. high. $224 £140

Sporting Squire, a Kingsware flask made for Dewar's, 6$\frac{3}{4}$in. high, circa 1909. $208 £130

Tony Weller, a Royal Doulton Kingsware flask with the inscription, 'Tony Weller Bevare of the Vidders', 8in. high. $208 £130

Sporting Squire, a Royal Doulton Kingsware flask, made for Dewar's Whisky, Royal cypher on reverse, 6³/₄in. high, circa 1909. $352 £220

Peace flagon, a Kingsware flask with brown border, made for Dewar's, No. 181, 7¹/₂in. high, circa 1919. $400 £250

Micawber, a Royal Doulton Kingsware whisky flask made for Dewar's Scotch Whisky, 7in. high, issued 1909. $208 £130

Monks In the Cellar, a Royal Doulton Kingsware flask, Dewar's Scotch Whisky, circa 1905, 8¹/₂in. high. $208 £130

Dickens' Characters, a Royal Doulton Kingsware water jug, 7in. high. $208 £130

Bonnie Prince Charlie, a Royal Doulton Kingsware flask made for Dewar's Whisky, 7in. high, circa 1913. $208 £130

Crusader, a Royal Doulton Kingsware whisky flask, Greenlees Bros. Scotch whisky, circa 1913, 8in. high. $384 £240

Nightwatchman, a Kingsware water jug, by Noke, 5¹/₂in. high. $112 £70

Don Quixote, a Royal Doulton Kingsware flagon, 10¹/₂in. high, circa 1913. $464 £290

Mr. Pickwick Proposes The Toast, a Royal Doulton Kingsware flask, signed Noke, circa 1912, 8in. high. $352 £220

Mr. Pickwick, a miniature Royal Doulton Kingsware jug with silver hallmarked rim, circa 1907, 2½in. high. $112 £70

The Jovial Monk, a Kingsware flask made for Dewar's, 8in. high, circa 1908. $224 £140

Oyez, Oyez, ewer shaped Kingsware flask made for Dewar's Scotch Whisky, 10½in. high, issued 1909. $192 £120

Royal Doulton Kingsware mug with silver rim, 4in. high. $112 £70

Church-Warden, a Kingsware flask made for Dewar's Whisky, 9½in. high, circa 1907. $448 £280

George The Guard, a Royal Doulton Kingsware whisky flask, Dewar's Scotch Whisky, circa 1908, 10in. high. $208 £130

The Alchemist, a Royal Doulton Kingsware flask, by Noke, circa 1913, 8¼in. high. $400 £250

Pied Piper, a Royal Doulton Kingsware milk jug with silver mounts, circa 1905. $96 £60

Bill Sykes, a miniature Royal Doulton Kingsware loving cup with silver hallmarked rim, circa 1907, 2¹/₂in. high.
$128 £80

Witches, a small pair of Royal Doulton Kingsware two-handled vases, circa 1912, 4¹/₂in. high.
$176 £110

Sam Weller, a miniature Royal Doulton Kingsware loving cup, hallmarked silver rim, circa 1909, 1³/₄in. high.
$128 £80

Royal Doulton Kingsware single-handled jug depicting a golfer and his caddie.
$448 £280

Nelson, a Royal Doulton Kingsware triangular flask, 8in. high, 6in. wide, 1914.
$352 £220

Pirates, a Royal Doulton whisky flask, by Noke, circa 1909, 6in. high.
$448 £280

Ben Jonson, a Kingsware flask made for Dewar's Scotch Whisky, issued 1909, 7in. high.
$192 £120

Sydney Harbour, a Royal Doulton triangular Kingsware flask, Dewar's Scotch Whisky, 6¹/₂in. high, circa 1914.
$512 £320

Double Foxes (one curled), a Royal Doulton Kingsware tobacco jug with silver hall-marked rim, circa 1912, 7¹/₂in. high.
$512 £320

Darby and Joan, a Royal Doulton tea cup, circa 1912, 2³/₄in. high. $80 £50

Royal Doulton Kingsware sugar bowl with silver mounts, circa 1905. $112 £70

Mr. Pickwick, a Royal Doulton Kingsware tea cup in low relief, circa 1912, 2¹/₂in. high. $80 £50

He's A Jolly Good Fellow, Dr. Johnson at The Cheshire Cheese, a Royal Doulton Kingsware whisky flask, circa 1924, 8in. high. $352 £220

Royal Doulton Kingsware Duke of York water jug, 7¹/₄in. high. $288 £180

Admiral of the Fleet, a Royal Doulton Kingsware flask, Dewar's Scotch Whisky, circa 1916, 7¹/₂in. high. $464 £290

Don Quixote, a Royal Doulton Kingsware mug, 4¹/₂in. high, circa 1912. $112 £70

John Barleycorn, a Royal Doulton Kingsware flask, circa 1931, 7in. high. $240 £150

Squire, a Kingsware Toby jug, hallmarked silver rim, 6¹/₂in. high. $480 £300

Peace flagon, a Kingsware flask with green border, made for Dewar's, No. 187, 7¹/₂in. high, circa 1919. $448 £280

Small fox, head down, a Royal Doulton Kingsware tobacco jar with hallmarked silver rim, circa 1912, 7³/₄in. high. $496 £310

Watchman, a Kingsware globular shaped flask, 8in. high, with modelled head. $224 £140

Royal Doulton Kingsware single handled jug depicting golfers, 9in. high. $432 £270

Huntsman, a Royal Doulton Kingsware loving cup, issued 1932, 8in. high. $224 £140

Pied Piper, a Royal Doulton Kingsware two-handled vase, signed Noke, circa 1910, 11¹/₄in. high. $224 £140

Don Quixote, a Kingsware water jug, 10¹/₂in. high, circa 1913. $216 £135

Memories, a Kingsware water jug depicting Dickens' characters. $120 £75

Pied Piper, a Royal Doulton Kingsware water jug with hallmarked silver rim and lid, 8¹/₂in. high. $240 £150

Bill Sykes, a Royal Doulton Kingsware pear-shaped whisky flask, circa 1905, 7³/₄in. high. $352 £220

One of the Forty, a Royal Doulton Kingsware ashtray, designed by H. Tittensor, circa 1921, 3³/₄in. high, HN423. $448 £280

The Crown, a Kingsware George VI commemorative flask, made for Dewar's Whisky, 1,000 issued 1937, 6in. high. $544 £340

Bardolph, a Royal Doulton Kingsware water jug, 7¹/₄in. high, circa 1902. $144 £90

Pair of Royal Doulton Kingsware candlesticks, a Hunting Scene in low relief, circa 1912, 11in. high. $400 £250

The Alchemist, a Royal Doulton Kingsware clock, 7¹/₂in. high, circa 1913. $640 £400

Parson Jones, a Royal Doulton Kingsware water jug, 7¹/₂in. high, circa 1935. $224 £140

Tony Weller, a Royal Doulton Kingsware whisky flask, circa 1912, 9¹/₂in. high. $560 £350

Pied Piper, a Royal Doulton Kingsware coffee pot with silver mounts, circa 1905. $240 £150

297

Huntsman, a Royal Doulton Kingsware Toby jug, 7¹/₂in. high. $400 £250

Mr. Pecksniff, a miniature Royal Doulton Kingsware vase with hallmarked silver rim, circa 1909, 2in. high.
$112 £70

Ben Johnson, a Royal Doulton Kingsware flask made for Dewar's Scotch Whisky, 7in. high, issued in 1909.
$48 £30

Falstaff, green hat, a Royal Doulton Kingsware whisky flask, Dewar's Scotch Whisky, 7¹/₂in. high, circa 1907.
$208 £130

Nelson, a Kingsware flat-shaped flask made for Dewar's, circa 1914, 8¹/₂in. high. $272 £170

Tavern Scenes, a Royal Doulton Kingsware two-handled vase, 6in. high, circa 1920.
$192 £120

Chadband (Bleak House), a Royal Doulton Kingsware whisky flask, 8in. high, circa 1912. $384 £240

Nightwatchman, a Royal Doulton Kingsware jug, by Noke, 7in. high. $144 £90

Parson Brown, a Royal Doulton Kingsware water jug, 7¹/₂in. high, circa 1935. $224 £140

Royal Doulton Kingsware whisky flask in the form of Tony Weller, 3¹/₂in. high. $400 £250

Memories, a Kingsware water jug depicting Dickens' characters. $120 £75

Jovial Monk, a Kingsware flask made for Dewar's Scotch Whisky, issued 1908, 7³/₄in. high. $240 £150

Fisherman, a Royal Doulton Kingsware flask, signed Noke, circa 1904, 7in. high. $352 £220

Royal Doulton jug in low relief by Charles Crombie, depicting a golfer, 9¹/₄in. high, circa 1910. $496 £310

A Hunting Scene, Kingsware water jug, 6¹/₂in. high. $160 £100

George V Coronation, a Kingsware jug with silver hallmarked rim, circa 1911, 6³/₄in. high. $352 £220

Mr. Pickwick and Sam Weller, a Royal Doulton Kingsware coffee pot with hallmarked silver rim, signed Noke, circa 1909, 6¹/₂in. high. $256 £160

Drink Wisely But Not Too Well, a Kingsware water jug of a pipe-smoking man, 8in. high. $208 £130

Wizard, a large Royal Doulton
Kingsware ewer, circa 1905,
16¹/₂in. high. $560 £350

Royal Doulton Kingsware coffee
pot, with silver mounts, circa
1905. $240 £150

Watchman, a Royal Doulton
Kingsware flask, circa 1930,
10¹/₂in. high. $208 £130

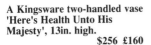

A Kingsware two-handled vase
'Here's Health Unto His
Majesty', 13in. high.
              $256 £160

Coachman, a Doulton Kingsware flagon, issued 1932, 10¹/₂in.
high. $240 £150

Wizard, a Royal Doulton Kingsware flask decorated with a
wizard standing over a cauldron,
designed by Noke, 10in. high,
issued 1904. $448 £280

LOVING CUPS & JUGS

ADMIRAL LORD NELSON LOVING CUP
Designed by C.J. Noke & H. Fenton, 10½in.
Issued 1935 in a limited edition of 600.

$640 £400

THE APOTHECARY LOVING CUP
Designed by C.J. Noke & H. Fenton, 6in. high,
Issued 1934 in a limited edition of 600.

$480 £300

CAPTAIN COOK LOVING CUP
Designed by C.J. Noke & H. Fenton, 9½in. high,
Issued 1933 in a limited edition of 350.

$2400 £1500

CAPTAIN PHILLIP JUG
Designed by C.J. Noke & H. Fenton, 9¼in. high,
Issued 1938 in a limited edition of 350.

$4800 £3000

CHARLES DICKENS JUG
Designed by C.J. Noke & H. Fenton, 10½in. high,
Issued 1936 in a limited edition of 1000.
$560 £350

DICKENS DREAM JUG
Designed by C.J. Noke, 10½in. high,
Issued 1933 in a limited edition of 1000.
$640 £400

GEORGE WASHINGTON BICENTENARY JUG
Designed by C.J. Noke & H. Fenton, 10¾in. high, Issued 1932 in a limited edition of 1000, Colour
variation on handle. $7200 £4500

LOVING CUPS & JUGS

JACKDAW OF RHEIMS JUG
Designer - Unknown, 11in. high,
Issued - Trial Jug circa 1934. $4500 £3000

GEORGE WASHINGTON BICENTENARY JUG
Designed by C.J. Noke & H. Fenton, 10³/₄in. high,
Issued 1932 in a limited edition of 1000,
Variation on handle style. $3200 £2000

JAN VAN RIEBECK LOVING CUP
Designed by C.J. Noke & H. Fenton, 10¹/₄in. high,
Issued circa 1935 in a limited edition of 300.
                                   $2400 £1500

GUY FAWKES JUG
Designed by H. Fenton, 7¹/₂in. high, Issued 1934 in a limited edition of 600. $560 £350

JOHN PEEL LOVING CUP
Designer - Unknown, 9in. high,
Issued 1933 in a limited edition of 500.

$720 £450

KING EDWARD VIII CORONATION LOVING CUP (Small)
Designed by C.J. Noke, 6¹/₂in. high,
Issued 1937 in a limited edition of 1000.

$320 £200

KING EDWARD VIII CORONATION LOVING CUP (Large)
Designed by C.J. Noke & H. Fenton, 10in. high,
Issued 1937 in a limited edition of 2000.

$560 £350

KING GEORGE V AND QUEEN MARY SILVER JUBILEE LOVING CUP
Designed by C.J. Noke & H. Fenton, 10in. high,
Issued 1935 in a limited edition of 1000.

$560 £350

**KING GEORGE VI AND QUEEN ELIZABETH
CORONATION LOVING CUP (Large)**
Designed by C.J. Noke & H. Fenton, 10½in. high,
Issued 1937 in a limited edition of 2000.
$560 £350

**KING GEORGE VI AND QUEEN ELIZABETH
CORONATION LOVING CUP (Small)**
Designed by C.J. Noke & H. Fenton, 6½in. high,
Issued 1937 in a limited edition of 2000.
$400 £250

MASTER OF FOXHOUNDS PRESENTATION JUG
Designed by C.J. Noke, 13in. high, Issued 1930 in a limited edition of 500.　　　$560 £350

MAYFLOWER LOVING CUP
Designed by David Biggs, 10$^{1}/_{4}$in. high,
Issued 1970 in a limited edition of 500.
$160 £100

PIED PIPER JUG
Designed by C.J. Noke & H. Fenton, 10in. high,
Issued 1934 in a limited edition of 600.
$720 £450

POTTERY IN THE PAST LOVING CUP
Designed by Graham Tongue, 6in. high, Issued 1983.
$160 £100

QUEEN ELIZABETH II CORONATION JUG
Designer - Unknown, 6$^{1}/_{4}$in. high,
Issued 1953 unlimited.
$136 £85

QUEEN ELIZABETH II CORONATION LOVING CUP
Designed by C.J. Noke & H. Fenton, 10½in. high, Issued 1953 in a limited edition of 1000.
$560 £350

QUEEN ELIZABETH SILVER JUBILEE LOVING CUP
Designed by R. Johnson, 10½in. high, Issued 1977 in a limited edition of 250.
$640 £400

REGENCY COACH JUG
Designed by C.J. Noke, 10in. high, Issued 1931 in a limited edition of 500.
$640 £400

ROBIN HOOD LOVING CUP
Designed by C.J. Noke & H. Fenton, 8½in. high, Issued 1938 in a limited edition of 600.
$560 £350

SIR FRANCIS DRAKE JUG
Designed by C.J. Noke & H. Fenton, 10½in. high,
Issued 1933 in a limited edition of 500.
$560 £350

THE THREE MUSKETEERS LOVING CUP
Designed by C.J. Noke & H. Fenton, 10in. high,
Issued 1936 in a limited edition of 600.
$640 £400

TREASURE ISLAND JUG
Designed by C.J. Noke & H. Fenton, 7¹/₂in. high,
Issued in 1934 in a limited edition of 600.
$560 £350

TOWER OF LONDON JUG
Designed by C.J. Noke & H. Fenton, 9¹/₂in. high,
Issued 1933 in a limited edition of 500.
$560 £350

THE VILLAGE BLACKSMITH JUG
Designed by C.J. Noke, 7³/₄in. high, Issued 1936 in a limited edition of 600. $560 £350

THE WANDERING MINSTREL LOVING CUP
Designed by C.J. Noke & H. Fenton, 5$^1/_2$in. high, Issued 1934 in a limited edition of 600.
$320 £200

WILLIAM SHAKESPEARE JUG
Designed by C.J. Noke, 10$^3/_4$in. high, Issued 1933 in a
limited edition of 1000. $560 £350

WILLIAM WORDSWORTH LOVING CUP
Designed by C.J. Noke, 6$^1/_2$in. high, Issued 1933
unlimited. $1200 £750

MISCELLANEOUS WARE

ASH BOWLS

AULD MAC D6006
Size: 3in., 7.5cm.
Issued: 1939-1960
Price: $104 £65

FARMER JOHN D6007
Size: 3in., 7.5cm.
Issued: 1939-1960
Price: $104 £65

OLD CHARLEY D5925
Size: 3in., 7.5cm.
Issued: 1938-1960
Price: $104 £65

PADDY D5926
Size: 3in., 7.5cm.
Issued: 1938-1960
Price: $104 £65

PARSON BROWN D6008
Size: 3in., 7.5cm.
Issued: 1939-1960
Price: $104 £65

SAIREY GAMP D6009
Size: 3in., 7.5cm.
Issued: 1939-1960
Price: $104 £65

ASH TRAYS

DICK TURPIN D5601
Size: 2¾in., 7cm.
Issued: 1936-1960
Price: $104 £65

JOHN BARLEYCORN D5602
Size: 2¾in., 7cm.
Issued: 1936-1960
Price: $104 £65

OLD CHARLEY D5599
Size: 2¾in., 7cm.
Issued: 1936-1960
Price: $104 £65

PARSON BROWN D5600
Size: 2¾in., 7cm.
Issued: 1936-1960
Price: $104 £65

DICK TURPIN

JOHN BARLEYCORN

OLD CHARLEY

PARSON BROWN

311

BOOKENDS

MR MICAWBER HN1615
Size: 4in., 10cm.
Issued: 1934-c.1939
Price: $640 £400

MR PICKWICK HN1623
Size: 4in., 10cm.
Issued: 1934-c.1939
Price: $640 £400

SAIREY GAMP HN1625
Size: 4in., 10cm.
Issued: 1934-c.1939
Price: $640 £400

TONY WELLER HN1616
Size: 4in., 10cm.
Issued: 1934-c.1939
Price: $640 £400

BUSTS

HRH Princess Anne, designed by E. J. Griffiths, introduced 1973, 11in. high, limited edition of 750, to commemorate her marriage to Captain Mark Phillips. $120 £75

HM Queen Elizabeth II and HRH The Duke of Edinburgh, designed by E. J. Griffiths, 10½in. and 11¼in. high, introduced 1972, limited edition of 750. Royal Silver Wedding Anniversary. $240 £150

Sir Winston Churchill, designed by E. J. Griffiths, 11¼in. high, introduced 1974, limited edition of 750, to commemorate the centenary of his birth. $120 £75

BUSTS

BUZ FUZ D6048
Issued: 1939-1960
Price: $64 £40

MR MICAWBER D6050
Issued: 1939-1960
Price: $64 £40

MR PICKWICK D6049
Issued: 1939-1960
Price: $64 £40

SAIREY GAMP D6047
Issued: 1939-1960
Price: $64 £40

SAM WELLER D6052
Issued: 1939-1960
Price: $64 £40

TONY WELLER D6051
Issued: 1939-1960
Price: $64 £40

BUZ FUZ

MR MICAWBER

MR PICKWICK

SAIREY GAMP

SAM WELLER

TONY WELLER

DICKENS TINIES

ARTFUL DODGER D6678
Designer: P. Gee
Issued: 1982
Price: $35 £22

BILL SYKES D6684
Designer: M. Abberley
Issued: 1982
Price: $35 £22

BETSY TROTWOOD D6684
Designer: M. Abberley
Issued: 1982
Price: $35 £22

CHARLES DICKENS D6688
Designer: E. Griffiths
Issued: 1982
Price: $35 £22

DAVID COPPERFIELD D6680
Designer: M. Abberley
Issued: 1982
Price: $35 £22

FAGIN D6679
Designer: R. Tabbenor
Issued: 1982
Price: $35 £22

LITTLE NELL D6681
Designer: M. Abberley
Issued: 1982
Price: $35 £22

MR BUMBLE D6686
Designer: R. Tabbenor
Issued: 1982
Price: $35 £22

MRS BARDELL D6687
Designer: R. Tabbenor
Issued: 1982
Price: $35 £22

OLIVER TWIST D6677
Designer: R. Tabbenor
Issued: 1982
Price: $35 £22

SCROOGE D6682
Designer: M. Abberley
Issued: 1982
Price: $35 £22

URIAH HEEP D6682
Designer: R. Tabbenor
Issued: 1982
Price: $35 £22

MUSICAL JUGS

AULD MAC D5889
Issued: 1938-c.1939
Price: $768 £480

OLD CHARLEY D5858
Issued: 1937-c.1939
Price: $640 £400

OLD KING COLE D6014
Issued: 1939
Price: $1600 £1000

OLD KING COLE (Yellow Crown) D6014
Issued: 1939
Price: $2480 £1550

PADDY D5887
Issued: 1938-1939
Price: $720 £450

TONY WELLER D5888
Issued: 1938-1939
Price: $680 £425

OLD KING COLE

NAPKIN RINGS

FAT BOY M59
Issued: 1935-1939
Price: $288 £180

MR MICAWBER M58
Issued: 1935-1939
Price: $288 £180

MR PICKWICK M57
Issued: 1935-1939
Price: $288 £180

SAIREY GAMP M62
Issued: 1935-1939
Price: $288 £180

SAM WELLER M61
Issued: 1935-1939
Price: $288 £180

TONY WELLER M60
Issued: 1935-1939
Price: $288 £180

FAT BOY

MR MICAWBER

MR PICKWICK

SAIREY GAMP

SAM WELLER

TONY WELLER

SUGAR BOWLS

OLD CHARLEY D6012
Size: 2½in., 6.5cm.
Issued: 1939
Price: $400 £250

SAIREY GAMP D6011
Size: 2½in., 6.5cm.
Issued: 1939
Price: $320 £200

TONY WELLER D6013
Size: 2½in., 6.5cm.
Issued: 1939
Price: $400 £250

OLD CHARLEY

SAIREY GAMP

TONY WELLER

TABLE LIGHTERS

BACCHUS D6505
Size: 3½in., 9cm.
Issued: 1964-1974
Price: $96 £60

BEEFEATER D6233
Size: 3½in., 9cm.
Issued: 1958-1973
Price: $96 £60

BUZ FUZ D5838
Size: 3½in., 9cm.
Issued: 1958
Price: $120 £75

BACCHUS   BEEFEATER   BUZ FUZ

CAPTAIN AHAB D6506
Size: 3½in., 9cm.
Issued: 1964-1974
Price: $96 £60

CAP'N CUTTLE D5842
Size: 3½in., 9cm.
Issued: 1958
Price: $128 £80

FALSTAFF D6385
Size: 3½in., 9cm.
Issued: 1958-1973
Price: $96 £60

CAPTAIN AHAB   CAP'N CUTTLE   FALSTAFF

LAWYER D6504
Size: 3½in., 9cm.
Issued: 1962-1974
Price: $96 £60

LONG JOHN SILVER D6386
Size: 3½in., 9cm.
Issued: 1958-1973
Price: $96 £60

MR MICAWBER D5843
Size: 3½in., 9cm.
Issued: 1958
Price: $120 £75

LAWYER   LONG JOHN SILVER   MR MICAWBER

MR PICKWICK D5839
Size: 3½in., 9cm.
Issued: 1958-1961
Price: $104 £65

OLD CHARLEY D5527
Size: 3½in., 9cm.
Issued: 1959-1973
Price: $96 £60

POACHER D6464
Size: 3½in., 9cm.
Issued: 1958-1973
Price: $96 £60

PORTHOS D6453
Size: 3½in., 9cm.
Issued: 1958
Price: $208 £130

RIP VAN WINKLE D6463
Size: 3½in., 9cm.
Issued: 1958
Price: $240 £150

MR PICKWICK   POACHER   RIP VAN WINKLE

TEAPOTS

FALSTAFF D6854
Designer: W.K. Harper
Size: 6½in., 16.5cm.
Issued: 1989
Rec. Retail Price

LONG JOHN SILVER D6853
Designer: W.K. Harper
Size: 6½in., 16.5cm.
Issued: 1989
Rec. Retail Price

OLD BALLOON SELLER D6855
Designer: W.K. Harper
Size: 6½in., 16.5cm.
Issued: 1990
Rec. Retail Price

OLD CHARLEY D6017
Size: 7in., 18cm.
Issued: 1939
Price: $1360 £850

OLD SALT D6818
(Collectors' Club)
Designer: W.K. Harper
Size: 6½in., 16.5cm.
Issued: 1988
Price: $304 £190

SAIREY GAMP D6015
Size: 7in., 18cm.
Issued: 1939
Price: $1360 £850

TONY WELLER D6016
Size: 7in., 18cm.
Issued: 1939
Price: $1360 £850

OLD SALT

SAIREY GAMP

OLD CHARLEY

TOBACCO JARS

OLD CHARLEY D5844
Size: 5½in., 14cm.
Issued: 1938-1941
Price: $576 £360

PADDY D5854
Size: 5½in., 14cm.
Issued: 1938-1941
Price: $608 £380

OLD CHARLEY   PADDY

TOOTHPICK HOLDERS

OLD CHARLEY D6152
Size: 2¼in., 5.5cm.
Issued: 1940-1941
Price: $240 £150

PADDY D6151
Size: 2¼in., 5.5cm.
Issued: 1940-1941
Price: $240 £150

SAIREY GAMP D6150
Size: 2¼in., 5.5cm.
Issued: 1940-1941
Price: $240 £150

OLD CHARLEY PADDY SAIREY GAMP

WALL VASES

JESTER D6111
Size: 7¼in., 18cm.
Issued: 1940-1941
Price: $880 £550

OLD CHARLEY D6110
Size: 7¼in., 18cm.
Issued: 1940-1941
Price: $880 £550

JESTER   OLD CHARLEY

317

WALL MASKS

A Royal Doulton miniature face mask, 'Jester', possibly HN1611, 7.7cm. long, c.m. $992 £620

A Royal Doulton face mask, 'Jester', probably HN1630, 28.5cm. long, c.m.l. & c., date code for 1937. $256 £160

A Royal Doulton miniature face mask, 'Jester', possibly HN1609, 7.5cm. long, c.m. $1152 £720

A Royal Doulton 'Grey Friar' wall mask, 7¼in. high, circa 1940-41. $560 £350

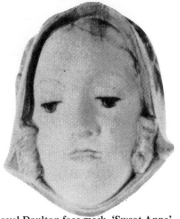

A Royal Doulton face mask, 'Sweet Anne', HN1590, design attributed to L. Harradine, 20.2cm. long, c.m.l. & c., impressed date 4.7.33. $400 £250

A Royal Doulton miniature face mask, possibly by L. Harradine, HN1614, 7cm. high, c.m. $480 £300

PANELS

In the early 20th century the Doulton works began producing decorative pottery tiles in large numbers for the embellishment of both interiors and exteriors of shops, bars and other establishments.

Making pictures and decorations from tiles was however far from being a new idea for as far back as the Egyptian Pharaohs the device had been used and some very beautiful tiles can still be seen in mosques of Iran and other Moslem countries. The Persian tile with its intricate foliage decoration and brilliant colours was an artistic masterpiece.

Doulton's idea of making whole pictures from tiles however was a new departure and their creations were used in the decoration of hospital wards, especially children's wards, where the artists let their fancies run free. The results were wonderful creations of nursery rhymes and fantasy children's scenes which must have diverted the minds of many small patients.

Tiled walls were not only decorative but they also had the advantage of being easily washed down and cleaned for it was a time when medical authorities were beginning to realise the importance of hygiene in hospitals.

By the 1950's however, modernisation programmes meant that tiled walls were either torn out or covered over with boarding. Those that have survived are now being preserved as works of art. Prices range from a few hundred pounds for a pictorial set of six to as much as ten thousand pounds for a large pictorial wall panel.

HERE WE GO GATHERING NUTS IN MAY

SIMPLE SIMON MET A PIEMAN

HANSEL AND GRETEL

THE GOOSE GIRL

SLEEPING BEAUTY

OLD MOTHER HUBBARD

CINDERELLA

PUSS IN BOOTS

LITTLE MISS MUFFET

SLEEPING PRINCESS

THERE WAS AN OLD WOMAN WHO LIVED IN A SHOE

LADY QUEEN ANNE

LITTLE BOY BLUE

THE QUEEN OF HEARTS

HIGGLEDY, PIGGLEDY, MY BLACK HEN

LITTLE BO-PEEP

PUSS IN BOOTS

OLD KING COLE WAS A MERRY OLD SOUL

LITTLE JACK HORNER

DING, DONG, BELL, PUSSY'S IN THE WELL

LITTLE RED RIDING HOOD

SEE-SAW, MARGERY DAW

SERIES WARE

Gaffers Series sugar bowl, 3in. high, circa 1915, depicting a gaffer outside a cottage. $56 £35

Coaching Days, a Series ware jardiniere, 6½in. high. $160 £100

Monks in the Cellar Series sugar bowl, 3½in. high, circa 1909, depicting a monk drinking. $61 £38

Willow Pattern Series jar and cover, 6½in. high, circa 1912. $120 £75

English Cottages Series, two-handled cup, 4in. high, circa 1924, depicting an old English cottage. $56 £35

Silhouette Series biscuit barrel, silver plated rim and lid, 5½in. high, depicting Country Scenes. $61 £38

Oliver Twist tankard in low relief, designed by C.J. Noke, issued 1949-1960. $96 £60

The Gleaners, Series ware sandwich tray. $61 £38

Nightwatchman Series tobacco jar, 5½in. high circa 1909, by Noke, depicting a watchman carrying a pike. $77 £48

A Royal Doulton Cecil Aldin Series ware jardiniere, the decoration from the 'Old English Scenes', 18cm. high. $272 £170

A sampler pattern Series ware tankard, 7in. high. $64 £40

Shakespeare Series art pot, 7¹/₂in. high, 10in. diam., circa 1922. $192 £120

'Country Garden', Series ware tray 'Old Man with Scythe', 1929. $61 £38

Dickens' ware 'Friar' shape jug depicting 'Poor Joe', 4³/₄in. high. $56 £35

Rural England Series candlesticks, 7in. high, circa 1925. $88 £55

Hunting Series spirit barrel and stand, 7in. high, circa 1924. $640 £400

Sunday Smocks Series, two-handled bowl, 3in. high, circa 1936, depicting an old man holding a basket. $40 £25

Nightwatchman Series sugar bowl and cover, 3¹/₂in. high, circa 1909. $56 £35

Under The Greenwood Tree Series sugar bowl and cover, 4in. high, circa 1914, depicting life in Sherwood Forest. $56 £35

'Hastings Castle', Churches and Castle Series vase, 8in. high, circa 1901. $72 £45

'Country Garden' Series dish depicting the 'Maid at the Well', circa 1929. $61 £38

Royal Doulton Series ware coffee pot, 7¹/₂in. tall, D5506, 1934. $64 £40

Robert Burns portrait plaque with his cottage in the background, 10¹/₄in. diam. $45 £28

A Royal Doulton jug and basin set depicting Sydney Carton. $320 £200

Gallant Fishers large Series art pot, by Izaak Walton, 12in. high, circa 1908. $448 £280

JUGS

'Little Nell', Dickens' Series jug, 7in. high, circa 1908.
$72 £45

Countryside Series water jug, 7in. high, circa 1936. $72 £45

Country Garden Series jug and cover, 7¹/₂in. high, circa 1929.
$77 £48

Rural England Series jug, 7in. high, circa 1933, depicting lambs in a field. $61 £38

Gleaners and Gypsies Series water jug, 7in. high, circa 1909, depicting a gypsy with bundle of corn. $88 £55

Egyptian Series jug, 7in. high, circa 1902. $72 £45

Rural England (Welsh) Series water jug, 12¹/₂in. high, circa 1907, depicting a woman in traditional dress. $109 £68

Oliver Twist jug designed by C.J. Noke, depicting 'Fagin and Bumble', D5617. $104 £65

The Bayeux Tapestry Series jug, 6¹/₂in. high, circa 1907, depicting Harold on horseback.
$61 £38

JUGS

'Mr Pickwick', Dickens' Series jug, 7in. high, circa 1912. $72 £45

Desert Scenes Series water jug, 6in. high, circa 1909, depicting a woman on a camel. $64 £40

Gondoliers Series jug, 7in. high, circa 1909, depicting a Venice scene. $93 £58

Gallant Fishers Series jug, by Izaak Walton, 7in. high, circa 1906, depicting a fisherman on the bank. $88 £55

A Jacobean jug 'Ye Old Belle' depicting a serving wench and two cavaliers, 6½in. high. $104 £65

Sunday Smocks Series jug and cover, 8in. high, circa 1936, depicting a man under a tree. $77 £48

'Sam Weller', Dickens' Series jug, 7¼in. high, circa 1912. $77 £48

Under The Greenwood Tree Series jug, 8in. high, circa 1937, depicting Friar Tuck and Robin Hood. $77 £48

Nightwatchman Series water jug, by C.J. Noke, 6¾in. high, circa 1907. $80 £50

JUGS

Silhouette Series jug, 4in. high, depicting Country Scenes.
$40 £25

Old Moreton Hall Series water jug, 4¹/₂in. high, circa 1915, depicting gentlemen in a mid 16th century scene. $51 £32

Sir Roger de Coverley Series cream jug, 3¹/₂in. high, circa 1911, depicting Sir Roger on horseback. $51 £32

Canterbury Pilgrims Series jug, 7¹/₂in. high, circa 1909, depicting Pilgrims on Horseback. $77 £48

'Nightwatchman', a Series ware jug by C.J. Noke, 8¹/₂in. high, D1198, 1903. $88 £55

Shakespeare Series jug, 12in. high, circa 1912, depicting 'Wolsey'. $104 £65

Huntsman Series water jug, 11in. high, circa 1906, depicting two huntsmen at the inn. $104 £65

Rural England Series Country Gardens jug, 7in. high, circa 1929, depicting a cottage by a pond. $77 £48

Under The Greenwood Tree Series water jug, 8¹/₂in. high, circa 1937. $77 £48

JUGS

Water jug in low relief depicting 'Tony Weller', D6397.
$96 £60

'Old London' jug in low relief designed by C.J. Noke, issued 1949-1960, D6291. $120 £75

Famous Sailing Ships Series jug, 4¹/₂in. high, circa 1938.
$45 £28

Monks in the Cellar Series water jug, 8in. high, circa 1909.
$77 £48

Under The Greenwood Tree Series, jug, 7in. high, circa 1937, depicting Friar Tuck and Robin Hood. $72 £45

New Cavaliers Series water jug, 12in. high, circa 1907, depicting two cavaliers toasting.
$104 £65

'Sir Toby Belch', Shakespeare Series jug, 8¹/₂in. high, circa 1904, quotation 'Maria, I Say a Stoop of Wine'. $80 £50

'Fagin', Dickens' Series jug, 6¹/₂in. high, circa 1912.
$77 £48

Wedlock Series water jug, 11in. high, circa 1905, depicting a gentleman and a lady with a fan.
$104 £65

PLATES

'Sairey Gamp' rack plate,
Dickens' Series, 10¹/₄in. diam.,
circa 1912. $56 £35

'The Fleur-De-Lys, St. Albans'
rack plate, Old English Inns
Series, 10¹/₄in. diam., circa 1939.
          $56 £35

'Painted Feelings' rack plate,
Behind the Painted Masque
Limited Edition Series, 9in.
diam., 1982. $24 £15

'Thunder in the Air' rack plate,
Aged in Wood Limited Edition
Series, 10¹/₂in. diam. $48 £30

'Gibson Girl' rack plate
designed by Charles Dana
Gibson, circa 1901. $104 £65

'Marshlands' rack plate,
Collectors Limited Edition
Series, 10¹/₂in. diam., 1981.
          $24 £15

Early Motoring Series titled
'Deaf', 10¹/₂in. diam., circa 1906.
          $192 £120

Series ware rack plate 'Mother
Kangaroo and Toby', 10¹/₂in.
diam. $24 £15

'Noble Heritage' rack plate,
Collectors Series, Limited
Edition, 8¹/₄in. diam., 1981.
          $40 £25

PLATES

'Arabian Nights' rack plate, 'The Arrival of the Unknown Princess', 10¼in. diam. $56 £35

'Kathleen and Child' plate, Collectors Limited Edition Series, 8¼in. diam., 1981. $40 £25

Old English Inns Series ware rack plate depicting 'The Bear's Head', 10in. diam. $42 £26

'At the Cheshire Cheese', Dr. Johnson Series rack plate, 13in. diam., circa 1909. $61 £38

'Gibson Girl' rack plate, by Charles Dana Gibson, circa 1901. $104 £65

'Winning Colours' rack plate, Collectors Limited Edition Series, 10½in. diam. $24 £15

'Weathering the Storm' rack plate, Aged in Wood Limited Edition Series, 10¼in. diam., $35 £22

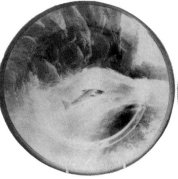

'Short Headed Salmon', a Royal Doulton rack plate, signed by J. Birbeck, 9½in. diam., circa 1913. $192 £120

'Edinburgh Castle', rack plate, 10½in. diam. $29 £18

337

PLATES

'The Old Balloon Seller' rack plate in low relief, 10½in. diam. $56 £35

'Make Me Laugh' rack plate, Behind the Painted Masque Limited Edition Series, 9in. diam., 1982. $24 £15

'Aero', a Royal Doulton commemorative rack plate, 1909. $224 £140

Rack plate 'Autumn' from 'The Seasons'. $29 £18

Charles Dickens portrait plate with a border of Dickens' characters, 10¼in. diam. $56 £35

Series ware rack plate 'The Seasons', 'Winter' $29 £18

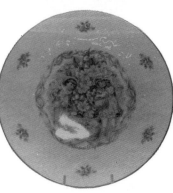

Royal Doulton rack plate 'Short Headed Salmon', signed J. Birbeck, 9½in. diam., circa 1909. $192 £120

'Valentine's Day' Series ware rack plate, 1985, 6¼in. diam. $24 £15

'Gibson Girl' rack plate designed by Charles Dana Gibson, circa 1901. $104 £65

TEAPOTS

'Gallant Fishers' teapot, by
Izaak Walton, 6in. high, circa
1906. $88 £55

Under The Greenwood Tree
teapot, 4¹/₂in. high, circa 1937,
depicting Robin Hood and Friar
Tuck. $93 £58

Gondoliers Series teapot, 5¹/₂in.
high, circa 1909. $88 £55

Silhouette Series teapot, 5in.
high, depicting Country Scenes.
                        $70 £44

A Series ware teapot, 5¹/₂in.
high, circa 1930, depicting the
Old Woman Who Lived in the
Shoe. $88 £55

Old Moreton Hall Series teapot,
4¹/₂in. high, circa 1915,
depicting Queen Elizabeth I
outside.
                        $88 £55

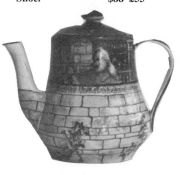

'Fagin', Dickens' Series teapot,
5¹/₂in. high, circa 1930.
                        $77 £48

Jackdaw of Rheims Series
teapot, 6¹/₂in. high, circa 1908,
depicting The Cardinal.
                        $88 £55

Sir Roger de Coverley Series
teapot, 5in. high, circa 1911,
depicting Sir Roger in the
garden. $88 £55

Arabian Nights Series teapot,
5in. high, circa 1909, depicting
the attendants. $88 £55

'Old Moreton Hall' Series ware
teapot, 5¹/₂in. high. $67 £42

Monks in the Cellar Series
teapot, 4¹/₂in. high, circa 1909,
depicting a monk inspecting the
food. $96 £60

VASES

Rural England (Welsh) Series, two-handled vase, 12¹/₂in. high, circa 1907, depicting a woman in traditional dress. $112 £70

Rural England Series vase, 4¹/₂in. high, circa 1916, depicting a girl gathering bluebells. $56 £35

'Orlando', Shakespeare Series vase, 8in. high, circa 1912.
                    $93 £58

Old Moreton Hall Series vase, depicting the hall at Moreton, 9in. high, circa 1915.
                    $93 £58

Gleaners and Gypsies Series vase, 7¹/₂in. high, circa 1909, depicting a Gypsy and Child.
                    $88 £55

Feminine Society Series vase, 7¹/₂in. high, circa 1934, depicting a family taking tea. $93 £58

Under The Greenwood Tree Series vase, 7³/₄in. high, circa 1937, depicting 'Robin Hood and Friar Tuck'. $93 £58

Royal Doulton two-handled vase, designed by Charles Crombie, depicting two golfers and a caddie, 8in. high.
                    $440 £275

'Old Houses, All-Saints St. Hastings', Rural England Series vase, 8in. high, circa 1930.
                    $88 £55

STONEWARE

A salt cellar with incised blue leaves and bead work, c.m., 1877, 2¼in. high. $88 £55

An hexagonal salt cellar, the interior glazed blue, o.u.m., circa 1872, 3in. diameter. $120 £75

A teaset by Edith Kemp comprising tea-pot, cream jug and sugar bowl, c.m., 1880, height of tea-pot 4¼in. $384 £240

A vase painted with yellow fruit and dark brown foliage on a brown field, c.m.l & c., circa 1912, 9in. high. $112 £70

A pair of candlesticks with incised geometric patterns in blue and brown on a buff ground, o.u.m., circa 1872, 11in. high. $512 £320

A mounted jug, the mottled brown ground with applied geometric and leaf patterns, c.m., 1878, 9½in. high. $112 £70

A tapered jug, with applied blue and green stylised flower heads, c.m., 1880, 9½in. high. $136 £85

A Punch and Judy clockcase, the buff stoneware with a bright blue glaze, c.m.l. & c., circa 1905, 11½in. high. $1200 £750

A jug, the light buff body with incised diamonds and applied blue slip flowers, impressed Doulton Lambeth, circa 1868, 9½in. high. $144 £90

A pepper pot by Alice Budden with incised leaves and bead work, c.m., 1880, 2½in. high. $112 £70

A massive pair of candlesticks by Alice E. Budden, incised overall, r.m., 1881, 11¾in. high. $512 £320

A jug by Jane S. Hurst with applied green and white geometric patterns in high relief, r.m., 1881, 9½in. high. $160 £100

A vase by Elizabeth Atkins, the buff ground with an incised scale pattern and four panels, r.m., 1883, 7in. high. $176 £110

A pair of vases by Margaret Aitken, the white ground with incised flowering foliage painted in green and white pâte-sur-pâte, r.m., 1881, 8in. high. $352 £220

A vase by Harry Barnard, the cream ground with incised bands of chevrons on which are painted tadpoles, r.m., 1882, 10¼in. high. $224 £140

A vase by Alberta L. Green with incised green leaves growing from a central ochre band, r.m., circa 1882, 8¾in. high. $128 £80

A pair of vases by Bertha Evans, the mottled blue ground with incised brown scrolls, r.m., 1883, 7in. high. $400 £250

A vase by Ellen Gathercole, the incised brown ground with green plants having white flowers, r.m., 1882, 8¼in. high. $240 £150

A vase possibly by Emily Welch, the grey-green ground with applied blue flowering branches, r.m., circa 1885, 11¾in. high. $208 £130

A pair of vases by Mary Capes painted with green flowers outlined in gilt, r.m., 1884, 7¾in. high. $272 £170

A white stoneware jug with an incised diamond pattern, glazed alternately blue and brown with applied flower heads, o.u.m., the silver cover hallmarked 1872, 7in. high. $352 £220

A jug by Ellen Gathercole decorated in the traditional manner with applied vignettes of sporting scenes, r.m., 1882, 8¾in. high. $416 £260

A pair of candlesticks by Nellie Garbott with incised brown and blue leaves, c.m., 1879, 6¾in. high. $416 £260

A large vase by Harry Barnard, the buff ground with incised foliage, r.m., 1881, 14¼in. high. $1360 £850

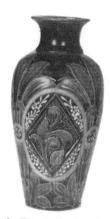

A vase by Annie Gentle, with painted white lattice-work and incised green and yellow foliage, c.m., 1879, 9¾in. high.
          $144 £90

A pair of vases by Margaret Aitken, with incised and carved brown and blue leaves, r.m., 1882, 7½in. $384 £240

A vase by Eliza S. Banks, with carved panels of blue foliage surrounded by painted white flowers, r.m., 1882, 8½in. high.
$240 £150

An unattributed jug moulded as a uniformed man with peaked hat, r.m., circa 1888, 9¼in. high. $400 £250

A small circular clockcase in buff stoneware with applied rough cast chips, circa 1890, 7¼in. high. $272 £170

An unattributed pair of vases, each with incised pale green and yellow foliage, r.m., circa 1885, 11½in. high. $572 £320

An unattributed beaker, the buff ground with painted white foliage and coloured lines, c.m.l. & c., circa 1902, 5½in. high. $96 £60

A late vase with stylised blue flowers and green leaves edged in white, c.m. & l., circa 1922, 7½in. high. $96 £60

A vase painted with formal purple flowers and green leaves against a white ground, c.m.l. & c., circa 1912, 7¾in. high. $104 £65

An unattributed salt cellar, the bowl with incised brown leaves, c.m., circa 1880, 3½in. high. $240 £150

A monumental clockcase glazed in shades of blue and brown with carved and incised details and applied bead work, c.m., 1879, 15½in. high. $2000 £1250

An unattributed vase with upright blue handles, c.m., 1879, 7½in. high. $152 £95

A vase, the mottled blue ground with incised lines, modelled in high relief with a dragon biting the neck, r.m., 1886, 10in. high.
$400 £250

An early architectural clockcase glazed ochre and blue, with incised blue, green, and purple leaves, o.m., 1875, 14½in. high.
$1440 £900

An unattributed jug, the combed buff ground with incised green fish and plants, DLE, circa 1895, 13¼in. high.
$352 £220

A vase with black and purple designs on a white ground, c.m.l. & c., circa 1920, 8¼in. high.
$96 £60

An architectural clockcase glazed in dark brown, blue and green, r.m., 1884, 10¼in. high.
$1360 £850

A cylindrical vase with blue, green and black geometric designs on a lovat ground, c.m.l. & c., circa 1920, 7¾in. high.
$96 £60

An unattributed jug, the buff ground with white bead work and incised blue and brown leaves, c.m., 1879, 7¾in. high.
$176 £110

An unattributed hexagonal open-work basket pierced with brown lattice, r.m., 1880, 5¼in. high.
$192 £120

An unattributed horn cup moulded with a blue and ochre sphinx, c.m., 1876, 9in. high.
$416 £260

A tapered jug with mottled brown glaze and applied blue flower heads, o.m., 1875, 10½in. high. $112 £70

A bulbous jug with applied geometric and floral patterns in purple and green, c.m., 1879, 7¼in. high. $304 £190

A jug by Harriet E. Hibbut, the blue ground with an applied carpet of large flowers predominantly blue, c.m., 1880, 9¼in. high. $128 £80

A vase by Bessie Youatt, the white ground with an incised spiral green leafy branch, c.m., 1879, 8in. high. $208 £130

A pair of vases by Emily A. London with a blue hatched ground, r.m., 1883, 4½in. high. $152 £95

A vase by Bessie Youatt, the white neck finely combed and the body painted with brown leaves, c.m., 1880, 9½in. high. $256 £160

A pâte-sur-pâte jug, the buff ground with finely incised and applied green leaves and bead work, r.m., circa 1882, 8½in. high. $120 £75

A shaped jug with applied blue geometric patterns in high relief, c.m., 1877, 8½in. high. $192 £120

A jug with an overall incised diamond pattern, glazed alternately in brown and blue, r.m., circa 1882, 8¾in. high. $96 £60

A jug, with applied dark green and white shell motifs within various applied borders, c.m., 1880, 9½in. high. $128 £80

A modelled owl with detachable head, the feathers formed by applied motifs in shades of blue, ochre and brown, r.m., circa 1880, 8in. high. $520 £325

A vase, the light buff body stencilled overall with impressed concentric circles, r.m., circa 1882, 12¼in. high. $128 £80

A jug by Bessie Youatt, incised and applied with a ring of blue flower heads, c.m., 1879, 8½in. high. $224 £140

A pair of vases by Bessie Youatt, each with four incised shaped panels, r.m., 1883, 10¾in. high. $576 £360

A baluster-shaped jug with incised blue shield-shaped panels on a brown ground, r.m., 1882, 9½in. high. $144 £90

A jug by Emma Shute with applied pale blue and white motifs, c.m., 1880, 9¼in. high. $112 £70

A mug by Constance E. Redford, the buff ground with white dots and incised blue scrolls, r.m., 1882, 5in. high. $120 £75

A jug by Harriett E. Hibbut, the mottled brown body with applied grey and blue leaves, and flower heads, c.m., 1976, 9in. high. $112 £70

A cylindrical jug with a dark brown glaze and applied flower heads, blue triangles and white beads, c.m., 1878, 6¾in. high.
$152 £95

A vase by Mary Aitken of baluster shape, with overall applied bands of graduated beads, r.m., 1880, 14½in. high.
$240 £150

A small bowl by Emily Welch with impressed gilt concentric circles, r.m., circa 1888, 4in. high.
$232 £145

A brown glazed jug with incised acorns, flowers, and leaves, filled with blue slip, o.u.m., circa 1871, 8in. high.
$176 £110

A cruet set by Charlotte Lamb, both bottles with incised flowering plants, c.m., 1879, 4¼in. high.
$288 £180

A blue stoneware jug with carved stylised leaves and a band of applied flower heads, the base incised F.M. and impressed with the letter B, o.u.m., circa 1871, 7¼in. high.
$144 £90

An incised jug, the light buff body with cattle and a goat below leaf bands filled with brown slip, o.u.m., circa 1871, 7in. high.
·$352 £220

A small bowl by Sarah Fisher, the cover pierced with green and blue scrolls, c.m., 1879, 4in. high.
$208 £130

A baluster-shaped jug with a mottled blue glaze, applied blue leaf motifs, and brown bead work, r.m., 1883, 8¼in. high.
$176 £110

A mounted jug with applied
geometric patterns and a frieze
of multi-coloured applied
circles, r.m., 1880, 9½in. high.
$152 £95

An egg cup stand by Mary
Davies, the ochre stand with
incised green foliate scrolls,
r.m., 1884, 6in. diameter.
$256 £160

A jug, the cream body with
incised and applied blue lily of
the valley, o.u.m., circa 1871,
7¼in. high. $192 £120

An inscribed vase by Alice
Groom, the buff body with
incised green and brown leaves
and blue flowers, r.m., 1886,
6½in. high. $208 £130

A large vase attributed to Cund,
with two modelled monkeys
clinging to the sides, r.m., 1881,
18in. high. $1360 £850

A jug by Jane S. Hurst with
overall applied green and grey
motifs, c.m., 1879, 9¼in. high.
$144 £90

A pair of vases by Nellie Garbott
with incised pale blue flowers on
a dark blue ground, r.m., 1881,
6in. high. $256 £160

A jug covered with a pale brown
glaze, with applied clusters of
green shells. o.m., 1875, 6½in.
high. $144 £90

A slip-cast vase by William
Rowe with green leaves and a
black and white checkered
design, s.c.m., circa 1920,
9in. high. $88 £55

Nelson's Centenary, a moulded statuette of the admiral glazed green, c.m.l. & c., circa 1905, 8¼in. high. $480 £300

A vase modelled with shaped panels in relief, on each an applied moulded portrait glazed dark green, r.m., 1888, 9¾in. high. $336 £210

An unattributed jug with an incised green and brown scale pattern, r.m., 1884, 7in. high. $152 £95

An unattributed vase, the pale blue ground with carved green flowering plants, r.m., 1880, 14¼in. high. $272 £170

A pair of unattributed cylindrical vases, each with applied medallions of fish and a lobster, r.m., circa 1885, 10¼in. high. $352 £220

An unattributed vase decorated with natural coloured foliage, r.m., circa 1885, 11½in. high. $416 £260

A vase painted with plums against buff, purple and pink bands, c.m.l. & c., circa 1912, 7½in. high. $96 £60

A ribbed vase moulded with a cellular pattern and glazed olive-green, s.c.m., circa 1920, 6½in. high. $96 £60

A vase painted with stylised yellow chrysanthemums against a mottled pink ground, c.m.l. & c., circa 1912, 9in. high. $120 £75

CLARA BARKER

A vase by Clara Barker, with incised green scrolls on a hatched blue ground, r.m., 1884, 6in. high. $176 £110

A small tazza by Clara Barker, the stem moulded with eight blue dolphins, c.m., 1878, 3¾in. high. $192 £120

A vase by Clara Barker, the white ground with an incised continuous green foliate band, r.m., 1882, 6½in. high.
$176 £110

ARTHUR BARLOW

A jug with incised green, blue and brown leaves on a white background, o.m., 1875, 10in. high. $272 £170

A pair of vases decorated with incised blue and green stylised leaf designs on a buff ground, o.m., circa 1873, 8³/₄in. high.
$480 £300

A ewer with deeply incised foliage and geometric patterns, and applied flower heads, o.m., 1874, 10½in. high. $280 £175

A jug with incised green and brown scrolling foliage on a white ground, o.m., 1873, 8¾in. high. $288 £180

A candlestick with lightly incised leaves glazed brown and blue, and applied borders, o.m., 1874, 9½in. high.
$224 £140

A jug with incised blue foliate scrolls on a white ground, o.m., the silver mount hallmarked 1872, 8in. high. $400 £250

ARTHUR BARLOW

A jug with incised pink and blue
foliage on a pale green ground,
o.m., 1874, 10¼in. high.
$264 £165

A flask with incised brown
foliage on a ground impressed
with stars, o.m., 1875, 8¼in.
high. $165 £110 $240 £150

A pierced vase, the outer wall
with foliage glazed dark brown
on a buff ground, o.u.m., circa
1872, 7¼in. high. $224 £140

A pepper pot by Arthur Barlow,
o.u.m., the silver cover hallmarked 1872, 3¼in. high.
$112 £70

A jug with carved scrolling
foliage and applied flower heads
and beads in brown, green and
blue, o.m., 1874, 6¼in. high.
$192 £120

A large jug with incised brown
foliage, applied bead decoration
and blue flower heads, o.m.,
1876, 12¼in. high. $512 £320

A ewer, the body with unusual
leaf motifs incised in blue, white
and green, assistants
monogram: Mary A. Thomson,
o.m., 1875, 10in. high.
$320 £200

A jug with incised mottled
brown leaves on a pale buff
ground, o.u.m., circa 1871,
7¼in. high. $224 £140

A vase with incised brown
foliate scrolls and applied white
flowers on a buff ground, o.m.,
1874, 9½in. high. $256 £160

ARTHUR BARLOW

A vase with incised leaves glazed bright blue on a hatched ground, glazed brown, o.u.m., circa 1872, 9in. high. $400 £250

A mug by Arthur Barlow, the light buff body with an incised blue leaf band and applied shell motifs, o.u.m., the silver rim hallmarked, 1871, 4½in. high. $136 £85

A ewer with incised foliate scrolls in blue and green on a buff ground, o.m., 1873, 9¾in. high. $272 £170

A large jug with incised blue and green foliage below various incised and applied borders, o.m., 1874, 14³/₄in. high. $720 £450

A dish with incised concave flower heads surrounded by bands of leaves and basketwork in green, brown and blue, o.m., 1874, 10¹/₂in. diam. $240 £150

A ewer, the light buff body with incised stiff leaves glazed mottled brown, signed A. B. Barlow, o.u.m., circa 1872, 11in. high. $400 £250

A jug with incised dark brown foliage on a mottled pink ground, o.m., 1874, 10in. high. $272 £170

A beaker with applied bead decoration and blue flowerheads, c.m., 1876, 5¹/₄in. high. $120 £75

A vase with finely incised blue and pale green foliage on a brown ground, o.m., 1874, 10in. high. $272 £170

FLORENCE BARLOW

A turkey vase painted in bright green and brown pâte-sur-pâte with a frieze of turkeys, r.m. & e., circa 1895, 14in. high. $432 £270

A biscuit barrel with plate cover and mounts, the sides painted in pâte-sur-pâte with four cockatoos, r.m., 1886, 5½in. high. $240 £150

A doubled-handled vase with various incised leaf and scroll designs, c.m., 1878, 11¼in. high. $512 £320

A vase by Florence Barlow, with three panels of young birds amongst coloured grasses, DSL, 1885, 10½in. high. $448 £280

A pair of vases, the alternating panels with incised and cut out stylised flowers and foliage in various shades of blue, c.m., 1878, 10¾in. high. $432 £270

A pair of vases incised on the buff ground with finches amongst grasses, c.m., 1878, 11in. high. $512 £320

A vase with incised brown foliate scrolls on a buff ground, the base with incised green and blue leaves, c.m., 1878, 10in. high. $320 £200

An oil lamp, the stoneware stand modelled on both sides with fox-gloves and a field mouse in high relief, r.m., 1882, 15¼in. high. $608 £380

A vase decorated in pâte-sur-pâte, the four oval panels each with a garden bird, r.m., 1883, 8in. high. $424 £265

FLORENCE BARLOW

A jug, the stippled buff ground painted in pâte-sur-pâte with two green and white crested birds, r.m., circa 1885, 5½in. high. $192 £120

A tall vase, decorated with five pâte-sur-pâte tit-mice perched on a branch, r.m. & e., circa 1895, 16in. high. $432 £270

A jug with incised scrolling brown foliage and applied white bead work, c.m., 1876, 6¾in. high. $176 £110

A jug painted in pâte-sur-pâte with a hen and her chicks in a shaped panel, r.m., circa 1885, 9in. high, with a beaker en suite, 5½in. high. $320 £200

A pair of ewers, each with two shaped panels painted in pâte-sur-pâte with a parrot on a branch, r.m. & e., circa 1895, 10¼in. high. $640 £400

A tapering jug painted in white, with ducks amongst rushes on a buff ground, c.m., 1879, 9½in. high, with two beakers en suite, 5¼in. high. $352 £220

A jug with incised horses in blue and brown slip on a buff ground, c.m., 1877, 6¾in. high. $280 £175

A massive vase painted in green and white pâte-sur-pâte with garden birds amongst branches and numerous ducks amongst rushes, circa 1880, 26½in. high. $1088 £680

A jug decorated with a shaped panel containing two pâte-sur-pâte black swans reserved on a buff ground, r.m., 1884, 7¾in. high. $288 £180

FLORENCE BARLOW

A vase decorated with brown leaves and blue birds on a buff lace ground, impressed date for 1880 and Doulton Lambeth, 10in. high. $264 £165

A jug with incised squirrels on a buff ground, the base with incised stiff green and blue leaves, c.m., 1877, 7¾in. high, with a beaker en suite, 4½in. high. $432 £270

An early jug, incised in a white ground with herons standing in water, o.m., 1874, 7½in. high. $320 £200

A pair of vases, each with incised horses and sheep in shaped panels with garden birds in pâte-sur-pâte, the animals by Hannah Barlow; the birds by Florence Barlow, r.m. & e., circa 1895, 16½in. high. $1088 £680

Australiana, a tall vase painted in green and brown pâte-sur-pâte with cassowaries, r.m. & e., circa 1895, 28¼in. high. $992 £620

A pair of vases, each painted in green and white pâte-sur-pâte with storks standing amongst grasses, c.m.l. & c., date letter for 1906, 14¼in. high. $720 £450

A doubled-handled vase painted in pâte-sur-pâte with a green and white titmouse perched on a branch, DLE, circa 1895, 9½in. high. $288 £180

A pair of covered vases with upright handles, c.m., 1878, 7¾in. high. $592 £370

A vase painted on either side with a swallow-tailed butterfly, c.m.l. & c., circa 1906, 11¾in. high. $424 £265

FLORENCE BARLOW

A large vase painted with herons fighting over a fish, the reverse side with herons and a bat against the moon, r.m. & e., circa 1895, 19¾in. high.
$528 £330

A large pair of vases, each with three shaped panels painted with garden birds amongst foliage, r.m. & e., circa 1895, 14½in. high. $944 £590

A vase, modelled in high relief, with two budgerigars perched on green leafy branches, r.m., 1886, 12¼in. high. $400 £250

A pair of vases, each with three panels decorated in relief with garden birds perched amongst blossom, c.m.l. & c., date letter for 1903, 11½in. high.
$928 £580

A lavishly decorated vase commemorating the 1897 Jubilee, the central panel with painted white VR monograms and applied moulded portraits of the Queen, signed in full: F. E. Barlow, r.m. & e., circa 1897, 24¼in. high. $1152 £720

A small pair of vases painted in green and white pâte-sur-pâte with a frieze of ducks, r.m. & e., circa 1895, 6¾in. high.
$272 £170

A large vase with three stippled buff panels painted with garden birds, r.m., circa 1885, 25½in. high. $736 £460

A pair of vases with a frieze of ducks and grass, r.m. & e., circa 1895, 9¾in. high.
$560 £350

A vase painted in pâte-sur-pâte, with a green bunting perched on a branch, r.m. & e., circa 1895, 13¼in. high. $512 £320

HANNAH BARLOW

A pepper pot by Hannah Barlow, o.u.m., the silver cover hallmarked 1872, 3in. high.
$144 £90

A mug with an incised frieze of running deer on a buff ground, c.m., 1878, 3½in. high.
$160 £100

A cream jug with incised puppies and blue and brown leaves on a buff ground, o.m., 1874, 4¾in. high. $224 £140

An early jug with incised stiff leaves filled with blue and brown slip on a buff ground, o.m., silver mount hallmarked, 1872, 6¾in. high. $264 £165

A large pair of vases, each with two quatrefoil panels, one of cats and the other of dogs, the birds by Florence Barlow, the background by Eliza Simmance, r.m. & e., circa 1895, 18in. high. $1424 £890

A cup and saucer with incised sheep and lambs on a buff ground, r.m., 1884, the cup 2in. high. $200 £125

A vase with three shaped panels, each painted with a cat in pâte-sur-pâte, r.m., 1884. 9in. high.
$320 £200

A jug with an incised white dog wearing a ruff, DLE, circa 1895, 6½in. high. $288 £180

A vase with finely incised ponies and goats in a landscape, c.m., 1878, 8in. high. $416 £260

HANNAH BARLOW

A small jug with incised goats in pasture on a dark buff ground, o.m., 1874, 5¾in. high.
$240 £150

A tobacco jar and cover, the body with incised brown glazed cows frolicking amongst incised green foliage, r.m. & e., circa 1895, 6½in. high. $288 £180

A small jug with an incised bird on a branch and flowering plants, o.m., circa 1872, 6in. high. $264 £165

A tall jug with incised deer in a wreath of foliage below incised scrolls, o.m., 1873, 10¾in. high. $272 £170

A large pair of vases with a boldly incised frieze of goats, borders by Frank Butler, r.m. & e., circa 1895, 21½in. high.
$1680 £1050

A jug with an incised pride of lions on a buff ground, DLE, circa 1895, 8½in. high.
$320 £200

A jug, the buff body incised with a dog and plants, titled 'Lost', o.u.m., circa 1871, possibly the work of Hannah Barlow, 6³/₄in. high. $288 £180

A tyg with three incised groups of rabbits in a landscape, the handles with incised flowers, o.m., 1873, 5¾in. high.
$264 £165

A jug with incised lions in a landscape, filled with a dark blue slip on a light buff ground, o.m., circa 1872, 8in. high.
$352 £220

HANNAH BARLOW

A small jug with an incised fox stalking a rabbit, filled with a blue slip on a buff ground, o.m., 1875, 6½in. high. $272 £170

A loving cup in buff glazed stoneware, with two boldly incised lions, o.m., silver rim hallmarked 1872, 6½in. high. $264 £165

A jug with incised cat and rabbits between incised stiff leaves, o.m., circa 1872, 8in. high. $320 £200

A jug with incised stiff leaves, scrolls, and a frieze of rabbits, o.m., circa 1872, 7½in. high. $320 £200

A terracotta picture, titled 'So near and yet so far', the animals modelled in high-relief in buff terracotta, 1890, 10 x 7in. $768 £480

A large vase with an incised frieze of frightened deer being pursued by wolves, o.m., circa 1872, 15¾in. high. $880 £550

A waisted beaker with an incised frieze of running dogs, o.m., 1873, 6¼in. high. $240 £150

A large tankard with incised water rats stealing eggs from an enraged swan, o.m., circa 1872, 6¾in. high. $264 £165

A tall tankard with an incised heron and ears of corn, filled with a bright blue slip, o.m., circa 1872, 10in. high. $280 £175

HANNAH BARLOW

A waisted beaker with incised sheep and lambs above stiff leaves, o.m., 1873, 6in. high.
$240 £150

A salt cellar by Hannah Barlow of hexagonal trencher type, o.u.m., circa 1872, 3in. diameter. $160 £100

A vase with incised herons flying amongst reeds, glazed blue on a white ground, c.m., 1876, 8¼in. high. $352 £220

A tapering jug with incised sheep by a fence, filled with blue slip on a white ground, c.m., 1877, 9¼in. high. $288 £180

A massive vase, the white ground impressed with blue flower heads and with incised lions in two shaped buff panels, further decorated by Frank Butler, r.m., 1886, 33in. high.
$6800 £4250

A jug with an incised band of pheasants above blue and brown leaves, o.m., 1873, 6in. high. $264 £165

A two-handled vase with incised horses between borders of stiff blue leaves on a buff ground, o.m., circa 1872, 10in. high.
$384 £240

A vase, the sides modelled in high relief with wolves chasing deer, o.m., circa 1872, 11¼in. high. $1200 £750

A jug with incised leaves and flowers glazed dark blue on a pale blue ground, r.m., 1880, 7in. high. $224 £140

361

HANNAH BARLOW

A vase with incised horses grazing in a field, filled with blue slip on a buff ground, r.m., circa 1882, 13½in. high.
$560 £350

A double-handled jardinière with an incised frieze of horses, r.m., 1880. 6¾in. high.
$576 £360

A vase with two modelled brown glazed dogs, the body with incised blue, green and brown leaves, r.m., 1889, 14in. high.
$752 £470

A jug with an incised frieze of cows in pasture on a white ground, c.m., 1878, 9in. high.
$320 £200

A pair of vases, one with incised children playing with puppies, the companion with a girl watching dogs chase a rabbit, r.m., 1885, 10¾in. high.
$1040 £650

An amusing jug with an incised dog growling at a bristling cat defending its kittens playing on a tree, r.m., 1883, 9¼in. high.
$352 £220

A jug with incised gun dogs sniffing a scent and a fox hiding behind the handle in long grass, c.m., 1880, 9¹/₂in. high.
$336 £210

A tankard with incised farm horses in a landscape, one ploughing, o.m., silver rim hallmarked 1872, 6³/₄in. high.
$304 £190

A jug with incised herons amongst reeds, in a bright blue slip on a buff ground, c.m., 1877, 9in. high. $312 £195

HANNAH BARLOW

A two-handled vase with an incised frieze of kangaroos, filled with blue slip on a white ground, r.m., 1886, 14¼in. high. $720 £450

A jardinière with an incised frieze of deer in a landscape on a light buff ground, c.m., 1877, 6½in. high. $544 £340

An unusual vase, with an incised frieze of sheep in pasture, c.m.l. & c., circa 1905, 7¾in. high. $264 £165

A mounted jug with incised horses in a landscape on a white ground, c.m., 1878, 9¼in. high. $352 £220

A large pair of vases, each with an incised frieze of wolves and their cubs amongst foliage, r.m., 1885, 16½in. high. $1088 £680

A large vase painted in green and white pate-sur-pâte with a frieze of cattle, r.m. & e., circa 1895, 18½in. high. $768 £480

A jug with the incised figure of a young girl behind a tree watching pigs, r.m., 1883, 8¾in. high. $464 £290

A jardinière with a frieze of incised lions, and borders with incised foliage, r.m., 1882, 9¾in. high. $624 £390

A vase with an incised frieze of horses, and foliate borders in green, blue and brown, r.m., 1883, 9in. high. $400 £250

HANNAH BARLOW

A vase decorated with incised goats grazing, with blue and brown slip designs on a brown ground, r.m., 13³/₄in. high.
$608 £380

A ewer decorated with incised goats grazing, leaves and bead designs on a stippled brown ground, DLE, 12in. high.
$368 £230

A vase decorated with incised goats, beads and foliage designs on a blue brown ground, r.m., impressed date for 1881, 9³/₄in. high.
$432 £270

A tea-set, comprising a teapot, cream jug and sugar bowl, each piece with an incised frieze of goats on a buff ground, o.m., 1875, the teapot 4¹/₄in. high.
$880 £550

A vase decorated with incised lions, stiff leaves and beads on a blue ground, r.m. & e., 1891-1902, 10¹/₂in. high. $608 £380

A tea-set, comprising a teapot, cream jug and sugar bowl, each with an incised frieze of rabbits above green and blue leaves, c.m., 1880, 1886, 4¹/₂in. high.
$912 £570

A vase decorated with an incised frieze of goats and donkeys with slip design scroll borders on a brown and green ground, r.m. & e., 12in. high. $512 £320

A large pair of vases with an incised frieze of white deer in a mountainous landscape, borders by Florence Barlow, DLE, circa 1895, 17¹/₄in. high.
$1600 £1000

A jug with an incised farm worker and a donkey pulling a cart loaded with tree branches, r.m., 1887, 9¹/₄in. high.
$368 £230

HANNAH BARLOW

A vase with three incised donkeys in a landscape on a buff ground, r.m. & e., circa 1892, 9in. high. $512 £320

A pair of ewers, each with incised lions in a landscape on a white ground, r.m., 1883, 11¾in. high. $896 £560

A vase with incised horses in a landscape, borders by Bessie Youatt, c.m., 1879. 10¼in. high. $608 £380

A tea-set, comprising a teapot, cream jug and sugar bowl, each piece with incised kangaroos and emus, c.m., 1878, the teapot 4½in. high. $944 £590

A vase decorated with incised moorland ponies, a band of stiff leaves and flowers on a blue green ground, impressed date 1880 and Doulton Lambeth, 9½in. high. $512 £320

A tea-set, comprising a teapot, cream jug and sugar bowl, each piece with an incised frieze of rabbits, borders by Lucy Barlow, r.m., 1883, the teapot 4½in. high. $896 £560

A jug with an incised frieze of goats in a rocky landscape, c.m., 1879, 10½in. high. $400 £250

A vase with a quatrefoil panel incised with two kittens, r.m. & e., circa 1895, 10in. high. $512 £320

A tapering jug with incised stags and does in a landscape, c.m., 1878, 9½in. high. $368 £230

JOHN BROAD

"The Boer War Soldier", a buff glazed figure of an infantry man, r.m. & e., circa 1900, 12½in. high. $640 £400

A modelled group, on a circular base with a buff glazed donkey, c.m., 1879 6½in. high. $560 £350

A terracotta statuette of King Edward VII standing against a column, the base inscribed ERI, c.m.l. & c., circa 1901, 16¾in. high. $1120 £700

A slip-cast figure of "The Bather", the white glazed nude seated on a purple sphere, s.c.m., circa 1912, 13in. high. $1360 £850

Queen Victoria, a buff salt-glaze figure commemorating her life, incised Doulton Co. Ltd. Lambeth, circa 1901, 11¾in. high. $1360 £850

Pitt's Centenary, a grey terracotta portrait-bust of the statesman, the shaped based inscribed "William Pitt 1759-1806", Sc., c.m.l. & c., circa 1906, 13¾in. high. $832 £520

ROSINA BROWN

A large vase with running green glaze by Rosina Brown, c.m.l. & c., 14½in. high. $136 £85

A jug by Rosina Brown, the shaded green ground with incised scrolls, r.m. & e., circa 1892, 7¼in. high. $232 £145

A pierced vase by Rosina Brown cut with geometric patterns, r.m., circa 1885, 7in. high. $256 £160

FRANK BUTLER

A small early jug, the buff body with deeply incised foliate scrolls, o.u.m., silver mount hallmarked 1873, 5in. high.
$240 £150

A candlestick with incised geometric and leaf designs, o.m., 1874, 5in. high. $208 £130

A flask of flattened circular shape incised in green, brown and purple, c.m., 1878, 8in. high. $448 £280

A jug with incised stiff leaves and scrolls in green, blue and brown, o.m., 1873, 7in. high.
$256 £160

A jardinière decorated with a frieze of applied moulded bust-portraits representing Queen Victoria, Victor Emmanuel of Italy, Napoleon III, Empress Eugenie and Kaiser Wilhelm of Germany, o.m., 1874, 8¼in. high. $960 £600

A jug with incised blue leaves on a brown ground, o.m., 1874, 5¼in. high. $216 £135

A jug with deeply incised brown and blue foliage, o.m., 1873, 9 in. high. $272 £170

A vase with shaped projections, incised leaves in blue and brown, o.m., 1874, 9½in. high.
$288 £180

A vase with incised blue leaves, applied white beads on a sepia ground, c.m., 1876, 7½in. high.
$240 £150

FRANK BUTLER

A vase modelled in relief with a stylised plant, r.m., circa 1890, 12in. high. $512 £320

A shaped bowl richly decorated on the inside and outside with incised leaves and foliate scrolls, c.m., 1880, 10¼in. diameter. $640 £400

An egg cup by Frank Butler with incised blue leaves on a buff ground, circa 1872, 3½in. high. $176 £110

A jug with carved and incised blue leaf patterns on a stippled buff ground, r.m., 1881, 13½in. high. $672 £420

A large pair of vases, the three panels with incised foliate scrolls in lovat, blue and ochre, r.m., 1882, 17½in. high. $1392 £870

A portrait jug, the dark blue ground with impressed flower motifs, c.m., 1877, 10½in. high. $448 £280

A vase with incised green and blue foliage and brown cross-hatched panels, r.m., 1884, 7¾in. high. $288 £180

An inscribed bowl with incised blue flowers and scrolls on an olive-green ground, 1894, 8¼in. diameter. $352 £220

A large vase, the central panel with carved brown scrolls on a hatched blue ground between incised leaf and scroll borders, r.m., 1884, 14¼in. high. $1072 £670

FRANK BUTLER

A goblet-shaped vase, with
applied stylised blue flowers on
a brown panel, c.m.l. & c.,
circa 1905, 8½in. high.
$232 £145

A shallow dish with incised
scrolls and the name K. B.
Smallfield, 1897, on a green
ground, r.m., 6½in. diameter.
$264 £165

A tall vase with incised dark
green plants on a brown
ground, c.m.l. & c., date letter
for 1909, 17½in. high.
$640 £400

A large jug, ornately decorated
with incised, applied and
impressed work. o.m., 1874,
17in. high. $784 £490

A pair of vases, each with
incised scrolls and leaves, c.m.,
1876, 14¼in. high. $1088 £680

A jug with a profusion of incised
leaves in blue, green, pink and
brown, o.m., 1875, 14½in.
high. $496 £310

A jug with incised green and
purple leaves on a brown
ground, c.m., 1878, 10in. high.
$352 £220

A shell-shaped bowl painted
with white flowers on a green
panel, r.m. & e., circa 1895,
4¾in. high. $512 £320

A jug, modelled in relief with
depressed fan-shaped motifs,
c.m., 1879, 8¼in. high.
$576 £360

FRANK BUTLER

  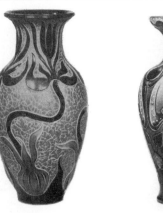

A vase with flowering plants against a brown background, r.m. & e., circa 1895, 13in. high. $672 £420

A pair of vases, modelled with stylised plants having green bulbs, brown stems and leaves, and blue flowers, DLE, circa 1895, 9¾in. high. $608 £380

A vase with stylised flowering plants in blue and brown, r.m. & e., circa 1895, 13¼in. high. $752 £470

A covered sprinkler, the squashed body with incised blue and green flowers, FAB., 1894, 10¼in. high. $336 £210

A pair of vases, modelled with projecting brown forms growing from a green ground, c.m.l. & c., date letter for 1906, 7in. high. $448 £280

An Art Nouveau vase with dark blue flowers and seed pods on a pale blue ground, DLE, circa 1900, 13in. high. $416 £260

 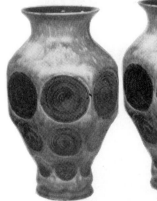 

A shaped flask, each side decorated with pierced and carved green foliate scrolls, r.m. & e., circa 1895, 9½in. high. $480 £300

A pair of vases, the mottled green ground modelled with projections divided by graduated brown and blue circles, r.m. & e., circa 1895, 9¾in. high. $432 £270

A vase modelled with projecting flowers, with green leaves and brown stems, c.m.l. & c., date letter for 1909, 14¾in. $672 £420

LOUISA DAVIS

A mounted jug, the incised buff
ground with impressed flowers,
c.m., 1880, 9½in. high.
$272 £170

A jug, the brown ground with
impressed flower motifs, c.m.,
1876, 6in. high. $240 £150

A vase, the white ground with
an incised spiral band of foliage
with blue flowers, c.m., 1877,
11¾in. high. $280 £175

A vase, the buff ground with
incised long lovat leaves, brown
foliage, and blue flowers, c.m.,
1877, 9¾in. high. $336 £210

A bowl, the brown ground with
incised blue flowers and
scrolling, c.m., 1878, 7½in.
high. $576 £360

A vase decorated with incised
blue leaves and flowers with
bands of applied beads and
florets, on a blue ground,
impressed dated for 1878 and
Doulton Lambeth, 9¼in. high.
$256 £160

W. EDWARD DUNN

A small vase by W. Edward
Dunn, painted in green and
white pâte-sur-pâte with a dog's
head, r.m., 1883, 5¼in. high.
$152 £95

A pilgrim bottle by W. Edward
Dunn, one side with incised
sheep in a landscape glazed
green, the other with women
gleaning, r.m., 1883, 9in. high.
$496 £310

A vase by W. Edward Dunn,
each side with an incised blue
bird on a buff panel, r.m., 1882,
12in. high. $512 £320

STONEWARE

EMILY EDWARDS

A jug by Emily J. Edwards with
a mottled brown glaze and
applied flower heads within
incised borders, o.u.m., circa
1872, 7in. high. $224 £140

A flower-shaped dish, the brown
ground with incised lines and
green and purple leaves,
impressed Doulton Lambeth,
1876, 10½in. diameter.
$256 £160

A jug with incised green scrolls
and blue leaves on a scored
brown ground, o.m., 1873,
7¼in. high. $224 £140

LOUISA EDWARDS

A jug with incised dark brown
leaf scrolls on a buff ground,
c.m., 1878, 10¾in. high.
$288 £180

A jug with incised green and
yellow plants with blue flowers,
c.m., 1878, 7¼in. high.
$224 £140

A vase, the pale blue ground
with finely incised foliage, r.m.,
1881, 10in. high. $224 £140

A jug, the buff ground with fine
incised lines and impressed
flower heads, c.m., 1879, 9½in.
high. $264 £165

A vase with incised blue
flowering foliage on a pale blue
ground, c.m., 1879, 11in. high.
$288 £180

A jug, the body with incised
bands of stylised leaves in green
and purple, c.m., 1879, 9½in.
high. $224 £140

STONEWARE

HERBERT ELLIS

A cream coloured terracotta figure of a partly draped woman holding a plaque, impressed Doulton & Co., Lambeth, incised H. Ellis Sc., circa 1910, 13½in. high. $400 £250

An unglazed cream coloured terracotta figure of a nude woman kneeling on a net, incised H. Ellis Sc., circa 1910, 9½in. high. $400 £250

An unglazed moulded terracotta figure, the partly draped woman holding a branch of foliage. Impressed Doulton & Co., Lambeth, circa 1910, 11in. high. $400 £250

ELIZABETH FISHER

A jug, the brown ground with incised panels in green, purple and brown, c.m., 1876, 9in. high. $288 £180

A pair of vases with incised foliate scrolls in two shades of blue, r.m., 1883, 11in. high. $672 £420

A jug, the blue ground with incised leaves, buff panels with impressed flower heads, c.m., 1878, 8½in. high. $256 £160

A beaker, the brown ground with impressed flower heads, c.m., 1876, 5¼in. high. $144 £90

A pair of candlesticks with incised blue leaves and applied flower heads and bead work, c.m., 1877, 8½in. high. $464 £290

A jug, incised in blue and brown on a buff ground, r.m., 1881, 9¼in. high. $208 £130

LESLIE HARRADINE

A brown salt-glaze spirit flask modelled as John Burns, the Labour leader, DLE, circa 1912, 7¼in. high. $360 £225

A cast figure of Sairey Gamp, the light buff glaze, s.c.m., circa 1913, 8in. high. $560 £350

A brown salt-glaze spirit flask modelled as David Lloyd George, DLE, circa 1912, 7¾in. high. $360 £225

A vase by Leslie Harradine cast into a square section and moulded with laburnum, s.c.m., circa 1912, 8¾in. high. $144 £90

A brown terracotta bust of George V, the reverse stamped Doulton Lambeth, L. Harradine Sc., circa 1910, 7½in. high. $448 £280

A vase after a design by Leslie Harradine with moulded yellow flowers, s.c.m., circa 1910, 9¾in. high. $192 £120

A slip-cast figure of Mr. Pickwick in a light buff glaze, s.c.m., circa 1913, 8½in. high. $560 £350

A white glazed figure of a peasant woman wearing a blue checkered dress, RDE, circa 1905, 8½in. high. $608 £380

A moulded figure of a farm labourer holding a scythe, wearing a blue shirt, circa 1905, 7½in. high. $608 £380

LESLIE HARRADINE

A brown salt-glaze spirit flask modelled as President Roosevelt, DLE, circa 1912, 7½in. high. $360 £225

"Motherhood", a white glazed figure of a mother cradling her baby, the dress with blue flowers, RDE, circa 1912, 6in. high. $560 £350

A brown salt-glaze spirit flask modelled in the traditional style with Austen Chamberlain, DLE, circa 1912, 7¾in. high. $360 £225

A brown salt-glaze figure of Mr. Pecksniff, s.c.m., circa 1913, 9¼in. high $560 £350

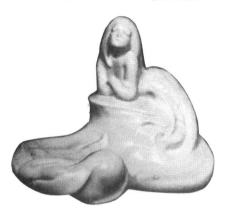
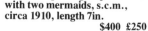

A white slip-cast group modelled with two mermaids, s.c.m., circa 1910, length 7in. $400 £250

Dickens, a moulded white glazed stoneware figure of Mr. Squeers, s.c.m., circa 1913, 9¼in. high. $560 £350

VERA HUGGINS

A large vase with incised green flowering foliage on a mottled blue ground, c.m. & l., circa 1925, 12¾in. high. $224 £140

A bowl painted with pink and blue flowers against a brown field, c.m. & l., 1926, 5in. high. $112 £70

A vase glazed in green, blue and brown with incised and raised borders, c.m. & l., circa 1925, 11¼in. high. $200 £125

FRANCES LEE

A vase, the buff ground with impressed concentric circles, heightened with gold, c.m., 1886, 10in. high. $320 £200

A pair of vases, the panels with incised green leaves and bordered by purple leaves, c.m., 1877, 9¾in. high.
$512 £320

A vase, the royal blue ground with four stippled buff panels painted with dolphins, c.m., 1883, 9¾in. high. $288 £180

A jug with four oval panels with incised green foliage, c.m., 1878, 5¼in. high. $176 £110

A shallow bowl with incised green and blue panels supported by three columns, c.m., 1884, 8¼in. high.
$512 £320

A jug, the neck with incised blue flowers on a brown ground, c.m., 1879, 6¾in. high.
$216 £90

A jug, the incised brown leaves with applied bead work and flower heads, c.m., 1877, 9¼in. high. $264 £165

A pair of vases, with finely incised foliage, painted overall in pâte-sur-pâte with blossom, c.m., 1882, 9in. high.
$448 £280

A jug carved with green flower heads on a blue ground, c.m., 1881, 9½in. high. $224 £140

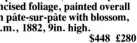

EDITH LUPTON

A jug with incised green, blue and brown leaves, o.m., 1875, 6½in. high. $160 £100

A large pierced vase with three shaped panels painted in pâte-sur-pâte with wild flowers, r.m., 1882, 14in. high.
$576 £360

A jug with incised stiff blue leaves and carved seed pods, c.m., 1876, 8¼in. high.
$208 £130

A small jug with incised green foliage on a brown ground, c.m., 1876, 7½in. high.
$240 £150

A pair of salt cellars with incised leaves, o.m., 1875, 3¼in. high.
$560 £350

A candlestick modelled with three buff cranes between incised green and blue columns, c.m., 1875, 8in. high. $224 £140

A mounted jug with incised blue and green leaves, o.m., 1875, 6¾in. high. $208 £130

A vase by Edith Lupton with chocolate panels painted with blue flowers, DSL, 1884, 9½in. high. $272 £170

A large vase by Edith Lupton, pierced overall with flowering plants and foliage, DSL, 1884, 15¼in. high. $512 £320

EDITH LUPTON

A large vase with incised
mottled foliage and seed pods,
r.m., 1886, 14in. high.
$480 £300

A vase with incised green leaves
and painted blossom and
berries, r.m., 1886, 6¾in. high.
$144 £90

A jug with incised blue and
white leaves on a brown ground,
c.m., 1876, 7½in. high.
$208 £130

An ecclesiastical vase modelled
in the form of a tower, and on
each corner the letters IHS in
brown shields, r.m., 1881,
13¾in. high $512 £320

A small pair of church vases, the
quatrefoil necks with incised
blue scrolls, r.m. & e., circa
1892, 6in. high. $416 £260

A jug with incised dark brown
scrolls on a royal blue ground,
c.m., 1880, 9in. high.
$280 £175

A tapering jug with incised green,
brown and blue scrolls, 9½in.
high, with two beakers en suite,
5½in. high, c.m., 1879. $440 £275

A globular vase, the stippled
buff ground with incised
fruiting vine, r.m., 1886, 10in.
high. $560 £350

A mounted jug with incised
foliate scrolls in shades of blue
and green, r.m., 1880, 9½in.
high. $264 £165

MARK V. MARSHALL

A large vase, one side modelled with a profile female portrait, the other with a bird amongst flowers, r.m. & e., circa 1895, 15in. high. $1040 £650

A paperweight modelled as a smiling creature glazed brown, RDE, circa 1902, 2½in. high.
$448 £280

A vase after a design by Mark V. Marshall with purple foliage and sepia fruit, c.m. & l., circa 1922, 8¼in. high. $256 £160

A vase with pink swirling panels painted with blue flowers and green leaves, c.m.l. & c., date letter for 1905, 12in. high.
$608 £380

A pair of vases pressed from the inside with pink fruits against green foliage on a pale pink ground, c.m.l. & c., date letter for 1903, 10¾in. high.
$832 £520

A vase painted with pink flowers and brown veined white leaves, c.m.l. & c., date letter for 1906, 11½in. high.
$416 £260

A buff coloured vase with two modelled monkeys grasping the neck of the vase, r.m. & e., circa 1895, 6¾in. high. $736 £460

An unusual bowl of flattened disc shape painted with purple foliage in shaped sepia panels, c.m., circa 1890, 4in. height, 14½in. diameter. $400 £250

An elaborate jug with incised lip and blue neck, the base of the handle modelled with the head of a dark-skinned Arab wearing a kefiya, r.m. & e., circa 1895, 11¼in. high. $1520 £950

MARK V. MARSHALL

A tankard, the grey-green ground indented with purple foliate scrolls and a grotesque mask, DLE, circa 1895, 6½in. high. $208 £130

A jug modelled as a fabulous fish with legs and cloven feet, c.m., circa 1885, 9in. high. $1360 £850

A vase pressed from the inside with russet and lovat foliate scrolls, r.m. & e., circa 1895, 10¾in. high. $416 £260

A paperweight modelled as a duck with mottled blue and green glaze, c.m.l & c., circa 1902, 2¾in. high. $368 £230

An inkwell modelled as a stylised bird glazed blue and green, RDE, circa 1902, 2¼in. high. $368 £230

A paperweight modelled as a green glazed cat with grinning features, RDE, circa 1902, 3¼in. long. $368 £230

A dark blue glazed vase, the body modelled in high relief with a sinuous dragon rising from blue waves, c.m., 1880, 10in. high. $1520 £950

An Art Nouveau jug, the base of the handle modelled with a hare's head, c.m.l & c., date letter for 1909, 10¾in. high. $688 £430

A standing bowl attributed to Mark V. Marshall, supported by three moulded and modelled heraldic beasts, c.m.l. & c., circa 1902, 9in. high. $816 £510

MARK V. MARSHALL

A gourd-shaped vase, incised and modelled in relief with fruiting foliage in brown and white, c.m.l. & c., date letter for 1904, 10½in. high.
$720 £450

An early grotesque bowl modelled as a fish, 8½in. high.
$768 £480

A vase, the glaze shading from white through purple to blue at the base, around which climbs a fabulous buff scaly creature, c.m.l. & c., date letter for 1904, 10½in. high. $1152 £720

A salt cellar modelled as a frog glazed brown, DLE, circa 1900, 1¾in. high. $336 £210

A 'Borogove' vase modelled as a hedgehog-like creature, r.m., circa 1890, 8in. high. $800 £500

An unattributed model of a rabbit glazed light brown, c.m. & l., circa 1922, 2¾in. long.
$144 £90

A vase painted on either side with a stylised plant in shades of green, r.m. & e., circa 1895, 8¼in. high. $352 £220

An inkwell modelled with two fabulous beasts glazed ochre, blue and brown, r.m., 1884, 5¼in. high. $768 £480

A jug modelled in low relief with brown leaves against a royal blue ground, DLE, circa 1895, 8½in. high. $448 £280

MARK V. MARSHALL

A trumpet-shaped vase, incised overall and glazed blue, circa 1879, 10¼in. high. $640 £400

A paperweight modelled as a bird glazed brown, c.m.l. & c., circa 1902, 3in. high. $352 £220

A vase modelled in low relief, with purple and pink sea-weed on a claret ground, r.m. & e., circa 1895, 9in. high. $352 £220

A tall jug, decorated with rambling blue and pink roses on which perch garden birds, c.m., circa 1880, 19¼in. high.
$992 £620

A pair of vases, each decorated with four ribbed panels in brown and pale green, c.m.l. & c., date letter for 1903, 12½in. high. $1088 £680

A large covered vase, each side modelled in relief, one with a music conductor with human head and the body of a bird, the other with a lizard and flowering plants, c.m., circa 1885, 26¾in. high. $5200 £3250

A slender vase painted in outline with three long-tailed birds perched amongst foliage, c.m.l. & c., circa 1902, 10in. high. $416 £260

A pot-pourri bowl with pierced blue cover overlaid with green foliate scrolls in high relief, r.m. & e., circa 1895, 5½in. high.
$240 £150

A shaped vase, the mottled blue ground with incised green markings and white neck, c.m., circa 1890, 8½in. high.
$352 £220

ISABELLA MILLER

A vase by Isabella Miller, the mottled purple ground with incised green and blue scrolls, c.m., 1880, 7¼in. high.
$240 £150

A vase by Isabella Miller, the green and ochre ground with incised dark green scrolls and plants, r.m., 1884, 10¼in. high.
$288 £180

A ewer by Isabella Miller with incised green and blue leaves and flowers, c.m., 1880, 6½in. high. $240 £150

MARY MITCHELL

A vase by Mary Mitchell, with the incised figures of two girls playing with a ball, r.m., 1881, 10¾in. high. $496 £310

A jug by Mary Mitchell, with two oval panels, with incised children in a landscape, c.m., 1879, 9¼in. high $416 £260

A vase by Mary Mitchell, the white ground with incised green foliage and purple flowers, c.m., 1879, 7in. high.
$200 £125

WILLIAM PARKER

A massive jug carved in high relief with green and brown flowers, c.m., 1879, 15¼in. high. $672 £420

A vase with incised flowers on a pale buff ground, r.m., 1883, 7½in. high. $272 £170

An inscribed jug with carved and incised pale green leaves, the neck with incised patterns and blue borders, c.m., 1881, 13¼in. high. $720 £450

WILLIAM PARKER

A vase with incised foliate scrolls in shades of blue, c.m., 1879, 11¾in. high. $368 £230

A vase incised through the celadon ground with blue and white flowering plants, r.m., 1883, 7in. high. $352 £220

A vase with finely incised flowering plants in mottled blue and green, r.m., 1884, 8¼in. high. $240 £150

A vase with finely incised blue convolvulous, sweet-peas, and clover, r.m., 1883, 9½in. high. $256 £160

A pair of vases, with an incised continuous blue branch bearing yellow fruits, r.m., 1884, 9½in. high. $512 £320

A vase carved with a frieze of green foliage scrolls within blue and green incised borders, c.m., 1881, 13¼in. high. $624 £390

FRANCIS POPE

A bottle with applied handle, and incised blue and green foliage, c.m.l. & c., silver rim hallmarked 1913, 8¼in. high. $192 £120

A slip-cast vase of gourd-shape with projecting ribs and a mottled blue glaze, circa 1920, 5¾in. high. $128 £80

A vase painted with green flowers growing from black stems, c.m.l. & c., circa 1905, 10in. high. $208 £130

FRANCIS POPE

An unusual vase, modelled in relief with a mermaid riding on a fish amongst underwater plants, c.m.l. & c., circa 1905, 11¾in. high. $352 £220

A pair of tall vases, each with incised mottled blue, pink and green leaves, c.m.l. & c., date letter for 1904, 15¼in. high. $720 £450

A handled bottle or spirit decanter with incised green leaves, c.m.l. & c., silver hall-marked 1913, 7½in. high. $176 £110

A slip-cast vase, the mottled blue body with brown ribs and pale blue scrolls in relief, s.c.m., circa 1920, 6¼in. high. $176 £110

A slip-cast vase moulded with arched panels covered in a mottled ochre and pale blue glaze, s.c.m., circa 1920, 6¼in. high. $120 £75

A vase with deeply incised black and brown scrolls on a green ground, c.m.l. & c., 5½in. high. $136 £85

A vase modelled in relief with a white bird amongst white foliage, c.m.l. & c., circa 1905, 9¾in. high. $240 £150

A pair of slip-cast vases of hexagonal section with a mottled green glaze, s.c., circa 1910, 11in. high. $592 £370

A slip-cast vase of square section, moulded on each side with a blue bird, s.c.m., circa 1920, 8¾in. high. $224 £140

FLORENCE ROBERTS

A mug by Florence C. Roberts,
the combed buff ground with
impressed flowers, r.m., 1884,
5¼in. high. $96 £60

A pair of vases by Florence C.
Roberts, the buff ground
modelled in relief with green,
blue and brown stylised flowers
and leaves, r.m., 1884, 10¼in.
high. $672 £420

A vase, the buff ground stippled
and modelled in relief with blue
flowers and mottled green
foliage, r.m., 1885, 12in. high.
$400 £250

EDITH ROGERS

A vase with incised blue flowers
heightened with white, r.m.,
1883, 7¾in. high. $272 £170

A jug, the silicon body painted
in rust and blue, DSL, 1884,
7¼in. high. $224 £140

A vase, with finely incised blue
flowering plants, the ground
over-glazed in brown, r.m.,
1883, 8in. high. $256 £160

A vase painted in green and
white pâte-sur-pâte with foliate
scrolls on an orange ground,
r.m., 1881, 10½in. high.
$272 £170

A pair of vases with overall
incised white and buff scrolls,
one with three plaques inscribed
'Burns, Scott and Keats', r.m.,
1882, 11½in. high. $752 £470

A vase, the white ground with a
thick dark olive-green glaze,
r.m., 1882, 10¼in. high.
$352 £220

MARTHA ROGERS

A vase, the buff ground with
finely incised foliage, r.m.,
1881, 7¾in. high. $240 £150

A vase, the buff ground with
painted white foliage, r.m.,
1881, 12¾in. high. $480 £300

A vase, the dark blue ground
with incised pale blue foliage
edged with gilt piping, r.m.,
1884, 11in. high. $352 £220

A vase, the pale ground with
incised brown foliate scrolls
bordered by incised blue leaves,
r.m., 1883, 12¼in. high.
$384 £240

A pair of vases, the orange
ground with painted white
motifs, r.m., 1882, 8¾in. high.
$480 £300

A vase by Martha M. Rogers,
the stippled frieze glazed blue,
with pale blue scrolls, DSL,
1883, 10½in. high. $240 £150

ELIZA SAYERS

A flask of flattened shape, each
side with incised green berried
foliage, c.m., 1880, 8½in. high.
$288 £180

A jug with incised dark brown
and blue stylised foliage
enriched with white bead work,
c.m., 1877, 9in. high.
$352 £220

A jug with incised green foliage
and applied beads on a brown
ground, c.m., 1877, 7in. high.
$240 £150

387

HARRY SIMEON

A vase painted with ears of corn in brown, green and purple against a mottled blue ground, c.m. & l., circa 1922, 9in. high. $192 £120

A vase painted with a parrot amongst green tropical foliage, c.m. & l., circa 1922, 10½in. high. $240 £150

A vase painted in polychrome colours with a cockerel and a blue pheasant, c.m. & l., circa 1922, 9¾in. high. $224 £140

ELIZA SIMMANCE

A jug painted with vine leaves and purple grapes against a pink ground, c.m.l. & c., date letter for 1910, 8½in. high. $240 £150

A ewer with incised brown foliage and impressed clusters of fruit, r.m. & e., circa 1895, 12in. high. $400 £250

A jug with incised yellow leaves and impressed brown berries against a mottled blue ground, c.m.l. & c., date letter for 1909, 9in. high. $272 £170

A vase with incised pale blue flowers and brown foliage edged in white, DLE, circa 1895, 14in. high. $576 £360

A waisted jar and cover painted with rings of white flowers, c.m.l. & c., date letter for 1907, 6½in. high. $224 £140

A large ribbed vase painted with blue leaves and pale blue flowers, c.m.l. & c., date letter for 1906, 15in. high. $560 £350

ELIZA SIMMANCE

A vase modelled with orange trees against a blue sky with birds, c.m.l. & c., date letter for 1905, 13in. high. $512 £320

A pair of vases with incised and painted pale blue cornflowers, r.m. & e., circa 1895, 11¼in. high. $720 £450

A vase painted with purple and green flowering plants, c.m.l. & c., date letter for 1915, 12¾in. high. $416 £260

A vase painted with purple berried trees against a pale blue background, c.m.l. & c., date letter for 1907, 13¾in. high. $512 £320

A pair of ribbed vases with incised green leaves, c.m.l. & c., date letter for 1910, 10in. high. $480 £300

A vase with a frieze of green trees edged in white, c.m.l. & c., circa 1907, 13½in. high. $448 £280

A vase painted with pink roses, the stems brown against a pale pink ground, c.m.l. & c., date letter for 1910, 11in. high. $256 £160

A pair of vases after Charles Rennie Mackintosh, with incised green roses, c.m.l. & c., date letter for 1910, 9in. high. $608 £380

A tall vase painted with pink pomegranates growing against a green ground, c.m.l. & c., date letter for 1910, 19¼in. high. $624 £390

ELIZA SIMMANCE

A vase with incised blue flowers against a buff panel of white scrolls, r.m. & e., circa 1895, 14in. high. $512 £320

A pair of vases by Eliza Simmance, the smooth cream ground with incised and painted flowering plants, r.m., circa 1890, 7¾in. high. $368 £230

A vase painted with green and white pâte-sur-pâte blossom on a stippled buff ground, r.m. & e., circa 1892, 8¼in. high.
$256 £160

A vase painted with pale green foliate scrolls on a darker green ground, r.m., 1884, 8¼in. high.
$256 £160

A stoneware bracket clockcase by Eliza Simmance, inspired by 18th century models, r.m. & e., circa 1895, 14½in. high.
$1600 £1000

A vase with shaped panels painted in pâte-sur-pâte natural colours with blackberries, r.m., 1881, 10¾in. high. $432 £270

A vase with shaped panels of incised stylised flowers in blue and green, r.m., 1884, 11in. high. $416 £260

A pair of vases with incised blue foliage and modelled green chrysanthemums, r.m. & e., circa 1895, 9¾in. high.
$704 £440

A vase painted with pale green and blue leaf sprays, r.m., 1883, 9¼in. high. $320 £200

ELIZA SIMMANCE

A vase painted with blue dolphins and green sea-weed on a pale pink ground, c.m.l. & c., date letter for 1910, 10½in. high. $352 £220

A bowl painted with alternate floral panels in pale green and blue on a dark green ground, r.m., 1883, 7in. high. $448 £280

A vase with incised green and brown sea-weed on an undulating green ground, c.m.l. & c., circa 1905, 9in. high. $288 £180

A jug with incised green and blue leaves on a buff ground, silver mount hallmarked 1875, 8in. high. $304 £190

A pair of vases by Eliza Simmance, the light grey ground with incised and painted brown plants, DSL, 1884, 7¼in. high. $512 £320

A pepper pot attributed to Eliza Simmance with pottery sprinkler and pierced base, r.m., 1884, 3¼in. high. $120 £75

An Art Union vase and cover painted with green and white pâte-sur-pâte blossom on a buff stippled ground, r.m. & e., circa 1895, 11½in. high. $960 £600

A vase by Eliza Simmance, the brown ground with three shaped panels, DSL, 1884, 8in. high. $224 £140

An octagonal plate painted with white pâte-sur-pâte flowers on a brown ground, c.m., 1878, 10in. diameter. $288 £180

ELIZA SIMMANCE

A cachepot with a broad pâte-sur-pâte band of Renaissance scrollwork and grotesques on an olive-green ground, dated 1882, 20cm. high. $640 £400

A vase by Eliza Simmance, the glazed buff ground with incised scrolls, r.m., 1881, 3¾in. high. $104 £65

A vase modelled with yellow apples growing from green branches, r.m., 1887, 9½in. high. $464 £290

A vase with incised royal blue flowers and leaves, r.m., circa 1887, 10in. high. $400 £250

A pair of cylindrical vases incised through the pale blue glaze onto the white body, c.m., 1879, 6¾in. high. $320 £200

One of a pair of vases with incised and modelled blue flowers, c.m.l. & c., date letter for 1909, 9¾in. high. $672 £420

A vase painted with green and white pâte-sur-pâte blossom on a Doulton and Slater buff lace ground, r.m., circa 1889, 6½in. high. $208 £130

A tazza, the surface with an incised blue and brown leaf pattern, c.m., 1877, 6½in. high. $384 £240

A vase with an incised foliate design in pale green and dark blue, c.m., 1876, 7¼in. high. $240 £150

STONEWARE

ELIZA SIMMANCE

A small vase by Eliza Simmance, the brown ground painted with white blossom and dark brown leaves, DSL, 1884, 4in. high. $112 £70

A vase with incised blue and white flowers and green foliage on a dark green ground, r.m. & e., circa 1895, 14in. high. $432 £270

A three-handled loving cup with green and white pâte-sur-pâte flowering scrolls, r.m., 1881, 6in. high. $256 £160

A pair of vases painted with long-tailed blue birds, c.m.l. & c., date letter for 1916?, 15¾in. high. $880 £550

A mustard pot by Eliza Simmance, the handle and body with incised blue leaves, o.m., 1875, 2¼in. high. $120 £75

A pair of vases by Eliza Simmance, with incised and painted brown garden birds and white daisies, DSL, 1885, 10¼in. high. $592 £370

ELIZABETH SMALL

A vase, the mottled blue ground with incised bright blue flowering foliage, r.m., 1884, 12½in. high. $480 £300

A pair of vases with incised blue and brown berried foliage on a mottled pale blue ground, r.m., 1884, 10¼in. high. $512 £320

A beaker, the buff ground with incised blue foliage, the entwined panels painted with white flowers, r.m., 1882, 4¾in. high. $152 £95

393

EMILY STORMER

A pair of vases, each with incised brown foliage above stiff green leaves, c.m., 1877, 10¾in. high $640 £400

A pair of flasks, with white bead work and an incised green, blue, and brown flower, c.m., 1878, 8¼in. high. $608 £380

A vase, the handles modelled as brown peacocks, the body with incised blue and yellow foliate scrolls, r.m. & e., circa 1892, 12½in. high. $720 £450

A candlestick, the base with carved green stylised leaves, r.m., 1886, 7in. high, $288 £180

A mounted jug with incised green flowers on a blue ground with incised brown scrolls, r.m., 1884, 6¾in. high. $240 £150

A jug, the buff body with impressed white circles and incised blue foliage and leaves, c.m., 1879, 9¼in. high. $272 £170

GEORGE H. TABOR

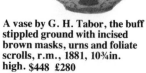

A vase by G. H. Tabor with carved blue oak branches and acorns, r.m., 1883, 9¼in. high. $256 £160

A pair of vases by G. H. Tabor, the green ground with overall incised blue masks, r.m., 1884, 9½in. high. $752 £470

A vase by G. H. Tabor, the buff stippled ground with incised brown masks, urns and foliate scrolls, r.m., 1881, 10¾in. high. $448 £280

GEORGE TINWORTH

A baluster vase, the mottled brown ground with incised blue foliate scrolls, r.m. & e., circa 1892, 12½in. high. $480 £300

A frog and mouse group with frogs riding mice over a water jump, o.m., circa 1875, 4½in. high. $1600 £1000

A large jug, the hatched pale green ground with incised green and brown scrolls, o.m., 1874, 11¼in. high. $608 £380

A brightly glazed jug, the green ground with an incised shaped blue panel, c.m., 1876, 9¾in. high. $480 £300

A terracotta picture tile moulded and carved in low relief with Christ in the Garden of Gethsemane, DLE., circa 1880, 8½in.×8½in. $640 £400

A mounted jug, with an incised green foliate meander, c.m., 1877, 9½in. high $480 £300

An early pair of candlesticks glazed blue, with incised leaves each supported by two buff winged putti, o.m., 1875, 7in. high. $1120 £700

A monkey group inscribed A United Family, sitting on a bench and sheltering under an ochre umbrella, r.m. & e., circa 1892, 5in. high. $1600 £1000

An early vase, the burnt sienna ground with incised blue and pale green scrolls, o.u.m., circa 1871, 9¾in. high. $480 £300

GEORGE TINWORTH

A carpenter's bag attributed to George Tinworth, glazed in shades of brown, c.m., circa 1880, length 5in. $1040 £650

The young carpenter, a brown salt-glaze model of a young boy planing at a bench, DLE, circa 1892, 5¼in. high. $1200 £750

A salt cellar, the bowl and stand glazed blue and brown, the moulded drummer boy glazed buff, r.m., circa 1885, 3½in. high. $672 £420

A jug, the lovat ground with an incised blue and buff fence decorated with pale blue bead work, c.m., 1879, 9½in. high. $480 £300

A blue glazed frog playing cricket with a brown bat, r.m., circa 1880, 4¾in. high.
                    $1360 £850

A tapering jug, the dark brown ground with an incised spiral band, c.m., 1878, 9¾in. high.
                    $480 £300

A jug, the light buff ground with incised scrolling blue foliage, o.u.m., circa 1872, 10½in. high.
                    $480 £300

A blue glazed group of two frogs riding on the backs of two mice, o.m., circa 1875, 3¾in. high.
                    $1360 £850

One of a pair of vases, the buff ground with a painted white cellular pattern, c.m.l. & c., date letter for 1903, 10¾in. high.
                    $832 £520

GEORGE TINWORTH

A candlestick with incised blue leaves on a brown ground, c.m., 1876, 8¼in. high. $880 £550

A quatrefoil inkwell with cover and liner, the body with incised blue leaves, c.m., 1879, 4in. high. $1152 £720

Mr Pickwick, the modelled figure glazed green and standing on a brown chair inscribed Pickwick Bachelor, DLE, circa 1895, 5in. high. $672 £420

A vase with a mottled blue ground with incised dark brown scrolls and applied flower heads, o.u.m., circa 1872, 9½in. high. $480 £300

A model of a green frog riding a yellow and brown penny farthing, r.m., circa 1880, 4½in. high. $1600 £1000

A vase, the brilliant royal blue ground with incised mottled brown scroll-work, r.m. & e., circa 1892, 8in. high.
$448 £280

A standing salt cellar, supported by moulded blue and brown dolphins, incised Doulton & Co., Lambeth, with the monogram GT, 4in. high. $432 £270

A double vase, the moulded buff putti with a blue garland standing on a brown sphere, r.m., circa 1885, 5¼in. high.
$640 £400

The eagle and the fox, a fable group with a brown trumpet-shaped vase, incised Doulton & Co., Lambeth, circa 1882, 7in. high. $1600 £1000

GEORGE TINWORTH

A letter rack, the stoneware compartments with incised leaves and flowers in brown, blue and green, r.m., circa 1885, length 14in.
$1400 £900

The drunken husband, a modelled fable group with an old man wearing a blue night-gown, sitting on the detachable lid of a coffin, r.m., 1881, length 7¾in. $1928 £1250

A brown salt-glazed group modelled with a frog painting and a country mouse holding an upturned basket of fruit, circa 1885, length 7in. $1920 £1200

A pair of mantle ornaments, each moulded with a kneeling figure of a young Egyptian boy, r.m., circa 1885, 9in. high.
$1040 £650

An umbrella stand modelled naturalistically with a brown glazed kangaroo holding a dark brown ring, incised Doulton Lambeth, circa 1885, 38¾in. high. $6400 £4000

A pair of salt cellars attributed to George Tinworth, supported by three buff winged putti, o.m., 1875, 3½in. high.
$1040 £650

A brown glazed stoneware mirror frame carved in low relief with a head and shoulders portrait of a young girl, c.m., circa 1880, 18in. high.
$880 £550

The Fables Clock, the stone-ware case modelled with the interior of a house and numerous figures and animals, the base inscribed: H. Doulton & Co., Lambeth, and G. Tinworth, circa 1882, 11¼in. high. $5600 £3500

The vain jackdaw, a fable group with the peacock's display forming a fan-shaped vase, incised H. Doulton, Lambeth, circa 1882, 6in. high.
$1760 £1100

A boy kicking a tambourine, DLE, incised Doulton Lambeth, circa 1895, 5in. high.
$1200 £750

A kneeling boy playing a harp, RDE, circa 1902, 3³/₄in. high. $1200 £750

A moulded and modelled figure of a seated boy with a cittern, DLE, circa 1895, 4³/₄in. high.
$1200 £750

A cello played by a seated boy, DLE, circa 1895, 4¹/₂in. high. $1200 £750

A boy with a white face playing a cello, RDE, circa 1902, 4³/₄in. high.
$1360 £850

An upright piano played by a boy seated on a stool, printed circle mark: Doulton Lambeth England, circa 1895, 4in. high. $1360 £850

A brown glazed figure of a boy playing a rebec, DLE, circa 1895, 5¹/₄in. high. $1200 £750

A seated boy playing a harp, DLE, circa 1895, 4in. high.
$1360 £850

A cornet played by a seated cross-legged boy, RDE, circa 1902, 4¹/₂in. high. $1200 £750

A boy leaning against a cylinder playing a concertina, DLE, circa 1895, 4¹/₂in. high.
$1360 £850

A boy playing a fiddle supported on his foot, DLE, circa 1895, 4¹/₄in. high. $1360 £850

A seated figure with a light buff face playing a French horn, RDE, circa 1902, 4³/₄in. high.
$1200 £750

GEORGE TINWORTH, MOUSE FIGURES

A mouse group with a white mouse playing a tuba and a little mouse playing the cornet, o.m., circa 1875, 3¾in. high.
$1360 £850

A knight from a chess set glazed white, r.m., 1884, 3¼in. high.
$520 £325

Play Goers, the group glazed pale brown with a blue and brown shaped base, r.m., 1886, 5¼in. high. $2000 £1250

A mouse group with a green vase and pale green mice playing ochre double-basses, r.m., circa 1885, 5¼in. high.
$1360 £850

A tea party with pale green mice seated on brown chairs, the hollow oval base inscribed Tea-Time Scandal, r.m., circa 1885, 3½in. high. $1760 £1100

A green vase on an oval base modelled with a pale green mouse playing a brown harp, and a little mouse playing a cornet, r.m., circa 1885, 5¼in. high. $1360 £850

A blue spill vase, with a mouse sleeping on the ground with a broom, r.m., circa 1885, 4in. high. $600 £375

A menu holder with a white mouse playing a harp and a little mouse playing a double bass, r.m., 1885, 3¾in. high.
$1360 £850

A bishop from a chess set, glazed white with a blue mitre, r.m., 1884, 3in. high. $520 £325

GEORGE TINWORTH, MOUSE FIGURES

A menu holder with two white mice playing a double-base and a cornet, inscribed Doulton Lambeth, circa 1880, 3¾in. high. $1360 £850

A brown glazed mouse-pawn holding an axe, r.m., 1884, 2½in. high. $520 £325

A tobacco jar, the lid with a green mouse sitting on a blue cushion smoking a brown pipe, r.m., circa 1885, 7in. high. $560 £350

A musical group with a blue vase and pale green mice, one playing an organ and the other a triangle, r.m., circa 1885, 5½in. high. $1360 £850

A mouse group moulded with three minstrels on a green mound, r.m., circa 1885, 3¾in. high. $1440 £900

A mouse-pawn glazed white, inscribed Pawn, r.m., 1884, 2¹/₂in. high. $520 £325

A model of a blue mouse eating a currant taken from the brown bun on which he sits, circa 1880, 2¾in. high. $480 £300

A blue spill vase modelled with a pale green mouse sitting comfortably in a brown chair, r.m. & e., circa 1895, 4½in. high. $600 £375

A menu holder with a little mouse about to steal an apple from a stall, r.m., circa 1885, 3¾in. high. $1360 £850

GEORGE TINWORTH,
PLAQUES

A Guard's Chapel maquette glazed green, blue and brown, and modelled with the parable of the lost piece of silver, inscribed H. Doulton & Co., Lambeth, G. Tinworth, circa 1877, 12in. x 9in. $1040 £650

A cream coloured terracotta self-portrait plaque inscribed G. Tinworth, circa 1913, 5³/₄in. x 4³/₄in. $608 £380

Tinworth's boyhood, a terracotta plaque modelled in high relief with George Tinworth as a young boy carving a small wooden bust in his father's wheelwright's workshop while his mother looks on, and a small boy watches for the possible arrival of his father, circa 1877, 8in. x 8in. $960 £600

A terracotta tile picture moulded and carved in low relief with Samson, DLE, circa 1880, 8¹/₂in. x 8¹/₂in. $560 £350

A terracotta tile picture moulded and carved in low relief with the Saviour and woman at the well, DLE, circa 1880, 8¹/₂in. x 8¹/₂in. $560 £350

A stoneware maquette with blue and brown glaze of David and Goliath, inscribed: H. Doulton & Co., Lambeth, G. Tinworth, with impressed oval stamps Doulton & Co., Lambeth London, circa 1877, 12in. x 9in. $1040 £650

GEORGE TINWORTH,
PLAQUES

A Station of the Cross, a terracotta plaque modelled in high relief with some free-standing figures, incised: H. Doulton & Co., Lambeth, G. Tinworth, circa 1878, 6in. x 13in. $720 £450

The Four Seasons, a set of four plaques in salt-glaze stoneware carved in high relief and glazed in shades of brown and blue, circa 1875, 8½in.×4in. $2560 £1600

Zacchaeus, a terracotta plaque modelled in high relief and inscribed Make Haste and Come Down for Today I Must Abide at Thy House and He Made Haste and Come Down, and Received Him Joyfully, in ebonised frame, circa 1878, 6in.×13in.
                                                                $720 £450

A religious plaque glazed in brown and blue and carved in high relief with the
Resurrection, circa 1880, 12¼in.×4½in. $720 £450

A religious terracotta plaque modelled in high relief and inscribed When She Had
Heard of Jesus Came in the Press Behind and Touched His Garment, inscribed: H.
Doulton & Co., Lambeth, G. Tinworth, circa 1878, 6in.×13in. $720 £450

John the Baptist, a terracotta plaque modelled in high relief with Salome demanding
the head of John the Baptist, circa 1878, 6in×13in. $720 £450

The Nativity, a terracotta plaque modelled in high relief and inscribed And They
Came with Haste and Found Mary, and Joseph, and the Babe Lying in a Manger, the
Poor of this World Rich in Faith, circa 1878, 5½in. x 12in. $720 £450

A small plaque, the stoneware glazed blue and brown on a white ground and carved in
high relief, circa 1875, 8½in.×4in. $720 £450

A Parable, a terracotta plaque modelled in high relief and incised And Jesus Called
a Little Child Unto Him and Set Him in the Midst of Them, Humble Yourselves
Therefore Under the Mighty Hand of God, circa 1878, 5¹/₂in. x 12in. $720 £450

BIBELOTS

A match striker advertising Dewar's Whisky, c.m.l. & c., 2½in. high. $80 £50

A tray glazed green and brown, with a central blue horse's head, c.m.l. & c., circa 1910, 4¼in. diameter. $144 £90

A match striker with Art Nouveau designs, DLE, 4in. high. $56 £35

A moulded tray centred by a brown mouse and a tree stump, s.c.m., circa 1925, 4in. high. $192 £120

The Suffragette Movement, an inkwell modelled as a baby with hinged head, R.D.E., circa 1905, 3¼in. high. $160 £100

A circular ring tray, slip-cast with a glazed brown rabbit, s.c.m., circa 1925, 3¼in. high. $136 £85

An inkwell moulded with a grumpy old lady, the green apron inscribed 'Votes for Women', c.m.l. & c., circa 1905, 3½in. high. $160 £100

A book-end glazed dark brown and modelled with a monkey clutching its young, DLE, circa 1900, 6½in. high. $224 £140

A moulded ring tray edged with green leaves on which sits a bird, DLE, Made in England, circa 1925, 4in. high. $144 £90

BIBELOTS

A group of two white ducklings squatting on a blue rockwork base, c.m.l. & c., circa 1920, 4¼in. high. $144 £90

An ashtray match holder, 'Queen Anne's Mansion', DLE. $88 £55

A ring tray attributed to Vera Huggins with a brown and buff owl. s.c.m., circa 1925, 4in. high. $120 £75

A trump indicator attributed to Leslie Harradine, RDE, circa 1910, 4in. high. $176 £110

A slip-cast ring tray modelled with a nymph seated on a ring of flowers, s.c.m., circa 1925, 4¼in. high. $152 £95

A match striker attributed to Harry Simeon, modelled with an old soldier seated next to a hollow drum, DLE, 4¾in. high. $152 £95

A shaped blue and brown ring tray on which perches a large billed bird, s.c.m., circa 1925, 4¼in. high. $136 £85

A match striker attributed to Harry Simeon with a toper wearing a blue coat, s.c.m., circa 1925, 3¾in. high. $272 £170

A whist booby attributed to Leslie Harradine, moulded with a skeleton, RDE, circa 1910, 4¼in. high. $176 £110

COMMEMORATIVE WARE

A jug with white relief lettering 'Christopher Columbus sighted America Oct 12 1491', flanking a buff portrait of the explorer, r.m. & e., 6¼in. high.
$144 £90

A shallow bowl, with applied moulded celadon portraits of the young Queen Victoria, r.m., circa 1885, 6in. diameter.
$400 £250

A jug commemorating Benjamin Disraeli, the buff portrait in high relief flanked by a quotation, r.m., 6½in. high
$120 £75

A tankard designed by John Broad commemorating the 1897 Jubilee, DLE, circa 1897, 6½in. high.
$144 £90

A bellarmine jug commemorating Queen Victoria's Golden Jubilee, r.m., 9in. high.
$240 £150

A coronation jug commemorating the accession of Edward VII and Queen Alexandra, DLE, circa 1902, 7½in. high.
$152 £95

A jug with a portrait of H. M. Stanley below the inscription 'Emin Pasha Relief Expedition 1887-1889', r.m. & e., 7½in. high.
$128 £80

A vase with a grey Doulton & Slater lace ground with an applied white bust of the Prince of Wales, r.m. & DSP., circa 1885, 6¼in. high.
$208 £130

General Gordon, a jug commemorating his death at Khartoum in 1884, the buff ground with applied motifs and inscriptions, r.m., dated 1884, 7½in. high.
$128 £80

COMMEMORATIVE WARE

A three-handled mug commemorating the coronation of King George V in 1911, moulded with relief portraits in pale green and blue, c.m.l. & c., 6¼in. high.
$144 £90

A jug commemorating the Golden Jubilee of Queen Victoria, with green glazed portraits of the Young and Old Queen on a blue ground, DLE, 9in. high. $176 £110

A three-handled mug commemorating the hoisting of the flag at Pretoria, DLE, 6½in. high.
$136 £85

A jug commemorating the hoisting of the flag at Pretoria, DLE, circa 1900, 8¼in. high.
$176 £110

A double-handled tankard commemorating War in the Sudan, r.m., 1883, 6in. high.
$136 £85

An oviform vase made to commemorate the Coronation of Edward VII and Queen Alexandra in 1902, c.m.l. & c., 27.5cm. high. $240 £150

William Ewart Gladstone, the jug printed with quotations below the title, 'England's Great Commoner', DLE, 7½in. high.
$136 £85

A small jug designed by John Broad commemorating the 1887 Jubilee, DL, 4½in. high.
$104 £65

A Nelson jug, moulded with a portrait of the famous admiral flanked by naval battle scenes, c.m.l. & c., 8in. high.
$336 £210

DOULTON & SLATER'S PATENT

A jug, overlaid with a grey and brown lace pattern on which mistletoe is applied, r.m. & DSP, circa 1888, 7¾in. high. $144 £90

A pair of ewers with rough brown lace ground decorated with floral sprays, Slater's Patent 'Chine', DLE, 8in. high. $176 £110

A dated vase with brown lion's head handles and applied green foliage on a brilliant blue ground, r.m. & DSP, 1886, 11in. high. $512 £320

A jug, the dark green elaborate lace ground overlaid with two celadon classical portraits, r.m. & DSP, circa 1888, 7½in. high. $144 £90

A jug, the blue lace ground with the impressions of large ferns and overlaid with bouquets of ochre flowers, r.m. & DSP, circa 1890, 7in. high. $128 £80

A jug, with a grey lace panel overlaid with moulded white and brown foliage enclosing six oval medallions, r.m. & DSP, circa 1888, 6in. high. $136 £85

A vase decorated with bands of applied stiff leaves on a blue ground, Slater's Patent 'Chine', DLE, 11³/₄in. high. $136 £85

A pair of vases, each with three panels of white flowering foliage, r.m. & e. & DSP, circa 1895, 10in. high. $416 £260

One of a pair of vases with rough brown lace ground decorated with floral sprays, Slater's Patent 'Chine', c.m.l. & c., 14¹/₄in. high. $208 £130

DOULTON & SLATER'S PATENT

A vase with four moulded blue-glazed cupids and numerous stars superimposed on a plain dark green lace ground, r.m. & DSP, circa 1888, 10¼in. high.
$176 £110

A pair of vases moulded with celadon fish and dragon medallions, r.m. & DSP, 1885, 9¼in. high. $208 £130

A vase with rough brown lace ground decorated with floral sprays, Slater's Patent 'Chine', r.m. & e., 10¾in. high.
$112 £70

A jug with applied pale blossom in high relief and two moulded medallions, one of a snake and a mouse, r.m. & DSP, circa 1888, 7½in. high. $152 £95

A teapot with rough brown lace ground decorated with floral sprays, Slater's Patent 'Chine', r.m., 4¾in. high. $104 £65

A jug, with two impressed lace patterns and decorated round the centre with three white medallions, r.m. & DSP, circa 1888, 6¾in. high. $128 £80

A vase with blue handles and neck, the rough brown lace ground with incised brown and blue foliage, r.m. & e. & DSP, circa 1895, 12in. high.
$256 £160

A pair of oriental vases, applied flower head and brown dragons supporting beige lace impressed medallions, r.m. & DSP, circa 1888, 8in. high. $480 £300

A small vase with a blue lace frieze in which are the impressions of dark green ferns, r.m. & DSP, circa 1890, 5½in. high. $128 £80

MINIATURES

Miniature Doulton Lambeth
stoneware mug with silver
hallmarked rim and decorated
with applied toping scenes.
$48 £30

A narrow vase with incised blue
leaves and bead work, c.m.,
1877, 5in. high. $104 £65

Miniature Doulton Lambeth
stoneware jug with applied
toping scenes. $40 £25

A bowl by Alberta Green, the
buff ground with white bead
work, r.m., 1887, 3¼in. high.
$104 £65

A double-handled vase with
incised blue and green flowers,
r.m. & e., circa 1892, 5in. high.
$120 £75

Doulton Lambeth miniature
stoneware mustard pot with
'Colman's' in relief and applied
moulding. $48 £30

A handled bottle with overall
applied pink, brown, and white
fan-shaped patterns, r.m.,
1882, 3¼in. high. $88 £55

A miniature Doulton Lambeth
stoneware caster with plated lid
and applied moulding.
$56 £35

A jug by Edith Lupton with
green panels painted in pâte-
sur-pâte, c.m., 1878, 4¾in.
high. $104 £65

NATURAL FOLIAGE WARE

A 'natural foliage-ware' vase with the impression of veined leaves glazed olive-green, c.m.l. & c., circa 1905, 8¾in. high.
$176 £110

A pair of 'natural foliage-ware' vases with the impression of veined leaves, r.m. & e., 16¼in. high. $576 £360

A 'natural foliage-ware' vase, the rough ochre ground impressed with two types of reddish-brown leaves, DLE, circa 1895, 12½in. high
$240 £150

SIMULATED WARE

Cast iron, a covered box in silicon ware, simulating an iron 14 lb. weight, DSL & e., the silver handle hallmarked 1898. 5in. high. $88 £55

A silicon jug, the dark brown body simulating leather with stitched joints, 9¾in. high, with two beakers en suite, hallmarked 1899, 4¼in. high, DSL & e. $296 £185

A jug, the silicon body with copper coloured glaze and imitation joints, 7in. high, DSL & e., 1900. $112 £70

A Doulton & Slater's patent mug, simulating brown leather with stitched panels, r.m. & e. & DSL, the silver rim hallmarked 1893, 6¼in high.
$144 £90

A Doulton Lambeth silicon stoneware match holder with silver rim, simulating a leather cricket ball, 3in. diam.
$192 £120

A stoneware jug simulating a black jack, the dark brown leather with stitched joints, DLE, the silver rim hallmarked 1897, 9in. high. $144 £90

SILICON WARE

A small vase of hexagonal section inscribed on either side 'The Waning of the Honey-Moon', supported on an oval base with two hares sitting defiantly at either end, r.m., 1880, 4³/₄in. high.　$448　£280

A pair of ewers decorated with applied slip flower, leaf and bead designs, DSL, circa 1891, 7¹/₄in. high.　$118　£74

A jug with impressed flower and leaf motifs, and applied blue flower heads, DSL, 1884, 5½in. high.　$104　£65

A jardiniere decorated with applied and incised flower and leaf designs on a blue ground, DSL, 7¹/₂in. high.　$144　£90

A modelled owl with brown wings and feet, the detachable head and the body decorated with applied blue, green and white motifs, DSL, circa 1880, 7½in. high.　$464　£290

A jardiniere decorated with blue floret and incised designs on a buff ground, DLE, impressed date for 1884, 6³/₄in. high.　$136　£85

A water filter with incised, carved and applied decoration on a buff ground, DSL, 14¹/₂in. high.　$336　£210

A tobacco jar decorated with applied blue and white beads, r.m., impressed date for 1888, 4¹/₄in. high.　$56　£35

A tapering jug with overall incised diamond patterns, DSL, circa 1880, 8in. high. $96 £60

SPORTING SUBJECTS

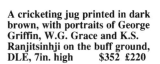

A cricketing jug printed in dark brown, with portraits of George Griffin, W.G. Grace and K.S. Ranjitsinhji on the buff ground, DLE, 7in. high $352 £220

A silver mounted cycling jug and two beakers, DLE, circa 1900, the jug 8in. high, the beakers 4³/₄in. high.
$368 £230

A sporting jug commemorating the untimely death of F.J. Archer, the champion jockey in 1886, r.m., 6¹/₂in. high.
$192 £120

A golfing jug, sprigged in white, with the panels of the 'Last Ball', 'Putting' and 'Driving', impressed Lambeth mark, circa 1880, 20cm. high. $608 £380

A waisted mug applied with moulded white figures of a bowler, wicket keeper, and a batsman, DLE, circa 1900, 6in. high. $240 £150

A cricketing jug, the moulded relief figures against the buff salt glaze ground within stylised floral borders outlined in white slip and coloured in blue and green, DLE, circa 1900, 9¹/₄in. high. $304 £190

A silver mounted sporting tyg, DLE, circa 1900, 6in. high, the silver rim maker's mark H.W., Sheffield. $304 £190

A cricketer's mug applied with moulded white figures of a bowler, wicket keeper and a batsman, circa 1880, 15.5cm. high. $272 £170

A cricketing tyg, impressed Registration mark, r.m., and dated 1884, 6¹/₄in. high.
$448 £280

415

SPORTING SUBJECTS

A mug with applied moulded golfing vignettes of 'the drive', and 'the lost ball', DLE, circa 1900, 5in. high. $464 £290

A beaker with relief white figures of a shot putter, a runner, and a long-jumper, DLE, the silver rim hallmarked 1900, 5in. high. $96 £60

A cycling mug with three applied white figures inscribed Military, Road, and Path, DLE, circa 1900, 4¾in. high. $160 £100

A cycling jug with three white vignettes, inscribed Military, Road and Path, DLE, circa 1900, 7¼in. high. $192 £120

A sporting jug with three moulded white vignettes, a man running, men playing football, and a man putting the shot, DLE, circa 1900, 8in. high. $160 £100

A cricket jug with applied vignettes of a bowler, wicket keeper and a batsman, DLE, circa 1900, 7in. high. $288 £180

A rugby football jug with vignettes of two men kicking a ball, a scrummage and two of the men running with a ball, r.m., 1883, 7½in. high. $240 £150

A cricket mug with three applied figures of batsmen in high relief, registration mark of 1880, r.m., 1882, 5¼in. high. $256 £160

A golfing jug with three applied white vignettes of 'the lost ball', 'putting', and 'driving', DLE, circa 1900, 7¾in. high. $512 £320

TOBY JUGS

ALBERT SAGGER THE POTTER D6745
(Collectors' Club)
Designer: W. Harper
Size: Small 4in., 10cm.
Issued: 1986
Price: $35 £22

CHARLIE CHAPLIN
Designer: Unknown
Size: Large 11in., 28cm.
Issued: c.1918
Price: $6400 £4000

CLIFF CORNELL
Designer: Unknown
Size: 9¼in., 23.5cm.
Issued: 1956 in a limited edition of 500
Price: $560 £350 (Blue Suit)

CLIFF CORNELL
Designer: Unknown
Size: 9¼in., 23.5cm.
Issued: 1956 in a limited edition of 500
Price: $560 £350 (Brown Suit)

CLIFF CORNELL
Designer: Unknown
Size: 9¼in., 23.5cm.
Issued: 1956 in a limited edition of 350
Price: $640 £400 (Beige Suit)

FALSTAFF D6062
Designer: C. Noke
Size: Large 8½in., 21.5cm.
Issued: 1939-
Rec. Retail Price

FALSTAFF D6063
Designer: C. Noke
Size: Small 5¼in., 13.5cm.
Issued: 1939-
Rec. Retail Price

GEORGE ROBEY
Designer: Unknown
Size: Large 10½in., 26.5cm.
Issued: c.1925
Price: $5600 £3500

HAPPY JOHN D6031
Designer: H. Fenton
Size: Large 8¾in., 22cm.
Issued: 1939-
Rec. Retail Price

HAPPY JOHN D6070
Designer: H. Fenton
Size: Small 5½in., 14cm.
Issued: 1939-
Rec. Retail Price

HONEST MEASURE D6108
Designer: H. Fenton
Size: Small 4½in., 11.5cm.
Issued: 1939-
Rec. Retail Price

HUNTSMAN D6320
Designer: H. Fenton
Size: Large 7½in., 19cm.
Issued: 1950-
Rec. Retail Price

ALBERT SAGGER THE POTTER

CHARLIE CHAPLIN

GEORGE ROBEY

CLIFF CORNELL
(Blue Suit)

CLIFF CORNELL
(Brown Suit)

CLIFF CORNELL
(Beige Suit)

FALSTAFF

HONEST MEASURE

HAPPY JOHN

JOLLY TOBY D6109
Designer: H. Fenton
Size: Medium 6½in.,
16.5cm.
Issued: 1939-
Rec. Retail Price

OLD CHARLEY D6030
Designer: H. Fenton
Size: Large 8¾in., 22cm.
Issued: 1939-1960
Price: $104 £65

OLD CHARLEY D6069
Designer: H. Fenton
Size: Small 5½in., 14cm.
Issued: 1939-1960
Price: $56 £35

SHERLOCK HOLMES D6661
Designer: R. Tabbenor
Size: Large 8¾in., 22cm.
Issued: 1981-
Rec. Retail Price

SIR FRANCIS DRAKE D6660
Designer: M. Abberley
Size: Large 9in., 23cm.
Issued: 1981-
Rec. Retail Price

SQUIRE D6319
Designer: H. Fenton
Size: Medium 6in., 15cm.
Issued: 1950-1969
Price: $144 £90

**THE BEST IS NOT TOO
GOOD D6107**
Designer: H. Fenton
Size: 4½in., 11.5cm.
Issued: 1939-1960
Price: $80 £50

TOBY XX D6088
Designer: H. Fenton
Size: 6½in., 16.5cm.
Issued: 1939-1969
Price: $112 £70

TOBY XX
Designer: Harry Simeon
Size: Large 7½in., 19cm.
Issued: 1922
Price: $240 £150

**WINSTON CHURCHILL
D6171**
Designer: H. Fenton
Size: Large 9in., 23cm.
Issued: 1941-
Rec. Retail Price

**WINSTON CHURCHILL
D6172**
Designer: H. Fenton
Size: Medium 5½in.,
14cm.
Issued: 1941-
Rec. Retail Price

**WINSTON CHURCHILL
D6175**
Designer: H. Fenton
Size: Small 4in., 10cm.
Issued: 1941-
Rec. Retail Price

HUNTSMAN THE BEST IS NOT TOO GOOD OLD CHARLEY

SQUIRE JOLLY TOBY SIR FRANCIS DRAKE

TOBY XX D6088 WINSTON CHURCHILL TOBY XX

DOULTONVILLE TOBIES

ALDERMAN MACE D6766
Issued: 1987-
Rec. Retail Price

BETTY BITTERS D6716
Issued: 1984-
Rec. Retail Price

CAPTAIN PROP D6812
Issued: 1988-
Rec. Retail Price

CAPTAIN SALT D6721
Issued: 1985
Rec. Retail Price

CHARLIE CHEER D6768
Issued: 1987-
Rec. Retail Price

DR. PULSE D6723
Issued: 1985-
Rec. Retail Price

FLORA FUCHSIA D6767
Issued: 1987-1988
Price: $29 £18

FRED FEARLESS D6809
Issued: 1989-
Rec. Retail Price

FRED FLY D6742
Issued: 1986-
Rec. Retail Price

LEN LIFEBELT D6811
Issued: 1988-
Rec. Retail Price

MADAME CRYSTAL D6714
Issued: 1984-1988
Price: $29 £18

MAJOR GREEN D6740
Issued: 1986-
Rec. Retail Price

MIKE MINERAL D6741
Issued: 1986-1988
Price: $29 £18

MISS NOSTRUM D6700
Issued: 1983-
Rec. Retail Price

MISS STUDIOUS D6722
Issued: 1985-1988
Price: $29 £18

MONSIEUR CHASSEUR D6769
Issued: 1987-
Rec. Retail Price

MR BRISKET D6743
Issued: 1986-
Rec. Retail Price

MR FURROW D6701
Issued: 1983-1988
Price: $29 £18

MR LITIGATE D6699
Issued: 1983-
Rec. Retail Price

MRS LOAN D6715
Issued: 1984-1988
Price: $29 £18

MR TONSIL D6713
Issued: 1984-
Rec. Retail Price

PAT PARCEL D6813
Issued: 1988-
Rec. Retail Price

REV. CASSOCK D6702
Issued: 1983-
Rec. Retail Price

SERGEANT PEELER D6720
Issued: 1985-
Rec. Retail Price

Designer: W. Harper
Size: 4in., 10cm.

ALDERMAN MACE

BETTY BITTERS

CAPTAIN PROP

CAPTAIN SALT

CHARLIE CHEER

DR. PULSE

DOULTONVILLE TOBIES

FLORA FUCHSIA

FRED FEARLESS

FRED FLY

LEN LIFEBELT

MADAME CRYSTAL

MAJOR GREEN

MIKE MINERAL

MISS NOSTRUM

MISS STUDIOUS

DOULTONVILLE TOBIES

MONSIEUR CHASSEUR

MR BRISKET

MR FURROW

MR LITIGATE

MRS LOAN

MR TONSIL

PAT PARCEL

REV. CASSOCK

SERGEANT PEELER

SMALL SEATED TOBIES

Designer: H. Fenton
Size: 4½in., 11.5cm.

MR PICKWICK D6261
Issued: 1948-1960
Price: $136 £85

MR MICAWBER D6262
Issued: 1948-1960
Price: $136 £85

SAIREY GAMP D6263
Issued: 1948-1960
Price: $136 £85

FAT BOY D6264
Issued: 1948-1960
Price: $136 £85

SAM WELLER D6265
Issued: 1948-1960
Price: $136 £85

CAP'N CUTTLE D6266
Issued: 1948-1960
Price: $136 £85

MR PICKWICK

MR MICAWBER

SAIREY GAMP

FAT BOY

SAM WELLER

CAP'N CUTTLE

ARTISTS & ASSISTANTS

Adelaide	**AARON**	aO
Christine	**ABBOT**	CA
Elizabeth J.	**ADAMS**	LA
Ella H.	**ADAMS**	aa 𝒜
Matilda S.	**ADAMS**	MsA
Margaret	**AITKEN**	𝕸
Mary	**AITKEN**	MA
Emily	**ALLEN**	EEA
Fannie J.	**ALLEN**	Æ
E.	**ARCHER**	𝓘
Helen A.	**ARDING**	𝒜
Mary M.	**ARDING**	M.M.A
Margaret M.	**ARMSTRONG**	𝕸
A.	**ASKEW**	⁚⁚ a
Elizabeth	**ATKINS**	EA
N.	**ATKINS**	♀
Lizzie	**AXFORD**	a⁚
Louisa	**AYLING**	a
Agnes E. M.	**BAIGENT**	ÆB
Clara	**BAKER**	bbb
Emily	**BAKER**	b⁚b
Edith H.	**BALL**	B̄ bq
E.	**BANFIELD**	bd
Eliza S.	**BANKS**	EℬB
Alice M. E.	**BARKER**	b⁚ B AMB
Clara S.	**BARKER**	CSB
G.	**BARKER**	-//-
Arthur B.	**BARLOW**	Æℬ
Florence E.	**BARLOW**	FℰB
Hannah B.	**BARLOW**	ℋB
Lucy A.	**BARLOW**	ℒL
Harry	**BARNARD**	ℬ
V.	**BARNES**	V
W.	**BARON**	W3
Mary A.	**BARRETT**	bbO MAB
Ethel	**BEARD**	EB
George W.	**BEARNE**	ℬ
Acidalia E. C.	**BECK**	ʌB
N.	**BEEDEN**	ℐ
Arthur	**BEERE**	ℬ
G.	**BENSON**	℅
A.	**BENTLEY**	↺
Augusta M.	**BIRNIE**	b̄ 𝒜B
Florence M.	**BIRT**	qb
Ernest R.	**BISHOP**	ℬ
Eborah	**BISSMIRE**	bOO
F.	**BLACKSTAFFE**	)-(
H.	**BLAKE**	|b|
O.	**BOUCHER**	br
Maud	**BOWDEN**	Mℬ
Florence	**BOWDITCH**	⁚b⁚
Jessie	**BOWDITCH**	ℬ
Eliza	**BOWEN**	bb⁚
L. F.	**BOWEN**	ℒfℬ
Winnie	**BOWSTEAD**	N.B
Jessie	**BOYCE**	J·B

Name	Mark		Name	Mark
N. BRAKE	∧		Miss COCKS	CO
Daisy BRIANT	D.B		Edith M. COLEMAN	EG.
John BROAD	B		F.M. COLLINS	CM
D. BROND	F		Rose COLLINS	RC
F. BROOKE	F		Miss CONGDON	c ∷
Rosina BROWN	RB		Alice COOKE	ccO
Alice E. BUDDEN	AEB. b		D. CORDERO	⌇
Mary BUDDEN	obo		Joan COWPER	Joan Cowper
C. BUNN	tU		Minna L. CRAWLEY	⋒ ⋒
Alice L. BURLTON	ALB. B		D. CROFTS	⧣
Georgina BURR	b+ G.D.B		Ellen CROSBY	E
Eleanor BURRELL	ⓑ		Emily CROSBY	cOO
Emma A. BURROWS	o b		James R. CRUICKSHANK	¢
Frank A. BUTLER	AB		Annie CUPIT	cc
Mary BUTTER	bb M.B		Lilian CURTIS	L.C. C c∎
Mary BUTTERTON	AB		Lizzie M. DAINTREE	dO
Alice CAFFIN	A		Olive DALE	d∎
Alice CAMPBELL	A.C.		A. DANIELS	⁊
Bertha M. CAPES	₿		Kate M. DAVIS	KD.
Mary CAPES	M		Louisa J. DAVIS	⊕
Annie M. CASTLE	A6.		Mary A. DAVIS	⋒⋒ d+
Kate J. CASTLE	c		W. DAVISON	D
M. CAUTY	c c m.b.		Elizabeth DAYTON	ⓓ
Margaret M. CHALLIS	M⋒		Mary DENLEY	Ⓜ
Emily M. CHANDLER	⌇ ᴣ		Ada DENNIS	AD A) d∎
J. CHANDLER	C		Florence DENNIS	≢ dd∎
Clara CHURCHER	∎c∎		Miss DOUTHWAITE	ddd
Emily CLARK	E.C.		Amelia A. DRAKE	A.D.
Fanny CLARK	FC		M. DRIVER	⊕
L. CLARK	C		A. DUNCAN	⅃
E. CLARKE	⌇		Edward DUNN	⅏ Ⅾ
Frances CLEMENTS	ⅎ		W. Edward DUNN	wED

Name	Mark		Name	Mark
M. DUNTON			Lizzie FRENCH	ff
Beatrice M. DURTNALL	D		A. E. FRENCH	ÆF
Josephine A. DURTNALL	J.D		M. FRICKER	f::
L. Imogen DURTNALL	LᴵD dd		Elizabeth A. GADSDON	g͟g
Alice K. EARL	:E:		Jessie GANDY	JG. go:
Florence EARL	e::		Walter GANDY	W G
Alice ECKENSTEIN	e▪ A.E.		Nellie GARBETT	g EG
Lottie ECKENSTEIN	eeO		Ellen GATHERCOLE	NGg g▪
M. EDERMANIGER			Sarah P. GATHERCOLE	ⓖ
Emily J. EDWARDS			Annie GENTLE	AG
Louisa E. EDWARDS			Kate R. GIBLIN	G go
Edward E. EGGLETON			Elizabeth M. GILLMAN	▪g▪
Fanny ELLIOTT			Emily J. GILLMAN	
Herbert ELLIS	HE		L. GOLDSACK	LG
Sarah ELLIS	SE		Mary A. GOODE	g g
C. EMERTON	E		Laura GOODERHAM	g gO
Bertha EVANS	E e		M. GOODING	:g
Kate EVERETT	e e		E. GRAVER	M
John EYRE	JE JEyre		M. GRAY	
Miss FELTON	f:		Alberta L. GREEN	AG
Ada E. FIMISTER	AF		Edith GREEN	G
Elizabeth FISHER			Laura GREEN	g▪
Sarah FISHER	SF ⓕ		Lydia GREIG	OgO
Emily A. FORSEY	fO E.A.F		A. GRIGGS	g::
Minnie FORSTER	ff		Alice E. GROOM	JG .G.
E. FORSYTH			Jessie GUEST	gOO
Constance FOSTER	ff		Alice HALL	
M. FOX	M.F.		Elizabeth HAMILTON	E.H.
D. FRAMPTON			J. B. HARDING	BH
Catherine FRANCIS	F		B. HARMAN	h
L. FRANCIS	f		A. Leslie HARRADINE	
May FREAKES	fr		Edith HARRINGTON	hOO

Name	Monogram
Rosina HARRIS	RH
Emma C. HARRISON	H
Nellie HARRISON	hn
W. HASTINGS	W
Lizzie HAUGHTON	Hl
Ethel HAWKINS	h k
Emily M. HAWKSBY	hh▪ E.M.H.
Emily HAYNES	hh
A. HAYS	AH
E. Violet HAYWARD	hd
L. HAYWARD	◿
Rosetta HAZELDINE	▪h▪
O. HEATH	hOh
Alice G. HELLIS	h
E. HENDERSON	(·)
Alice M. HERAPATH	H h▪ A.M.H
Edith HERAPATH	hh
F. HEWITT	h h h
K. HEYWOOD	◔
E. HIBBERD	⊏⊐
Harriett E. HIBBUT	HEH
Jessie HINCHLIFF	Ⓗ
Marion HOLBROOK	MH
Eliza J. HOLLIS	hhO E.H.
Joan HONEY	JH
Agnes S. HORNE	hO H̄
Annie HORTON	ho▪
Agnete HOY	AH
Eliza L. HUBERT	ELH
Vera HUGGINS	v·H ℋ YH
Kate HUGHES	h∷ K·H
Annie M. HULFORD	H.x.
Florence L. HUNT	J.H.
Jane S. HURST	H
John HUSKINSON	H
Ernest JARRETT	J
E. JESSETT	⊂
Doris JOHNSON	DJ
Florrie JONES	FJ
Gladys JOYCE	J
Ivy JOYCE	J
Rosa KEEN	R K
Edith KELSEY	J
Edith L. KEMP	K EK
Harriette E. E. KNIGHT	k
Alice LACY	ll O
Charlotte LAMB	CL
Ulrique LARCHER	UL
J. LASHAM	II
Marion LAYZELL	11
Francis E. LEE	FEL
Harriette E. LEE	L ll
Nellie LEGGE	⊣⊣1
Esther LEWIS	£
Florence E. LEWIS	£
Isabel LEWIS	⊥
Ada C. LILLEY	ll▪
Mary M. S. LILLEY	l▪
Frances M. LINNELL	⅏
Ada LONDON	l
Emily A. LONDON	L EA
Alice LONGHURST	l∷
Jessie LORD	ld
Edith D. LUPTON	EDL

Name	Mark		Name	Mark
Annie LYONS	⅄ A.L.		Annie NEAL	n
W. W. MACKAY	� monogram		Minnie NEAL	Z
B. MACNAE	(X		William J. NEATBY	WJN
Matilda MARLYN	m▪m		Bessie NEWBERY	BN
Emma MARRIOTT	ⴴⴳ		Josephine E. NEWNHAM	N
L. MARRIOTT	÷		Mary NEWSON	mn
Alice MARSHALL	A.M.		E. NOBLE	•n•
Mark V. MARSHALL	M·V·M		Lilla NOTTINGHAM	N
Susan MARSHALL	m		E. NORRIS	(monogram)
Eliza MARTIN	mm		F. NORRISH	(monogram)
Emma MARTIN	EM.		W. J. W. NUNN	(monogram)
M. MARTIN	m▪m		Gertrude NYE	(monogram)
Matilda MARTYN	mmm		A. ORCHIN	(monogram)
F. MASKELL	(monogram)		Lizzie PADBURY	P LP
Louisa MATTERSON	mO		D. PAINTER	P
Ada MAYCOCK	m▪		Ellen PALMER	Op
Emily MAYES	m		L. PARKER	◇
Emily W. MAYNE	EM.		William PARKER	ωp
John H. McLENNAN	JHMᶜ		Emily J. PARTINGTON	EP
L. MEAR	(monogram)		Lily PARTINGTON	LP
Miss MEDLICOTT	mt		Annie PARTRIDGE	P▪
Miss MIDDLEMISS	mi		Arthur E. PEARCE	(monogram) R
Alice MILBORROW	▪▪m		Georgina PEARSON	P▪P
Isabella MILLER	M (monogram)		S. PEARSON	P.
A. MILLS	⅄		Helena M. PENNETT	PP
Annie MILNE	(m)		F. PERRIN	(monogram)
Mary MITCHELL	MM		E. PHEBY	▪P▪
Ada MORGAN	mOO		E. PICKERSGILL	Pa
Joseph H. MOTT	JHM		F. POMEROY	FP
Iza M. MUNDAY	EM		Francis C. POPE	.P F·C·P
E. NAISH	⤢		A. POTTERTON	(monogram)
H. NAISH	(n)		R. PRITCHARD	R

M.	PRYCE	⋇
Jane	RABBIT	rrO
Emily	RANDALL	E.R.
L.	RAWLINGS	rg
Frank W.	READER	R ℛ
Constance E.	REDFORD	ℛ r:
George W.	RHEAD	ᵱᴹR
S.	RICKARDS	r:
Alice M.	RITCHIN	AR
Emma	ROBERTS	ER
Florence C.	ROBERTS	FR
Emily L.	ROBINSON	R
Alice	ROBJENT	ⓡ
Edith	ROGERS	EER
Isabel	ROGERS	ℛ
Kate	ROGERS	ℛ
L.	ROGERS	⦀
Martha M.	ROGERS	M̅M̅R
A.	ROHSS	F̵
Letitia	ROSEVEAR	r
William	ROWE	WR
M.	RUCKSTUHL	mr
E.	RUDDOCK	E.R
Agnes M.	RUFF	ℳ
Ellen	RUMBOL	ER RO
Jane	RUMBOL	rOO
Alice	RUSSELL	:r:
F.	RUSSELL	⚜
Kate E.	RUSSELL	rɹ
Louisa	RUSSELL	⌐ᴸ R LR
Clara	RYMER	rO
Susanna M.	SANDERSON	S.S
Agnes D.	SANDES	A.S.
F.	SAWYER	⁊
A.	SAYERS	sO AS.
Elizabeth A.	SAYERS	ƐAS
Fanny	SAYERS	sOO
Rosalie	SCOTT	ssO
G.	SHARPE	⨂
G.	SHEARS	sr
Elizabeth	SHELLEY	E.S
Annie	SHELTON	ss:
Lizzie	SHETTLEWORTH	ℒ
F.	SHIPMAN	⍏
A.	SHUTE	ss:
Emma	SHUTE	ℰS.
Harry	SIMEON	HS
Eliza	SIMMANCE	S ES
Alice M. M.	SKIDMORE	OsO
Mary	SLATTER	M.S.
Elizabeth M.	SMALL	ƷMS
Katherine B.	SMALLFIELD	KBS ℬ
Mildred B.	SMALLFIELD	MBS
Alice G.	SMITH	A.S.
Ellen B.	SMITH	E.B.S S. ss
E.	SMITH	ℐ
Frances	SMITH	F.S.
Georgie	SMITH	GS
Gertrude	SMITH	S̵ S̵
Catherine A.	SPARKES	CAS
E.	SPONG	Ⓢ
A.	SPURRELL	↓
Fanny	STABLE	F.S.
Mary	STAREY	SMS s:

Eliza	STOCK	s
Emily E.	STORMER	EES
N.	STRAKER	
Emilie M.	STRATFORD	s•s
E.	STRATTON	st
Katherine	STURGEON	
George Hugo	TABOR	GTH
Winifred	TALBOT	tl
N.	TAYLOR	
Florence	TEGETMEIER	to
A. Euphemia	THATCHER	
Elsie S.	THOMAS	tt
Margaret E.	THOMPSON	TM
Marie E.	THOMPSON	tx
Minnie G.	THOMPSON	MGT
Mary Ann	THOMSON	MT
Walter	THORNEMAN	
M.	THORNTON	
George	TINWORTH	
H.	TOLAND	
Louisa E.	TOMKINS	
F.	TOMLYN	
Ada	TOSEN	AT
A.	TOSEN	
Eleanor	TOSEN	ttt
Ellen C.	TOWNSEND	t••
A.	TRANTER	
Ethel	TRANTER	tOO
A.	TURNER	
M.	UNWIN	U•
C.	VARGAS	
R.	VARGAS	

Bessie M.	VARNEY	v
C.	VIGOR	C.V.
Emily M.	VINER	E.V.
E.	WAKELY	w•
Louisa	WAKELY	w LW
K.	WALKER	
Helen	WALTERS	
L.	WATERS	L.W.
Linnie	WATT	Watt
Minnie	WEBB	MW
Jenny F.	WEEKES	wO
Emily M. R.	WELCH	EW
M.	WELSBY	
Georgina	WHITE	G.W.
Onslow E.	WHITING	O.W.
K.	WHITTON	
H.	WILKINSON	
Arthur	WILLCOCK	W
A.	WILSON	
Edgar W.	WILSON	
Louie	WILSON	
R.	WILSON	
Ada M.	WOOD	wOO
Christina	WOOD	C.W
Emily	WOOD	ww
Edith H.	WOODINGTON	W
Rosetta S.	WOODS	RW
Ada L.	WORTHEY	A.W.
C. M.	WRAY	
Bessie J.	YOUATT	
L.	YOUNG	y
A.	ZURCHER	Z

MARKS

DOULTON & WATTS — Impressed or incised mark used on stoneware, 1827–1858.

 Circular mark impressed with date, used on Doulton Ware and Lambeth Faience, 1876–1880.

DOULTON & WATTS
LAMBETH POTTERY
LONDON — Impressed or incised mark used on stoneware, 1827–1858.

 Impressed or printed mark used on stoneware, with England added after 1891, 1879–1902.

 Impressed or incised mark used on stoneware, 1827–1858.

 Rosette Mark impressed or printed on Doulton Ware and Lambeth Faience, 1880-1891.

(r.m. – rosette mark)

DOULTON
LAMBETH — Impressed or printed mark used on stoneware, with England added after 1891, 1858–1910.

H. DOULTON & CO. — Incised on panels and plaques by George Tinworth.

 Oval undated mark impressed on early Doulton Ware, 1869–1872.

(o.u.m. – oval undated mark)

DOULTON & SLATERS
PATENT — Doulton and Slater's Patent, 1885–1939.

(DSP – Doulton & Slater's Patent)

 Oval mark impressed and dated used on Doulton Ware, 1872–1876.

(o.m. – oval mark)

 Doulton Silicon Lambeth, with England added after 1891, 1880–1932.

(DSL – Doulton Silicon Lambeth)

 Circular mark, impressed or printed, and sometimes dated in the centre, used on Lambeth Faience, 1873–1914.

(c.m. – circular mark)

 Rosette mark with England added, used on Doulton Ware and Lambeth Faience, 1891–1902.

(r.m. & e. – rosette mark and England)

 Impressed or printed mark, with England added after 1891, used on Lambeth Faience, 1873–1914.

DOULTON
LAMBETH
ENGLAND — Impressed or printed on small objects of Doulton Ware, 1891–1956.

Doulton Lambeth England, used on Doulton Ware and Lambeth Faience, 1891–1956.

(DLE – Doulton Lambeth England)

 Impressed or printed mark used on Crown Lambeth Ware, 1891–1905.

 Impressed or printed mark used on Impasto Ware, often dated in the centre and with England added after 1891, 1879–1914.

 Used on objects with a metallic coating, circa 1900.

 Printed mark used on Faience, with England added after 1891, 1880–1914.

 Printed on Morrisian Ware, 1901–1924.

 Impressed or printed on Marqueterie Ware, with England added after 1891, 1887–1906.

 Printed mark used on Brangwyn Ware.

 Impressed or printed on Marqueterie Ware, with England added after 1891, 1887–1906.

 Circle mark, lion and crown used on Doulton Lambeth and Burslem Ware, 1902–1956.

(c.m.l. & c. – circle mark, lion and crown)

 Impressed or printed on Marqueterie Ware, with England added after 1891, 1887–1906.

 Circle mark used on small objects of Doulton Lambeth and Burslem Ware, 1902–1956.

(RDE – Royal Doulton England)

 Impressed or printed on Marqueterie Ware, with England added after 1891, 1887–1906.

 Printed mark used on Royal Doulton Flambe, with 'Made in England' added from 1930, 1902–1930.

 Impressed or printed mark used on Carrara Ware, 1891–1924.

 Royal Doulton Flambe mark used on small pieces, 1904–1930.

 Printed on Velluma Ware, 1911–1914.

 Impressed or printed mark used on Persian Ware, 1920–1936.

 Impressed or printed mark used on Doulton Ware, 1912–1956.

(s.c.m. – slip cast mark)

 Printed mark used on Burslem stone-ware, 1922–1927.

 Printed mark used on Royal Doulton Titanian Ware, 1916–1929.

 Circle mark and lion, impressed or printed on Doulton Ware, 1922–1956.

(c.m. & l. – circle mark and lion)

 Printed mark used on Royal Doulton Titanian Ware, 1916–1929.

  Printed mark used on Chang Ware with the monogram of H. Nixon, 1925–1940.

 Printed mark used on hard-paste figures, 1918–1933.

 Printed mark used on Chinese Jade, 1920–1940.

 Mark used mainly on wall plaques, 1925–1939.

Printed mark used on Burslem earthen-ware, 1932 –present day.

 Printed Flambe mark with Sung in script, 1920–1940.

 Mark in current use, 1959–present day.

INDEX

A La Mode 101
A Parable 405
A Penny's Worth 101
A United Family 395
Abberley, M. 307, 419
Abdullah 101
A' Courting 101
Adele 101
Admiral of the Fleet 295
Adornment 101
Adrienne 101
Advertising Wares 16, 33—38
Aero 338
Affection 101
Afternoon Tea 101
Aged in Wood Series 336, 337
Aileen 101, 102
Aitken, Margaret 342, 343
Aitken, Mary 348
Ajax 102
Albert Embankment 15
Albert Medal 11
Albert Sagger 417
Alchemist 102, 293, 297
Alderman Mace 419
Aldin Series, Cecil 64, 330
Alexandra 102
Alfred Jingle 102
Alice 102
Alison 102
All-A-Blooming 102
All Aboard 102
Allen 22, 29
Allen, F. 63
Allure 102
Amanda 102
Amy 102
And One For You 102
And So To Bed 102
Andrea 102
Angela 102
Angelina 102
Animal Figures 17, 39—46
Ann 102
Anna 102
Annabel 103
Annabella 103
Anne Boleyn 65
Anne of Cleves 65
Annette 103
Annie Oakley 65
Anthea 103
Antique Dealer 65
Antony & Cleopatra 65
Antoinette 103, 104

Apothecary 65, 301
Apple Maid 104
April 104
April Shower 104
Arab 104, 211
Arabian Nights 337, 339
Aragorn 104
Aramis 66
Archer, F. J. 415
'Ard of Earing 66
Arding, Helen 55
Arding, Mary 53, 55
Army Club Cigarettes 34, 37
'Arriet 66, 86
Arrival of the Unknown
    Princess, The 337
'Arry 66, 85
'Arry & 'Arriet 25
Art Pottery 17, 47—64
Art Union 391
Artandia 38
Artful Dodger 104, 291, 313
Artists & Assistants 423
As Good As New 104
Ascot 104
Ash Bowls 311
Ash Trays 311
Asprey & Co. 33
At Ease 105
At The Cheshire Cheese 295,
    337
Athos 66
Atkins, Elizabeth 342
Aubrey 61
Auctioneer 66, 105
August 105
Auld Lang Syne 34
Auld Mac 66, 311, 314
Austen Chamberlain 375
Automne 105
Autumn 105, 338
Autumn Breezes 105
Autumn Time 105
Awakening 106

Baba 106
Babette 106
Babie 106
Baby 106
Baby Bunting 106
Bacchus 66, 68, 315
Bachelor 106
Bailey, Arthur 28
Bailey, Cuthbert 20
Ballad Seller 106

Ballerina 106
Ballet Class 106
Ballinese Dancer 106
Balloon Boy 106
Balloon Clown 106
Balloon Girl 107
Balloon Lady 107
Balloon Man 107
Balloon Seller 107
Banks, Eliza S. 343
Barbara 107
Bardolph 291, 297
Barker, Clara 351
Barliman Butterbur 107
Barlow, Arthur 11, 30, 351—
    353
Barlow, Florence 7, 11, 14, 30,
    47, 48, 49, 54, 354—357,
    364
Barlow, Hannah 7, 11, 12, 30,
    31, 48, 54, 55, 358—365
Barlow, Lucy 365
Barnard, Harry 342, 343
Basket Weaver 107
Bass 36
Bather 107, 366
Bathing Beauty 108
Battle of Britain 23
Bayes, Gilbert 15
Bayeux Tapestry Series 332
Beachcomber 108
Beam, Jim 33
Beard, Ethel 48
Bear's Head, The 337
Beat You To It 108
Beatrice 108
Becky 108
Bedtime 26, 104
Bedtime Story 108
Beefeater 34, 68, 289, 315
Beethoven 108
Beggar 108
Beggar's Opera 31
Behind the Painted Masque
    Series 336, 338
Belch, Toby 25
Belle 108, 109
Belle O' The Ball 27, 109
Bell's Whisky 33
Ben Jonson 294, 298
Benjamin Franklin 68
Benmore 109
Bernice 109
Bess 109
Beth 109

Betsy 109
Betsy Trotwood 313
Betty 109, 110
Betty Bitters 419
Bibelots 32, 406, 407
Biddy 110
Biddy Penny Farthing 110
Big Ben Scotch Whisky 35
Biggs, D. 300
Bilbo 111
Bill Sykes 111, 294, 297, 313
Bilton, Louis 21
Bing Boys, The 418
Birbeck, J. 21, 337 338
Black Prince Road 8, 15
Blacksmith 68, 111
Blacksmith of Williamsburg 111
Blighty 111
Blithe Morning 111
Blossom 111
Blue Beard 111, 112
Blue Pearly Boy 25
Blue Pearly Girl 25
Bluebird 112
Bo-Peep 112
Boatman 112
Boer War Soldier, The 366
Bolero 112
Bon Appetit 112
Bonjour 112
Bonnie Lassie 112
Bonnie Prince Charlie 68, 292
Bookends 312
Bootmaker 68
Borogrove 381
Boromir 112
Boudoir 112
Bouquet 112, 113
Bow 26
Boy Evacuee 113
Boy from Williamsburg 113
Boy On Crocodile 113
Boy On Pig 113
Boy With Turban 113, 114
Breezy Days 114
Breton Dancer 114
Bride 114, 115
Bridesmaid 115
Bridget 115
Bright Water 116
British Industry Fair 21
Broad, John 32, 366, 408, 409
Broad St. 8, 15

Broken Lance 116
Brown Pearly Boy 25
Brown, Rosina 366
Brussels Exhibition 11, 27
Buckingham Palace 11
Budden, Alice 342
Buddha 21
Buddies 116
Buffalo Bill 68
Bulldog 35
Bulloch & Lade 28, 289
Bumble 116
Bunny 116
Burns 386
Burns' Cottage 33
Burns, John 374
Burslem College of Art 27
Burslem Factory 11–32
Busker 68
Busts 312
Butler, Frank 7, 30, 31, 359, 361, 367–370
Buttercup 116
Butterfly 116
Butterton, Mary 53
Buz Fuz 68, 117, 312, 315

Cafe Royal 15
Called Love 117
Calumet 117
Camellia 117
Camilla 117
Camille 117
Canterbury Pilgrims Series 334
Capes, Mary 53, 343
Cap'n Cuttle 69, 309, 422
Captain 117
Captain Ahab 68, 70, 315
Captain Cook 117, 301
Captain Cuttle, 70, 117, 315
Captain Henry Morgan 70
Captain Hook 70
Captain MacHeath 117
Captain Phillip 301
Captain Prop 419
Captain Salt 419
Captain, 2nd New York Regt. 117
Cardinal 70, 339
Carefree 117
Carmen 117, 118
Carnival 118
Carol 118
Carolyn 118

Carpenter 118
Carpet Seller 118
Carpet Vendor 118, 119
Carrara Ware 18, 48
Carrie 119
Carter & Co., Owen J. 34
Cassim 119
Catherine 119
Catherine Howard 70
Catherine of Aragon 70
Catherine Parr 70
Cavalier 70, 72, 119
Celeste 119
Celia 120
Cellist 120
Cello 120
Centurian 120
Cerise 120
Chadband (Bleak House) 298
Chadwick, Edwin 10
Challis, Margaret 54
Championship Dog Range 17
Chang 12, 17, 18, 19, 50–52
Character Jugs 23–25, 65–94
Charisma 120
Charity 120
Charley's Aunt 120, 121
Charlie 418
Charlie Chaplin 25, 121, 417
Charlie Cheer 419
Charlotte 121
Charmian 121
Charrington 34
Chatcull Hall 17
Chatcull Range 17
Chelsea 26
Chelsea Pair 121
Chelsea Pensioner 72, 121
Cherie 122
Cherry Blossom 122
Cheryl 122
Chessington Zoo 36
Chic 122
Chicago Exhibition 11, 12, 19, 26
Chief 122
Chief Sitting Bull & George Armstrong Custer 72, 91
Chieftain 122
Child & Crab 122
Child from Williamsburg 122
Child Study 122, 123
Child's Grace 123
China Repairer 123
Chine 32, 410, 411

Chinese Dancer 123
Chinese Jade 12, 19, 52
Chitarrone 123
Chloe 124
Choice 124
Choir Boy 124
Chorus Girl 124
Christ in the Garden of
    Gethsemane 395
Christening Day 124
Christine 124
Christopher Columbus 408
Christmas Morn 124
Christmas Parcels 124
Christmas Time 124
Church-Warden 293
Churches & Castles Series 331
Churchill, Sir Winston 16, 23,
    72, 259, 312 418
Cicely 125
Cinderella 322
Circe 125
Cissie 125
City Gent 72
Clare 125
Claribel 125
Clarinda 125
Clarissa 125, 126
Clark Gable 72
Clear Water 126
Clemency 126
Cleopatra 126
Cleveland Flux Co. 16
Cliff, Clarice 27
Clockmaker 126
Clothilde 126
Cloud 126
Clown, 23, 72, 127
Clownette 181
Coaching Days 329
Coachman 127, 300
Cobbler 127
Cocktails 127
Collector 72
Collectors' International 30
Collectors' Ltd. Edn. Series
    336, 337
Collinette 127, 128
Colman's 412
Colonel Fairfax 128
Columbine 126, 128
Coming of Spring 128
Commemorative Ware 32,
    408, 409
Connoisseur, The 290

Constance 128
Contemplation 129
Contentment 26, 129
Cook and Cheshire Cat 72
Cookie 129
Copenhagen 12
Coppelia 129
Coquette 129
Coralie 129
Corinthian 129
Cornell, Cliff 16, 417
Corporal, 1st New Hampshire
    Regt. 129
Countess Mary Howie 129
Country Garden Series 330,
    331, 332
Country Girl 129
Country Lass 129, 201
Country Maid 129
Country Rose 129
Country Scenes 334, 339
Countryside Series 332
Court Shoemaker 129
Courtier 130
Covent Garden 130
Cradle Song 130
Craftsman 130
Craven 'A' Cigarettes 36
Crawford, J. Saxton 33
Crinoline 130
Crinoline Lady 130
Crombie, Charles 299, 340
Crouching Nude 130
Crown, The 297
Crown Lambeth 19, 49
Crusader 292
Crystal Palace 21
Crystalline Ware 20
Cyprus Ware 20
Cund 349
Cup of Tea 130
Curly Knob 130
Curly Locks 130
Curtsey 130, 131
Cymbals 131
Cynthia 132
Cyprus Ware 20
Daffy-Down Dilly 132
Daily Mirror 36
Dainty May 132
Daisy 132, 133
Damaris 133
Dancing Delight 133
Dancing Eyes & Sunny Hair
    133
Dancing Figure 133

Dancing Years 133
Dandy 133
Daphne 133
Darby 133
Darby & Joan 295
Darling 26, 133, 134
D'Artagnan 72
David Copperfield 134, 313
David & Goliath 402
Davies, Margaret (Peggy) 27
Davies, Mary 349
Davis, Louisa 7, 371
Davy Crockett/Santa Anna
    72, 90
Dawn 134
Daybreak 134
Daydreams 134
Deaf 336
Deauville 134
Debbie 134
Debut 135
Debutante 135
December 135
Deirdre 135
Delicia 135
Delight 135
Delphine 135
Demure 135
Denise 135
Denley, Mary 18, 55
Dennis, Ada 18, 55
Derby 26
Derrick 136
Desert Scenes Series 333
Despair 136
Detective 136
Devotion 136
Dewar, John & Sons 28, 34,
    35
Dewar's Whisky 38, 289—299
    406
Diana 136
Diana The Huntress 136
Dick Swiveller 136
Dick Turpin 23, 72, 74, 137,
    311
Dick Whittington 74
Dickens 30, 31, 292, 299,
    302, 313, 330, 332, 333,
    335, 336, 338, 339, 375
Dickens' Dream Jug 29, 302
Dickens' Tinies 313
Digger 137
Diligent Scholar 137
Dimity 137

Ding, Dong, Bell, Pussy's In
  The Well 328
Dinky Do 137
Disraeli, Benjamin 408
Do You Wonder 137
Doc Holliday 74
Doctor 137
Dolly 137
Dolly Vardon 137
Don Quixote 74, 292, 295
  296
Donna 138
Dorcas 138
Doreen 138
Doris Keene as Cavallini 138
Dorothy 138
Double Jester 26, 139
Doulton, Henry 7–32, 96
Doulton, John 7–32, 80
Doulton & Rix 21
Doulton & Slater's Ware 32,
  392, 408, 410, 411, 413
Doulton & Watts 9, 33
Doultonville Tobies, The
  419–421
Downey 36
Dr Johnson Series 337
Dr Pulse 419
Dr Scholl 15, 16
Dragon Vase 19
Drake, Sir Francis 25, 28, 74,
  419
Dream Weaver 139
Dreaming 139
Dreamland 139
Dresden 12
Dressing Up 139
Drink Wisely But Not Too
  Well 299
Drive, The 416
Driving 415, 416
Drummer Boy 139
Drunken Husband, The 398
Dryad of the Pines 139
Duchess of York 139
Duke of Edinburgh 312
Duke of Wellington 74
Duke of York 295
Dulcie 139
Dulcimer 139
Dulcinea 139, 140
Dunce 140
Dunn, Edward W. 371
Durtnall, Josephine 18, 48
Dwight, John 7

Eagle & The Fox, The 397
Earl Mountbatten of Burma
  74
Early Motoring Series 336
Easter Day 140
Eastern Grace 140
Eaton, A. 62, 63
Edinburgh Castle 337
Edith 140
Edward VIII 298
Edward VII & Queen
  Alexandra 408, 409
Edwards, Emily 372
Edwards, Louisa 372
Egyptian Series 332
Elaine 140
Eleanor of Province 140
Eleanore 141
Elegance 141
Elephant Trainer 74
Elfreda 141
Eliza 141
Elizabeth 141
Elizabeth Fry 141
Ellen 141
Ellen Terry as Queen
  Catherine 141
Ellis, Herbert 373
Elsie 141
Elsie Maynard 142
Elyse 142
Embroidering 142
Emin Pasha Relief
  Expedition 408
Emir 142
Emma 142
Empress Eugenie 367
Enchanting Evening 142
Enchantment 142
Encore 142
Engine Driver 74
England's Great Commoner
  409
English Cottages Series 329
Enigma 142
Entranced 142
Ermine Coat 142
Ermine Muff 143
Erminie 143
Esmeralda 143
Estelle 143
Ete 143
Eugene 143
Europa & The Bull 26, 143
Evans, Bertha 342

Eve 144
Evelyn 144
Eventide 144

Fables Clock, The 398
Fagin 144, 290, 313, 335,
  339
Fagin & Bumble 332
Faience 20, 52–55
Fair Lady 144
Fair Maiden 144, 145
Fairy 145, 146
Fairy Spell 146
Faith 146
Falconer 74
Falstaff 28, 34, 74, 76, 146,
  147, 298, 316, 417, 418
Family 147
Family Album 147
Famous Sailing Ships Series
  335
Faraway 147
Farmer 147
Farmer John 76, 311
Farmer's Boy 148
Farmer's Wife 148
Fat Boy 76, 148, 314, 422
Favourite 148
February 148
Feminine Society Series 340
Fenton, H. 24, 25, 28, 29,
  301–310, 417, 419, 422
Festival of Britain 17
Fiddler 148
Figures 26, 27, 95–288
Fiona 148, 149
Fireman 76
First Dance 149
First Love 149
First Steps 149
First Waltz 149
Fisher, Elizabeth 373
Fisher, Sarah 348
Fisherman 299
Fisherwomen 149
Fitzherbert, Mrs 150, 213
Flambe 12, 17–20, 56–59
Fleur 150
Fleurette 150
Flirtation 150
Flora 150
Flora Fuchsia 419
Florence 150
Florence Nightingale 150
Flounced Skirt 150, 151

Flower Arranging 151
Flower Seller 151
Flower Seller's Children 151
Flute 151
Foaming Quart 151
Folly 152
Foot Warmer 34
For Thy Sake Tobacco I
    Would Do Anything But
    Die 290
Forget-Me-Not 152
Fortnum & Masons 36
Fortune Teller 76, 152
Forty Winks 152
Four O'Clock 152
Four Season's 403
Fox 296
Foxes, Double 294
Fragrance 152
Francine 152
Francis Drake, Sir 25, 28,
    74, 419
Frangcon 152
Fred Fearless 419
Fred Fly 419
Free As The Wind 153
Free Spirit 153
Freedom 153
French Horn 153
French Peasant 153
Friar Tuck 76, 153
Friar Tuck & Robin Hood
    333, 335, 339, 340
Frodo 153
Fruit Gathering 153, 154

Gaffer 154
Gaffer Series 329
Gaiety 154
Gail 154
Gainsborough Hat 154, 155
Galadriel 155
Gallant Fishers Series 331,
    333, 339
Gamekeeper 155
Gandalf 155
Gaoler 76
Garbe, Richard 27
Garbott, Nellie 343, 349
Gardener 76, 155
Gathercole, Ellen 342, 343
Gay Morning 155
Gee, P. 307
Geisha 26, 155, 156
General Gordon 408

Genevieve 156
Genie 157
Gentle, Annie 343
Gentleman from Williamsburg
    157
Gentlewoman 157
George IV 9
George V 298, 299, 374
George VI 297, 299
George Harrison 76
George Robey 417
George The Guard 289, 291,
    293
George Washington 29, 76,
    157, 302, 303
George Washington At Prayer
    157
George Washington/King
    George III 76
Georgiana 157
Georgina 157
Geraldine 157
Geronimo 76
Gibson, Charles Dana 336-338
Gibson Girl 336, 337, 338
Giles, R. G. 37
Gillian 157
Gillie And Fisherman 289
Gillman, Emily 52
Gimli 157
Girl Evacuee 158
Girl With Yellow Frock 158
Giselle 158
Giselle, The Forest Glade 158
Gladiator 78
Gladstone, William Ewart 409
Gladys 158
Glasgow Exhibition 11, 31
Gleaner 158
Gleaners & Gypsies Series
    332, 340
Gleaners, The 329
Glen Garry Old Highland
    Whisky 38
Gloria 158
Gnome 158, 159
Golden Days 159
Golfer 78, 159
Gollum 159
Gollywog 159
Gondolier 78
Gondoliers Series 333, 339
Gone Away 78
Good Catch 159
Good Day Sir 159

Good Friends 159
Good King Wenceslas 159
Good Morning 159
Good Pals 159
Goody Two Shoes 160
Goose Girl, The 26, 321
Goosegirl 160
Gossips 161
Grace 161
Grace Darling 161
Grace, W. G. 32, 415
Grace, William 29
Graduate 161
Grand Manner 161
Grand Prix 27
Grandma 161
Grandma's Days 236
Granny 78, 161, 162
Granny's Heritage 162
Granny's Shawl 162
Grant, Wm. 16, 35
Green, Alberta L. 14, 342, 412
Greenaway, Kate 27
Greenlees Bros. 292
Greenlees & Watson 28
Greta 162
Gretchen 162
Grey Friar 318
Grief 162
Griffin, George 415
Griffiths, E. 307
Griselda 162
Grizel 163
Groom, Alice 349
Grossmith's Tsang Ihang 37, 163
Groucho Marx 78
Guard's Chapel 402
Guardsman 78
Gulliver 80
Gunsmith 80
Guy Fawkes 163, 303
Gwendolen 163
Gwynneth 163
Gypsy Dance 163, 164
Gypsy Woman With Child 164

Hamlet 80
Hampshire Cricketer 80
Hansel & Gretel 321
Happy Anniversary 164
Happy Birthday 164
Happy John 417
Happy Joy, Baby Boy 164
Harlequin 164
Harlequinade 164

Harlequinade, Masked 165
Harmony 165
Harold on Horseback 332
Harp 165
Harper, W. 27, 420, 421
Harradine, L. 26, 27, 31, 374
    375, 407, 422
Harriet 165
Harrison, Emma 49
Harvest Time 165
Hastings Castle 331
Hatless Drake 25
Hazel 165
He Loves Me 166
Heart to Heart 166
Heather 166
Heidi 166
Helen 166
Helen of Troy 166
Helmsman 166
Henri 22
Henri, F. 64
Henrietta Maria 166
Henry V 80
Henry VIII 80, 166, 167
Henry Irving As Cardinal
    Wolsey 167
Henry Lytton as Jack Point 167
Her Ladyship 167
Her Majesty Queen
    Elizabeth II 167
Her Majesty Queen
    Elizabeth, The Queen
    Mother 167
Here A Little Child I Stand
    167
Here We Go Gathering Nuts
    In May 319
Here's Health Unto His
    Majesty 300
Herminia 167,168
Hermione 168
He's A Jolly Good Fellow 295
Hibbut, Harriet E. 346,347
Hibernia 168
Higgledy Piggleday , My Black
    Hen 327
Highwayman 168
Hilary 168
Hinged Parasol 168
His Royal Highness Prince
History of Doulton 7-32
Hiver 168
Holbein Ware 60
Home Again 168

Homecoming 169
Honest Measure 417
Honey 169
Hope 169
Hornpipe 169
Hostess of Williamsburg 169
Huckleberry Finn 169
Hudson's Bay Co.28
Huggins, Vera 375,407
Hughes 37
Hunting Scene 291,297,299
Hunting Series 330
Hunting Squire 169,265
Hunts Lady 169
Huntsman 169,170,296,298,
    417
Huntsman Series 334
Hurdy Gurdy 170
Hurst, Jane S. 342,349
Hyde Park Exhibition 11

Ibrahim 170
Idle Hours 170
Illustrated London News 34
I'm Nearly Ready 170
Impasto 20,60
In Grandma's Days 170
In The Stocks 170, 171
Indian Brave 27,171
Indian Maiden 171
Indian Pavilion 11, 31
Indian Temple Dancer 171
Innocence 171
International Collection 16
Invitation 171
Iona 171
Irene 171
Irish Colleen 172
Irishman 172
Isadora 172
Isthmian Games 30
It Won't Hurt 172
Ivy 172
Izaac Walton 80,331,339

Jack 172
Jack Point 26,172,173
Jackdaw of Rheims 303,339
Jacqueline 173
James 173
Jan Van Riebeck 303
Jane 173
Jane Seymour 80
Janet 173,174
Janice 174

Janine 174
January 174
Japanese Fan 48,174
Jarge 80
Jasmine 175
Jean 175
Jefferson, Robert 17
Jemma 175
Jennifer 175
Jersey Milkmaid 175,207
Jessica 175
Jester 26,80,175,176,317,318
Jill 176
Jimmy Durante 80
Joan 176
Joanne 176
Jockey 80
John Barleycorn 23,80,295,
    311
John Doulton 80
John Lennon 82
John Peel 82,176,304
John The Baptist 404
Johnny Appleseed 82
Johnson, L.48
Johnson, R.29, 301
Joker 176
Jolly Sailor 176
Jolly Toby 418
Jones 9
Jovial Monk 176,293,299
Joy 176
Judge 176
Judge & Jury 176
Judith 176
Juggler 82
Jugs 332-335
Julia 176,177
Julie 177
July 177
June 177
Juno & The Peacock 177
Just One More 178

Kaiser Wilhelm 367
Karen 178
Karno Troupe 418
Kate 178
Kate Hannigan 178
Kate Hardcastle 178
Katharine 179
Kathleen 179,180
Kathleen And Child 337
Kathy 180
Katrina 180

INDEX

Keats 386
Keen, Rosa 60
Kelly 180
Kemp, Edith 341
Kerry 180
King Arthur 82
King Charles 180
King Edward VIII 304
King George V 304, 409
King George VI 305
King Phillip II 82
Kingsware 27, 28, 289–300
Kirsty 180
Kitty 180
Ko–Ko 181
Kurdish Dancer 181

L.C.C. 14
La Sylphide 181
Lady And Blackamoor 181
Lady And The Unicorn 181
Lady Anne 182
Lady Anne Nevill 182
Lady April 182
Lady Betty 182
Lady Charmian 182
Lady Clare 182
Lady Clown 182
Lady Diana Spencer 182
Lady Fayre 182
Lady from Williamsburg 182
Lady Jester 26, 182, 183
Lady of the Elizabethan
  Period 183
Lady of the Fan 183
Lady of the Georgian Period
  183
Lady of the Snows 183
Lady of the Time of
  Henry VI 184
Lady Pamela 184
Lady Queen Anne 324
Lady With Ermine Muff 184
Lady With Rose 184
Lady With Shawl 184
Lady Without Bouquet 184
Ladybird 184
Laird 184
Lalla Rookh 185
Lamb, Charlotte 348
Lambeth Factory 7–32
Lambeth Faience 20
Lambeth School of Art 10, 11, 30,
  31
Lambeth Studio 7–32
Lambeth Walk 185

Lambing Time 185
Land of Nod 185
Last Ball 415
Last Waltz 185
Laura 185
Laurianne 185
Lavender Woman 185, 186
Lavinia 186
Lawyer 82, 186, 315
Leading Lady 186
Leather Bottle, The 290
Leda and the Swan 186
Ledger, Joe 17
Lee, Francis 376
Legolas 186
Leisure Hour 186
Len Lifebelt 419
Leprechaun 82
Lesley 186
Lewis, Esther 52, 54, 55
Lewis, Florence 53
Lewis & Highland 36
Liberty 14, 187
Lido Lady 187
Life in Sherwood Forest 331
Lifeboat Man 187
Lights Out 187
Lilac Shawl 187, 236
Lilac Time 187
Lily 187
Limited Edition Loving Cups
  & Jugs 29
Linda 187
Linnell, Francis 60
Lisa 188
Lisette 188
Little Bo-Peep 188, 327
Little Boy Blue 188, 325
Little Child So Rare And
  Sweet 188
Little Jack Horner 189, 328
Little Lady Make Believe 189
Little Land 189
Little Lord Fauntleroy 189
Little Man 418
Little Mester 82
Little Miss Muffet 189, 323
Little Mistress 189
Little Mother 189, 190
Little Nell 190, 313, 332
Little Red Riding Hood 328
Lizania 190
Lizzie 190
Lloyd George, David 374
Lobster Man 82, 190

London Bobby 82
London Cry, Strawberries 190
London Cry, Turnips and
  Carrots 190, 191
London, Emily A. 346
London Exhibition 11
London Fire Brigade 10
Long John Silver 82, 84, 191,
  316
Lord Nelson 9, 84, 350, 409
Lord Olivier As Richard III
  191
Loretta 191
Lori 191
Lorna 191
Lorraine191
Lost 359
Lost Ball, The 416
Lost Piece of Silver, The 402
Louis Armstrong 84
Louise 191
Love Letter 191
Lovers 191
Loving Cups & Jugs 23, 301–
  310
Lucrezia Borgia 191
Lucy 192
Lucy Ann 192
Lucy Lockett 192
Lumberjack 84
Lunchtime 192
Lupton, Edith 31, 49, 377,
  378, 412
Luscian Ware 21
Lute 192
Lydia 192, 193
Lynne 193
Lynsey 193
Lyric 193

Macbeth 84
McCallum, D. & J. 35
McCallum, The 35
McLennan, John H. 52
Macnab, The 290
Mad Hatter 84
Madame Crystal 419
Madonna of the Square 193,
  194
Mae West 84
Magic Dragon 195
Magpie Ring 195
Maid at the Well 331

Maisie 195
Major Green 419
Major, 3rd New Jersey Regt. 195
Make Believe 195
Make Me Laugh 338
Mam'selle 195
Man In Tudor Costume 196
Mandarin 196, 197
Mandy 197
Mantilla 197
Maori 84
March 197
March Hare 84
Margaret 197
Margaret of Anjou 197
Margery 198
Margot 198
Marguerite 198
Marianne 198
Marie 198, 199
Marietta 200
Marigold 200
Marilyn 200
Marion 200
Mariquita 200
Marjorie 200
Mark Twain 84
Market Day 200
Marriage of Art & Industry, The 27, 201
Marshall, Mark 31, 379—382
Marshlands 336
Marqueterie Ware 21
Mary 201
Mary Had A Little Lamb 201
Mary Jane 201
Mary, Mary 201
Mary Queen of Scots 201
Mask 201, 202
Mask Seller 202
Masque 202
Masquerade 202, 203
Master 203
Master of Foxhounds Presentation Jug 29, 305
Master Sweep 203
Matador & The Bull 27, 203
Matilda 203
Maureen 203, 204
Maxine 204
May 204
Mayflower 306
Mayor 204
Maytime 204
Meditation 204

Meg 204
Meissen 26
Melanie 204
Melissa 204
Melody 204
Memories 205, 296, 299
Mendicant 205
Mephisto 205
Mephistopheles 24, 84
Mephistopheles and Marguerite 205
Meriel 205
Merlin 84
Mermaid 206
Merry Christmas 206
Merry Musicians 399
Meryll 206, 274
Mexican Dancer 206
Micawber 292
Michael Doulton 84
Michelle 206
Midinette 206
Midsummer Noon 206, 207
Mikado 84
Mike Mineral 419
Milady 207
Milking Time 207
Milkmaid 207
Miller, Isabella 383
Millicent 207
Mine Host 84, 86
Miniatures 32, 412
Minuet 207
Mirabel 207, 208
Miranda 208
Mirror 208
Miscellaneous Ware 311—328
Miss 1926 209
Miss Demure 208
Miss Fortune 209
Miss Muffet 209
Miss Nostrum 419
Miss Studious 419
Miss Winsome 209
Mitchell, Mary 383
M'Lady's Maid 209
Modena 209
Modern Piper 210
Modesty 210
Moira 210
Molly Malone 210
Monica 210
Monks in the Cellar 290, 292, 329, 335, 339
Monsieur Chasseur 419
Monte Carlo 210

Monty 86
Moon Dancer 210
Moor 210, 211
Moore 56
Moore, Bernard 20
Moore, F. 62, 63
Moorish Gateway 29
Moorish Minstrel 211
Moorish Piper Minstrel 211
Morgan, William De 21
Morning Glory 211
Morning Ma'am 212
Morris Dancers 21
Morrisian Ware 21, 60
Mother and Daughter 212
Mother Kangaroo and Toby 336
Mother's Help 212
Motherhood 212, 375
Mouse Figures 400, 401
Mr. Brisket 419
Mr. Bumble 313
Mr. Furrow 419
Mr. Litigate 419
Mr. Micawber 86, 212, 213, 312 314, 315, 422
Mr. Pecksniff 230, 231, 298, 375
Mr. Pickwick 86, 213, 290, 293, 295, 299, 312, 314, 315, 333, 374, 397, 422
Mr. Quaker 86
Mr. Squeers 375
Mr. Tonsil 419
Mrs. Bardell 213, 313
Mrs. Fitzherbert 213
Mrs. Loan 419
Musical Jugs 314
Musicale 213
My Love 213
My Pet 213
My Pretty Maid 214
My Teddy 214
Myfanwy Jones 214, 215

Nadine 215
Nana 215
Nancy 215
Nanny 215
Napkin Rings 314
Napoleon 9, 367
Napoleon & Josephine 86
Natalie 216
National Distillers 35
Nativity, The 405

Natural Foliage Ware 32, 413
Negligee 216
Nell 216
Nell Gwynn 216
Nelson 9, 84, 216, 289, 294, 298, 301, 350, 409
Neptune 86
Nestling Down 216
New Bonnet 216, 217
New Cavaliers Series 335
New Companions 217
Newhaven Fishwife 217
News Vendor 217
Newsboy 217
Nicola 217
Night Watchman 86, 292, 298
Nightwatchman Series 329, 331, 333, 334
Nina 217
Ninette 217
Nixon 19, 50—52
Noble Heritage 336
Noelle 217
Noke, C. J. 12, 17—23, 25, 26, 28, 29, 50—52, 58, 59, 62—64, 291—294, 296, 299, 300, 329, 332—335, 417
Noke, Cecil 29
Norma 217, 218
North American Indian 86
North American Indian Dancer 218
Nott, J. H. 14
Novelty Art Wares 29
November 218
Nude on Rock 218
Nunn, W. 60

October 218
Odds & Ends 218
Officer of the Line 218
'Oh Law' 26
Old Balloon Seller 26, 27, 31, 218, 316, 338
Old Balloon Seller And Bulldog 218
Old Charley 23, 88, 311, 314, 316, 317, 418
Old Cottage Bromley 54
Old English Inns Series 336, 337
Old English Scenes 330
Old Father Time 11
Old Houses, All-Saints St., Hastings 340

Old King 219
Old King Cole 24, 88, 219, 314, 327
Old Lavender Seller 219
Old London 335
Old Man 219
Old Man With Scythe 330
Old Meg 219
Old Moreton Hall Series 334, 339, 340
Old Mother Hubbard 219, 321
Old Salt 88, 316
Old Woman Who Lived In A Shoe 339
Olde Worlde England 30
Olga 219
Oliver Twist 219, 291, 313, 329, 332
Olivia 220
Omar Khayyam 220
Omar Khayyam and the Beloved 220
Once Upon A Time 220
One of the Forty 220—223 297
One That Got Away 223
Orange Lady 224
Orange Seller 224
Orange Vendor 224,
Organ Grinder 224
Orlando 340
Othello 88
Out For A Walk 224
Over The Threshold 224
Owd Willum 225
Oyez, Oyez 293
Oyster Bar 15

Paddy 88, 311, 314, 317
Painted Feelings 336
Painting 225
Paisley Shawl 225, 226
Palio 226
Pamela 226
Pan 12
Pan on Rock 226
Panels 319—328
Panorama 226
Pantalettes 226, 227
Paradise 227
Paris Exhibition 11, 30
Parisian 227
Park Parade 227
Parker, William 383, 384

Parson Brown 23, 88, 298, 311
Parson Jones 297
Parson's Daughter 227, 228
Past Glory 228
Pat Parcel 419
Patchwork Quilt 228
Pate-Sur-Pate 14, 30, 31
Patent 410, 411
Patricia 228, 229
Paul McCartney 88
Paula 229
Pauline 229
Pavlova 229
Peace 229, 292, 296
Pearce, A. E. 22
Pearly Boy 23, 88, 229, 230
Pearly Girl 23, 90, 230
Pearly King 90
Pearly Queen 90
Pearson Group 15
Pecksniff 230, 231
Pedlar Wolf 231
Peggy 231
Pendle Witch 90
Penelope 231
Penny 231
Pensive 231
Pensive Moments 231
Perfect Pair 231
Persian Ware 21
Philadelphia Exhibitions 11
Philippa of Hainault 231
Philippine Dancer 232
Phyllis 232
Picardy Peasant 232, 233
Pick-Kwik 16, 33, 34
Pickwick Bachelor 397
Picnic 233
Pied Piper 90, 233, 289, 291, 293, 296, 297, 306
Pierce, A. 21
Pierette 233, 234
Pierrot 26
Pilgrims on Horseback 334
Pillow Fight 234
Pinder Bourne & Co. 11
Pinkie 234
Piper 235
Pirate King 235
Pirouette 235
Pitt's Centenary 366
Plaques 402, 405
Plates 336—338
Play Goers 17, 400
Playmates 235

Please Keep Still 235
Poacher 35, 90, 235, 315
Pocahontas 235
Poke Bonnet 188, 235
Policeman 90
Polish Dancer 236
Polka 236
Polly 236
Polly Peachum 236—238
Polly Put The Kettle On 238
Pollyanna 238
Poor Joe 330
Pope, Francis 48, 384, 385
Pope John Paul II 238
Porthos 90, 315
Postman 90
Potter 238, 239
Pottery In The Past 306
Premiere 239
President Roosevelt 375
Pretty Lady 239, 240
Pretty Polly 240
Pride & Joy 240
Prime Minister Of Mirth, The 418
Primroses 240
Prince of Wales, The 10, 240 408
Princess 240, 241
Princess Alexandra 20
Princess Anne 312
Princess Badoura 26, 241
Princess of Wales 241
Printemps 241
Priscilla 241, 242
Private, Connecticut Regt. 242
Private, Delaware Regt. 242
Private, 1st Georgia Regt. 242
Private, Massachusetts Regt. 242
Private, Pennsylvania Rifle Bn. 242
Private, Rhode Island Regt. 242
Private, 2nd South Carolina Regt. 243
Private, 3rd North Carolina Regt. 243
Prized Possessions 243
Professor 243
Promenade 243
Proposal 243
Prudence 244
Prue 244
Puff and Powder 244

Punch & Judy 341
Punch & Judy Man 90, 244
Puppetmaker 244
Puss In Boots 323, 327
Pussy 244, 245
Putting 415, 416
Pyjamas 245

Quality Street 245
Queen Anne 245
Queen Anne's Mansion 35, 407
Queen Caroline 9
Queen Elizabeth 305
Queen Elizabeth I 90, 245
Queen Elizabeth II 27, 29, 164 245, 306, 307, 312
Queen Mary 26, 304
Queen Mother 245
Queen Mother As The Duchess Of York 245
Queen of Hearts 326
Queen of Sheba 246
Queen of the Dawn 246
Queen of the Ice 246
Queen Victoria 11, 12, 16, 92, 246, 366, 367, 408, 409

Raby 22
Rachel 246
Red Queen 92
Rag Doll 246
Rag Doll Seller 246
Ranjitsinhji, K. S. 415
Rebecca 246
Redford, Constance E. 347
Reflection 246
Reflections 246, 247
Reform Flasks 9, 31
Regal Lady 247
Regency 247
Regency Beau 92, 247
Regency Coach Jug 29, 307
Rendezvous 247
Rennie Mackintosh, Charles 389
Repose 247
Rest Awhile 247
Resurrection, The 404
Return of Persephone 247
Rev. Cassock 419
Reverie 247
Rhapsody 247
Rhoda 248
Rhythm 248
Ringo Starr 92
Rip Van Winkle 33, 92, 315

Rita 248
Ritz Bell Boy 248
River Boy 248
Rix, William 17, 21
Robert Burns 248, 331
Roberts, Florence 386
Robin 248, 249
Robin Hood 92, 249, 308
Robin Hood & His Merry Men 29
Robinson Crusoe 92
Rocking Horse 249
Rogers, Edith 386
Rogers, Kate 20, 54
Rogers, Martha 387
Romance 249
Romany Sue 249
Romeo 92
Ronald Reagan 92
Rosabell 249
Rosalind 249
Rosamund 249, 250
Rose 250
Rose Arbour 250
Roseanna 250
Rosebud 250, 251
Rosemary 251
Rosina 251
Rowe, W. 22, 349
Rowena 251
Royal Canadian Mounted Police 251
Royal College of Art 27
Royal Court Theatre 15
Royal Governor's Cook 251
Royal Society of Arts 11
Royal Worcester Co. 26
Royles Patent 19
Ruby 252
Rumpelstiltskin 252
Rural England Series 330, 332 334, 340
Rural England (Welsh) Series 332, 340
Ruskin, John 9
Rustic Swain 252
Ruth 252
Ruth, The Pirate Maid 252

Sabbath Morn 252
Sailor's Holiday 252
Sailor's Story 294
Sairey Gamp 23, 94, 252, 253, 311, 312, 314, 316, 317, 336, 374, 422

Salome 253, 404
Sally 253
Sam Weller 94, 253, 290, 294, 299, 312, 314, 333, 422
Samantha 253
Sampler Pattern 330
Samson 402
Samson and Delilah 94
Samuel Johnson 94
Samwise 253
Sancho Panza 94
Sandiman's Port 35
Sandra 253
Sanitary Fountain 34
Santa Anna/Davy Crocket 94
Santa Claus 94, 96, 254
Sara 254
Saucy Nymph 254
Save Some For Me 254
Saviour & Woman At The Well, The 402
Savoy Hotel 10, 15
Sayers, Eliza 7, 387
Scaramouche 96
Schoolmarm 254
Schorr, Raoh 17
Scotch Girl 254
Scotsman & Irishman 33
Scott 386
Scotties 254
Scottish Highland Dancer 254
Scribe 254, 255
Scrooge 255, 313
Sea Harvest 255
Sea Shore 255
Sea Sprite 255
Seafarer 255
Seasons, The 338
Seated Tobies (Small) 422
Secret Moments 255
Secret Thoughts 255
See-Saw, Margery Daw 328
Sentimental Pierrot 255
Sentinel 255
September 256
Serena 256
Serenade 256
Sergeant, 6th Maryland Regt. 256
Sergeant Peeler 419
Sergeant, Virginia 1st Regt. 256
Series Ware 29, 30, 329-340
Sets 61
Sevres 12, 26

Shakespeare Jug 29, 94, 304
Shakespeare Series 330, 334, 335, 340
Shakespearian Characters 12
Sharon 256
She Loves Me Not 256
Sheikh 256
Sheila 256
Shepherd 256, 257, 258
Shepherdess 257
Sherlock Holmes 418
Shirley 258
Shoolbred, Jas. 36
Shore Leave 258
Short Headed Salmon 337, 338
Shute, Emma 347
Shy Anne 258
Shylock 258
Sibell 258, 259
Siesta 259
Silhouette Series 329, 334, 339
Silicon Ware 32, 49, 414
Silks and Ribbons 259
Silversmith of Williamsburg 259
Simeon, Harry 25, 388, 407
Simmance, Eliza 7, 14, 30, 31, 358, 388-393
Simon The Cellarer 96
Simone 259
Simple Simon 96, 320
Simulated Ware 32, 413
Sir Edward 259
Sir Edward Lee 33
Sir Francis Drake 25, 28, 96, 308, 418
Sir Henry Doulton 7-32, 96
Sir Ralph 259
Sir Roger De Coverley Series 334, 339
Sir Thomas 259
Sir Thomas Lovell 259
Sir Thomas More 96
Sir Toby Belch 335
Sir Walter Raleigh 259, 260
Sir Winston Churchill 260
Sisterly Love 260
Sisters 260
Sitting Bull/George Armstrong Custer 96
Skater 260
Sketch Girl 260
Slater, John 32
Slater, Walter 61
Sleep 260, 261
Sleeping Beauty 261, 321

Sleeping Princess 323
Sleepy Darling 261
Sleepy Scholar 261
Sleepyhead 261
Sleuth 96
Small, Elizabeth 393
Small Seated Tobies 422
Smallfield, K.B. 18, 53, 55, 369
Smiling Buddha 261
Smuggler 96
Smuts 96
Snake Charmer 261
Sneyd Brickworks 37
So Near And Yet So Far 360
Soiree 261
Solitude 261
Sonata 262
Song of the Sea 262
Sonia 262
Sonny 262
Sophie 262
Sophistication 262
Southern Belle 262
Spanish Flamenco Dancer 262
Spanish Lady 263
Sparkes, John 10, 11
Spinning 263
Spirit of the Wind 263
Spook 263, 264
Spooks 264
Sporting Squire 28, 291, 292
Sporting Subjects 32, 415, 416
Spring 264, 265
Spring Flowers 265
Spring Morning 265
Springtime 265
Squire 265, 295, 418
St George 27, 94, 265, 266
St George and the Dragon 266
St. Louis Exhibition 20
Stable, Fanny 54
Staffordshire Figures 26
Stanley, H.M. 408
Stargazer 266
Statesman 266
Station of the Cross 403
Stayed at Home 266
Stephanie 266
Sterne, Laurence 25
Stick 'Em Up 266
Stiff & Sons 15
Stiggins 266, 291
Stitch In Time 266
Stoneware 30, 341-416
Stop Press 266

Stormer, Emily 394
Storytime 267
Strolling 267
Style & Winch Ltd. 38
Suffragette Movement, The 406
Sugar Bowls 314
Suitor 267
Summer 267
Summer Rose 267
Summer's Darling 267
Summer's Day 267
Summertime 267
Sunday Best 267
Sunday Morning 267
Sunday Smocks Series 331, 333
Sung 12, 13, 18, 21, 62-63
Sunshine Girl 268
Susan 268
Susanna 268
Suzette 268, 269
Sweet and Fair 269
Sweet and Twenty 269, 270
Sweet Anne 270, 271, 318
Sweet April 271
Sweet Dreams 271
Sweet Lavender 271
Sweet Maid 271
Sweet Perfume 271
Sweet Seventeen 271
Sweet Sixteen 271
Sweet Suzy 271
Sweet Violets 271
Sweeting 271, 272
Swimmer 272
Sydney Carton 331
Sydney Harbour 294
Sylvia 272
Sympathy 272
Symphony 272

Tabbenor, R. 307, 419
Table Lighters 315
Tabor, George H. 394
Tailor 272
Taking Things Easy 272
Tall Story 273
Tam O'Shanter 96, 97
Tango 61, 273
Tapestry Weaving 273
Tavern Scenes 289, 298
Teapots 316, 339
Teatime 273

Tea-Time Scandal 400
Teenager 273
Tenderness 273
Teresa 273
Tess 273
Tete-A-Tete 273, 274
Thank You 274
Thankful 274
Thanks Doc 274
Thanksgiving 274
The Best Is Not Too Good 418
The Fleur-de-Lys, St. Albans 336
Theaker, H. G. 47
There Was An Old Woman 323
Three Musketeers 308
This Little Pig 274
Thunder in the Air 336
Tiger On Rock 46
Tildy 275
Tinkle Bell 275
Tinsmith 275
Tinworth, George 7, 8, 11, 17, 26, 30, 31, 395-405
Tinworth's Boyhood 402
Tiny Tim 275
Titanian Ware 12, 22, 64
Tittensor 22, 26, 48, 297
To Bed 275
Tobacco Jars 317
Toby XX 418
Toby Ale 34
Toby Gillette 98
Toby Jugs 16, 25, 417-422
Toby Philpotts 98
Toinette 205, 274
Tom 275
Tom Bombadil 275
Tom Brown 275
Tom Sawyer 276
Tom, Tom, The Piper's Son 276
Tomorrows Dreams 276
Tongue, Graham 300
Tony Weller 98, 276, 291, 297 299, 311, 314, 316, 335
Tony Weller Bevare of the Vidders 291
Toothpick Holders 317
Tootles 276
Top O'The Hill 276, 277
Touchstone 98
Tower of London 309
Town Crier 98, 277

Toymaker 277
Toys 277
Tracy 277
Tranquility 277
Trapper 98
Travellers Tales 277
Treasure Island 277, 309
Treaty Of Berlin 20
Tristram Shandy 25
Trotty Veck 277
Tsang Ihang 38
Tulips 278
Tumbler 278
Tuppence A Bag 278
Tutankhamen 22
Twilight 278
Twinings 36
Two-A-Penny 278
Tz'u Hsi, The Empress Dowager 278

Ugly Duchess 98
Ulysses S. Grant & Robert E. Lee 98
Uncle Ned 278
Uncle Sam 290
Uncle Toby 25
Uncle Tom Cobbleigh 98
Under The Gooseberry Bush 279
Under The Greenwood Tree Series, 331, 333-335, 339, 340
Upon Her Cheeks She Wept 279
Uriah Heep 279, 313

Vain Jackdaw 398
Valentine's Day 338
Valerie 279
Vanessa 280
Vanity 280
Vases 340
Vauxhall 9
Veale Chifferiel Co. 37
Velluma Ware 22
Veneta 280
Vera 280
Verena 280
Veronica 280, 281
Veteran Motorist 98
Vicar of Bray 98

Victor Emmanuel 367
Victoria 281
Victorian Lady 281, 282, 283
Vienna Exhibition 11
Viking 98, 100, 283
Village Blacksmith 309
Viola D'Amore 283
Violin 283
Virginals 283
Virginia 283
Viscount Montgomery of
  Alemain 100
Vivienne 283
Votes for Women 283, 406
Vyse, Charles 26

W.C. Fields 100
W.G. Grace 100
Wade, George 418
Waldorf 37
Walklate Ltd., W. 33,34, 35
Wall Masks 318
Wall Vases 317
Walrus & Carpenter 100
Wandering Minstrel 284,310
Waning of the Honey-Moon
  414
War in the Sudan 409
Wardrobe Mistress 284
Washington, George 29,75,
  154
Watchman 289,296,300
Water Maiden 284
Watt, Linnie 14,54
Watts 9
Wayfarer 284
Weathering The Storm 337
Wedding Day 284
Wedding Morn 284
Wedding Vows 284
Wedlock Series 335
Wee Willie Winkie 284
Welch, Emily 343, 348
Weller, Snr. 290
Welsh Girl, 284, 285
Wendy 285
West Indian Dancer 285
West Wind 27, 285
White, G. 49
Wigmaker of Williamsburg 285
Wild Bill Hickock 100
Wilkinson & Co., Charles 33
Willow Pattern Series 329
Willy Won't He 285

Windflower 285,286
Windmill Lady 286
Windswept 286
Winner 286
Winning Colours 337
Winsome 286
Winter 286,287
Winter's Walk 287
Wintertime 287
Wistful 287
Witches 294
Wizard 287,300
Wolsey 334
Woman Holding Child 287
Woman of the Time of Henry
  VI 287
Woman on a Camel 333
Wood Nymph 287
Worcester Pottery 12
Wordsworth, William 310
Worthingtons 33
Wright's Coal Tar Soap 38
Writing 288
Wyatt Earp 100

Yachtsman 100
Ye Old Belle 333
Yearning 288
Yeoman of the Guard 288
Youatt, Bessie 346,347,365
Young Dreams 288
Young Knight 288
Young Love 288
Young Master 288
Young Miss Nightingale 288
Young Widow 288
Younger's 38
Yum-Yum 288
Yvonne 288

Zacchaeus 403
Zino Pads 16